HAWAI'I'S PLANTS AND ANIMALS

COVER ILLUSTRATION
'Apapane (*Himatione sanguinea*) on
'ōhi'a lehua (*Metrosideros polymorpha*);
watercolor by Joan Yoshioka

HAWAI'I'S PLANTS AND ANIMALS

Biological Sketches of Hawaii Volcanoes National Park

Charles P. Stone and Linda W. Pratt

With the Assistance of
Danielle B. Stone

Illustrations by
Joan M. Yoshioka

Hawaii Natural History Association,
National Park Service,
and
University of Hawaii
Cooperative National Park Resources Studies Unit

© 1994   Hawaii Natural History Association
         All Rights Reserved

Support for publication was provided by
the Cooperative National Park Resources Studies Unit,
the National Park Service, and
Hawaii Natural History Association

Camera-ready copy was prepared by the authors

Manufacture of this book was through
the production services of
University of Hawaii Press

The paper used in this publication meets the minimum
requirements of American National Standard for Information
Sciences/-permanence of Paper for Printed Library Materials

Library of Congress Cataloging-in-Publication Data

Stone, Charles P.
      Hawai'i's plants and animals : biological sketches of Hawaii Volcanoes
National Park / Charles P. Stone and Linda W. Pratt : with the assistance
of Danielle B. Stone : illustrations by Joan M. Yoshioka.

      p.   cm.
      Includes bibliographical references (p.   ) and index.
      ISBN 0-8248-1689-7
      1. Natural history--Hawaii--Hawaii Volcanoes National Park.
2. Botany--Hawaii--Hawaii Volcanoes National Park--Identification.
3. Zoology--Hawaii--Hawaii Volcanoes National Park--Identification.
4. Hawaii Volcanoes National Park (Hawaii)   I. Pratt, Linda W.,
1950-   . II. Stone, Danielle B., 1941-   . III. Title.
QH198.H3S74   1994
508.969'1--dc20   94-28177
                                                                       CIP

Distributed by
University of Hawaii Press
Honolulu, Hawaii 96822

To our parents,
who have supported and encouraged our efforts

Charles and Dorothy Stone,
William (Kelly) and Elizabeth Waldrup,
Waldron and Dorothy Barrère,
and
Haemi and Yoshiko Yoshioka

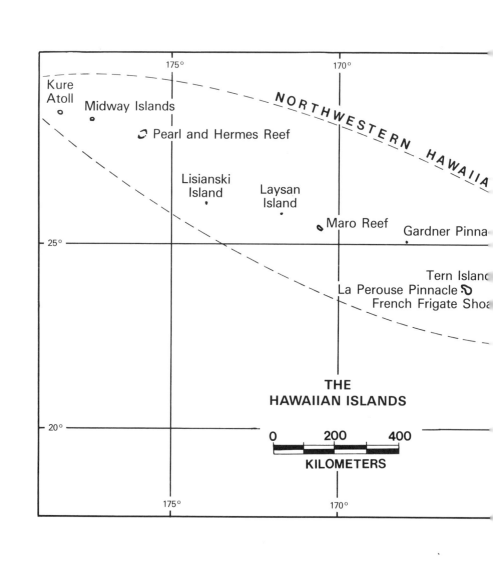

Kure
Atoll

Midway Islands

Pearl and Hermes Reef

NORTHWESTERN HAWAIIA

Lisianski
Island

Laysan
Island

Maro Reef

Gardner Pinna

25°

Tern Island

La Perouse Pinnacle

French Frigate Shoa

175°

170°

**THE
HAWAIIAN ISLANDS**

20°

0   200   400

KILOMETERS

175°

170°

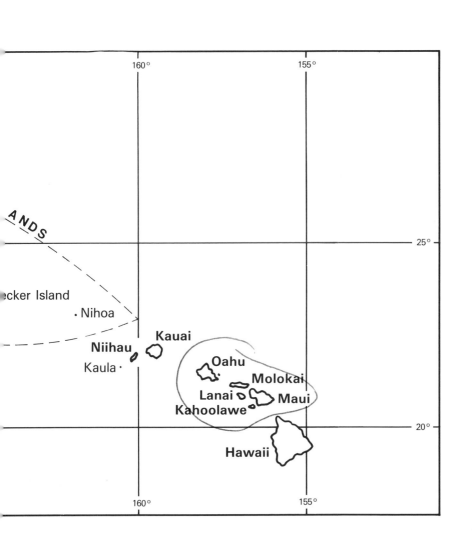

CONTENTS

ACKNOWLEDGMENTS

This book would not have been possible without the support of the Board of Directors of the Hawai'i Natural History Association, which funded the illustrations and half of the publishing costs. We thank those of the Board who initially approved the project, some of whom did not live to see the finished product. We appreciate the patience of Kathy English and the Hawai'i Natural History Association in adjusting deadlines when necessary and encouraging us in our efforts. It has been a pleasure working with Kathy.

A number of people helped assure the quality of this book by providing comments and criticisms of the written material. These include Paul Banko, Dorothy Barrère, Rob Cowie, Dick Cunningham, Clif Davis (deceased), Lu Eldredge, Suzanne Fellows, David Foote, Christina Heliker, Frank Howarth, Jim Jacobi, Larry Katahira, Lloyd Loope, Dieter Mueller-Dombois, Bill Mull, Thane Pratt, Dick Rasp, Cliff Smith, Lani Stemmermann, Tim Tunison, and Ron Walker.

Many colleagues assisted us in deciding which plants and animals to include in the book (we sent out a survey). These included Paul Banko, Clif Davis, David Foote, Frank Howarth, Jim Jacobi, Larry Katahira, Mardie Lane, Dan Taylor, and Tim Tunison.

Illustrations were critiqued by Donna Ball, Paul Banko, Kerry Brust, David Foote, Jim Jacobi, and Jack Jeffrey. Slides, photographs, or specimens used in the illustrations were made available by David Foote, Jack Jeffrey, Maile Kjargaard, Bill Mull, Gordon Nishida, and Nanci Sidaras. Some drawings were adapted (with permission) from Bill Mull's photographs in *Hawaiian Insects and Their Kin* and Hawaii Audubon Society's *Hawaii's Birds*. Three drawings originally used in *Conservation Biology in Hawai'i* (Stone and Stone, editors) are here used with permission of the University of Hawaii Cooperative National Park Resources Studies Unit. The cover illustration is used with the permission of C. and D. Stone and Joan Yoshioka.

We thank Dina Kageler for photos used in the zone accounts except for the Alpine/Aeolian Zones; Jane Takahashi and the Hawaiian Volcano Observatory allowed us to use the photo for the Alpine/Aeolian Zones. Dina also took many photos useful in drawing the Special Systems sections of the book. Thanks to Pamela Lockwood for preparing the maps following the sections on How to Use This Book and The Park.

We appreciate the tolerance of The Nature Conservancy of Hawai'i and especially Sam Gon III for allowing Joan Yoshioka a flexible enough schedule to complete the drawings. Joan also thanks Karen Kosasa, an inspirational art teacher and friend.

We owe special thanks to Danielle Stone, who typed numerous drafts of the accounts, wrote the Seacoast description and the Crabs and Mollusks accounts, prepared the index (with Pamela Lockwood), assembled the taxonomic list, critically reviewed and edited the entire manuscript, and helped us arrange the material.

Jan Heavenridge and Lucie Aono of University of Hawaii Press were again a joy to work with in completing the publication, and we appreciate their patience and competence.

Special thanks to Thane Pratt for marrying the former Linda W. Cuddihy before this book went to press, so that we could use her new name.

Finally, we are grateful for what has gone before -- not only for knowledge passed on by Hawaiian people, the early European naturalists, and various authors, but for the opportunity to have worked with many outstanding naturalists, resource managers, and scientists who have been associated with the Park in the past dozen years or so. This book would not have been possible without their work. May support for the efforts of people learning about and protecting Hawai'i's remarkable biota increase! Much remains to be done.

HOW TO USE THIS BOOK

We have arranged the pencil and prose sketches of plants and animals according to seven major ecological zones in Hawaii Volcanoes National Park (see Introduction). After a **Multizonal** section that includes biota readily found in many zones, coverage begins at the ocean (**Seacoast**) and ends at the top of Mauna Loa (**Alpine/Aeolian**). Each zone is described by photo and narrative account. Sketches of selected plants, then animals, follow for each zone. Where more than one plant or animal is illustrated, the identity of each is found in an underlined reference in the narrative (*e.g.*, upper right in illustration). Where more than one species is discussed, the identity of the illustrated species is noted by underlined reference (illustrated).

Species or group accounts are arranged in approximate order of size of organism (*e.g.*, trees precede grasses, house cats precede mice). Animals are arranged as follows: birds, mammals, reptiles and amphibians, and invertebrates. Thus, a large bird precedes a small bird, a large mammal precedes a small mammal, etc. You may find it handy to mark ecological zones and plant and animal sections within each with stick-on tabs for easy reference. Common, Hawaiian, and scientific names are given in each account where possible, and the status and distribution of each plant and animal discussed are also noted. Status as to native or alien (introduced) and Endangered or Threatened are given. The Endangered or Threatened Species category (capitalized) refers to those organisms that are Federally listed; State listings generally parallel the Federal listing.

Some ecological zones also contain **Special Systems** (*e.g.*, "Ka'ū Desert" or "Anchialine Pools"). Information about the plants, animals, and other characteristics of these distinct areas is presented in continuous narrative, and a pencil drawing depicting each area is included.

The **Introduction** and **The Park** sections prior to the Multizonal section provide information on native and alien species, endangerment and extinction, management and research, some basic background on the Park, and what you can do to help the Park maintain its biological resources. Toward the back of the book (after Alpine/Aeolian Zones), sections on **Rare and Missing Plants** and **Rare and Missing Birds** profile some of the plants and birds no longer present in the Park or of extremely rare occurrence. A **Systematic Classification** of the plants and animals discussed in the book is then included. A suggested list of **Further Reading and References** and an **Index** complete the volume.

The coverage of species and groups of plants and animals is obviously not exhaustive. Ask an interpreter, resource manager, researcher, or other employee of Hawaii Volcanoes National Park if you have questions, but PLEASE DO NOT COLLECT EXAMPLES to show them!

MAPS

Geographical locations mentioned in the text may be found on one of six maps near the front of the book. The first, showing the Hawaiian Archipelago, appears just before the full title page. The next four maps follow this section on How to Use This Book and include a map of Hawai'i Island with major features and administrative districts; a map of Hawaii Volcanoes National Park excluding higher elevations; an enlargement of the Kīlauea Caldera area; and an enlargement of the Mauna Loa Strip and Summit areas. The sixth map, showing ecological zones, is at the end of the section on The Park.

TAXONOMY

Plants and animals are universally known by their scientific names -- Latin "binomials" that definitively identify the genus and species to which they belong. For some organisms (especially plants and rare forms), subspecies or varieties are also important, and a three-part name, or "trinomial," is used to enable further definition of "taxon" (scientific category). The family and binomial have been generally used to identify taxa in this book, but because a wide range of plants and animals is covered, it is sometimes necessary to present information about broader classification categories. The general hierarchal breakdown of scientific nomenclature is:

Kingdom (Plants, Animals, etc.)
    Division (Plants) or Phylum (Animals)
        Class
            Order
                Family
                    Subfamily or Tribe
                        Genus
                            Species
                                Subspecies, Variety or Form

In Hawai'i, where many groups of organisms are poorly known and discoveries continue, scientific names change relatively frequently for some groups. Common names also change but are much less standardized than scientific names, except for birds. Hawaiian names also vary, even among districts and islands; many species do not have Hawaiian names, and the same Hawaiian name may apply to more than one species. Sources for scientific, common, and Hawaiian names that were used in this book are as follows:

Plants (except ferns): Wagner *et al.* 1990; St. John 1973; Pukui and Elbert 1981.
Ferns: Lamoureux (unpublished); Wagner and Wagner (unpublished).
Birds: Pratt *et al.* 1987; Hawaii Audubon Society 1993.
Mammals: Tomich 1986.
Reptiles and Amphibians: McKeown 1978.
Arthropods: Nishida *et al.* 1992.
Land Mollusks: R. Cowie, B.P. Bishop Museum Malacologist, pers. comm. March 1994.
Marine Mollusks: Kay 1979.

Marine Crustaceans: Fielding 1979; L.G. Eldredge, B.P. Bishop Museum, Pers. comm. March 1994.

Common and Hawaiian names are used with scientific names in narratives for each ecological zone and in special system accounts. However, only common or Hawaiian names are used in species or group accounts as a rule, to simplify reading and save space. The Index indicates the corresponding scientific, common, and Hawaiian names of each species or group mentioned in the book. In addition, a systematic classification of plants and animals discussed in the book is included; the list includes scientific, common, and Hawaiian names.

HAWAIIAN LANGUAGE
Macrons and glottal stops or 'okina are used in all words of Hawaiian origin where appropriate, except in some names of organizations or institutions. Spelling of Hawaiian names is according to Pukui and Elbert 1981 for the most part. Hawaiian place names follow Pukui *et al.* 1986. Hawaiian names for plants and animals are generally taken from the taxonomic sources listed above where possible, or (for plants) from Porter 1972, and (for marine invertebrates) from Titcomb 1978.

METRIC EQUIVALENTS
We decided to use English measurement units because this is still the accepted U.S. convention; conversion between English and metric for each measurement as it is given in the accounts reduces readability and takes considerable space. We apologize for the inconvenience to those used to the metric system and offer the following conversions as an aid:

When You Know	Multiply By	To Get
ft	0.31	m
in.	2.54	cm
mi	1.61	km
oz	28.35	g
lb	0.45	kg
acres	0.41	ha
^{o}F	0.556(^{o}F-32)	^{o}C

SOME DEFINITIONS
We have removed as much technical jargon (words not usually found in a dictionary of the English language) as possible. However, some things are simply difficult to paraphrase succinctly; there is sometimes just no substitute for the proper word. Hawaiian words that have found their way into common English usage -- as evidenced by their inclusion in a standard English dictionary -- have not been defined in the narratives. For those who object to words unknown to them, we suggest using any one of several leading general dictionaries.

We offer a few handy definitions to assist in understanding those few botanical or other technical words that were unavoidable.

Botanical Terms

Alternate: Arrangement of leaves, in which leaves are attached to the stem one to a node (place on stem where leaves originate), alternating along the stem.

Bract: A modified leaf, usually small and scalelike but sometimes large and brightly colored, from whose axil (upper angle between leaf and stem) grows a flower or inflorescence.

Calyx: The outer structure of a flower, which encloses the petals in the flower bud. The calyx is often green and leaflife. Calyx segments are called sepals.

Capsule: A dry fruit composed of more than one carpel (pistil section), which splits open when mature.

Compound: A leaf composed of separate and distinct segments or leaflets. Leaflets may be distinguished from leaves by the absence of any bud where they are attached.

Corolla: The part of the flower, often colored and showy, within the calyx. It may be composed of separate petals or shaped like a tube or cylinder.

Frond: The leaf of a fern, composed of a stipe and blade.

Inflorescence: A cluster of flowers.

Opposite: Arrangement of leaves in which the leaves are attached to the stem opposite one another.

Ovate: Leaf egg-shaped, widest below the middle.

Palmate, Palmately Compound: A leaf with leaflets attached at a central point like the fingers of a hand.

Petiole: The stalk of a leaf, which attaches the flattened leaf blade to the stem.

Pinnate, Pinnately Compound: A leaf with leaflets arranged along a stem-like axis like the segments of a feather.

Pistil: The female part of a flower, composed of a stigma (the part that receives the pollen), ovary (the seed-bearing organ), and style (the structure, often elongated, which connects the stigma and ovary).

Rachis: The stemlike axis of a compound leaf or frond, along which the leaflets are attached.

Rhizome: A prostrate stem, often growing underground. Used particularly for ferns.

Sporangia: The spore-bearing structures in ferns, visible under magnification as a round, stalked container. Sporangia are usually located on the underside of the frond and are often arranged in clusters called sori.

Stamen: The male part of a flower, composed of a pollen-bearing anther and a stalklike filament.

Stipe: The stalk of a fern frond, which attaches the rachis or leafy blade to the fern rhizome or stem.

Stipule: A small leaflike or scalelike appendage found at the base of leaves (usually in pairs).

Other Terms

Anticoagulant: A drug or substance that delays or prevents the clotting of blood.

Biocontrol, Biological Control: Reduction or elimination of pest animals or plants by introduction of natural enemies such as predators, parasites, and diseases.

Biological Niche: The role or function of an organism in the environment.

Caldera: A crater (bowl-shaped depression) more than one mile in diameter formed largely by collapse of the top of a volcano. A crater is a smaller depression and/or one at a volcanic vent and can be formed by various means.

Cere: A waxy, often brightly colored, fleshy area at the base of the bill of some birds, which contains the nostrils.

Chela: A pincerlike claw of a crab, lobster, scorpion, etc.

Epiphyte: A plant that grows on another plant but is not parasitic on it and is not rooted in the ground.

Feral: An animal with domesticated ancestors that has returned to the wild and is no longer dependent upon humans for survival.

Fumarole: A vent in a volcanic area from which smoke and gases arise.

Home Range: That area traversed by an individual mammal in a certain time period (*e.g.*, seasonal, yearly, lifetime).

Honeydew: A sweet excretion produced by certain insects such as aphids. Also, an exudate from the surface of some galls.

Keystone Species: A species upon which other species in the biological community depend and without which they cannot survive.

Kīpuka: Hawaiian word for an "island" of land (older lava flow with vegetation) surrounded by a more recent lava flow (often without vegetation).

Mycoplasma: A class of bacteria that lack cell walls and may cause disease in plants or animals.

Naiad: An aquatic nymph (young insect that leaves the egg in a relatively advanced developmental stage like the adult stage, but without wings and genitalia).

Operculum: The horny (or sometimes calcareous) plate serving to close the shell of many gastropods (seashells) when the animal is retracted.

Parthenogenesis: Reproduction without fertilization by the male.

Radula: A ribbonlike structure found in the mouth of most mollusks, bearing numerous rows of teeth, which are used to tear up food and take it into the mouth. The radular teeth differ in shape and arrangement according to the food items of the particular mollusk species.

Savannah: Grassland with scattered trees, especially in tropical or subtropical areas with seasonal rains.

Trophallaxis: Exchange of food between social Hymenoptera (bee, wasp, and ant order) and their larvae.

Ungulate: A mammal with hoofed feet. Examples are pigs, goats, cattle, deer, horses.

Windthrow: Uprooted by the wind or a tree or trees so uprooted.

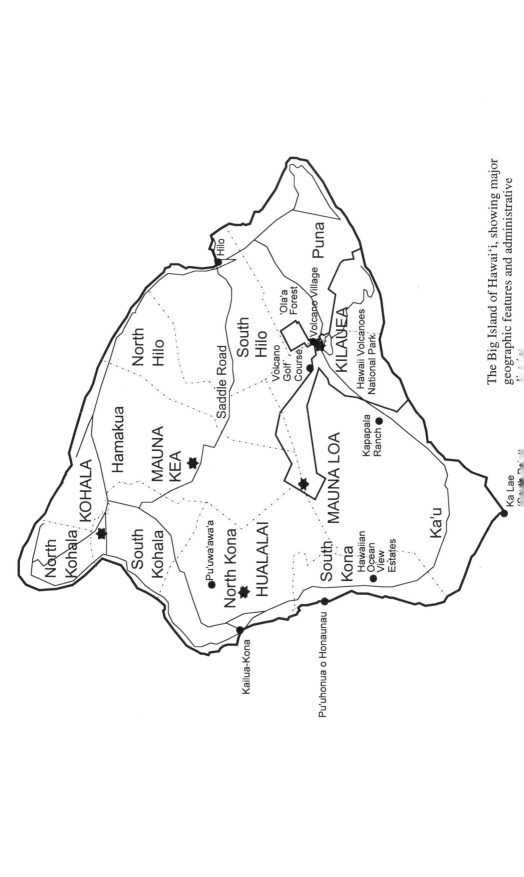

The Big Island of Hawai'i, showing major geographic features and administrative

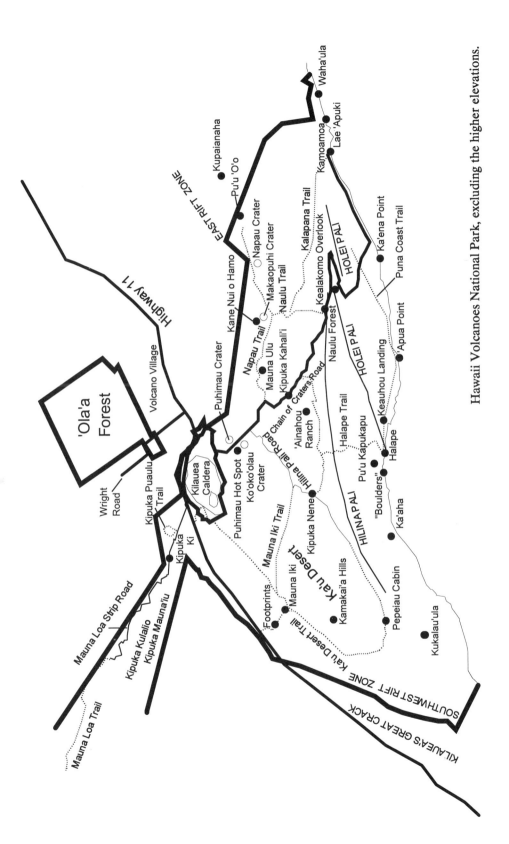

Hawaii Volcanoes National Park, excluding the higher elevations.

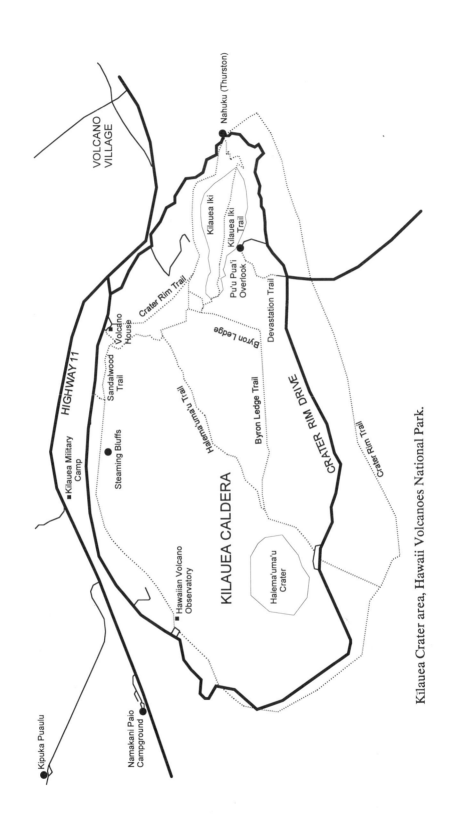

Kilauea Crater area, Hawaii Volcanoes National Park.

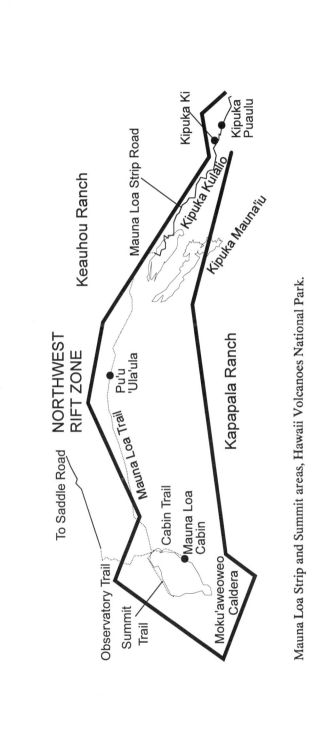

To Saddle Road

Observatory Trail
Summit
Trail

NORTHWEST
RIFT ZONE

Keauhou Ranch

Cabin Trail

Mauna Loa
Cabin

Mauna Loa Trail

Pu'u
'Ula'ula

Mauna Loa Strip Road

Moku'aweoweo
Caldera

Kapapala Ranch

Kipuka Kulalio

Kipuka Maunaʻiu

Kipuka Ki

Kipuka
Puaulu

Mauna Loa Strip and Summit areas, Hawaii Volcanoes National Park.

INTRODUCTION

The story of Hawai'i's plants and animals and the communities in which they exist is a fascinating blend of geology, ecology, and history. The effects of isolation and time, as well as the processes of evolution and colonization, are readily apparent in the face of Hawai'i today. And the impacts of human activities, including introductions of alien, or introduced, species, on flora and fauna that arrived and developed on their own are as striking in the Hawaiian Islands as anywhere on earth.

NATIVE SPECIES
From the volcanic origin of the Hawaiian Archipelago some 40 million years ago (70 million, if the now-submerged Emperor Seamounts are included) to the present day, certain plants and animals have arrived in the Islands without human help. These are the "native species" and can be thought of in two groups: those that are **endemic,** or found only in Hawai'i, and those that are **indigenous,** or found in Hawai'i and elsewhere in the world. Endemic species evolved in Hawai'i from ancestral colonizing forms from which they are now distinct. Indigenous forms may have evolved here or elsewhere, but like endemics they arrived without human assistance.

The majority of Hawai'i's native species are those whose ancestors were able to fly here (for example, birds and bats); those colonizers (or their propagules) carried on wind or ocean currents (for example, fern spores and insects or seeds tolerant of salt water or light enough to be wind dispersed); and those carried to Hawai'i on or in birds (for example, the seeds of some flowering plants, some insects and spiders, and snails). Of course, getting here was only part of the problem; ancestral plants and animals also had to be able to endure and to reproduce successfully enough to overcome competition, inbreeding, and mortality of various sorts -- all detrimental to survival of small numbers of individuals. To reproduce successfully on arrival, it probably helped to be hāpai (with unborn young) or to be able to breed without an opposite sex -- easier for plants and "lower" life forms such as some invertebrates, as a rule.

For the species with the "right stuff" to arrive and survive, the Islands became a land of opportunity -- a cradle of evolution. Hawai'i's isolation and diverse environment, the small size and juxtaposition of different soil and climatic zones on individual islands, the proximity of some islands in the Hawaiian Archipelago to each other, and the absence of flora and fauna present in continental areas but unable to overcome dispersal barriers, encouraged the process of **adaptive radiation,** the formation of numerous diverse species to exploit newly available environments and biological niches. Such groups as the tarweeds, lobelioids, Hawaiian honeycreepers, pomace flies, and long-horned woodborers exhibit remarkable adaptive radiation. Hawai'i is one of the best places in the world to study evolutionary processes.

1

ALIEN SPECIES

Plants and animals brought to Hawai'i by humans can be thought of as either **Polynesian introductions** or **aliens**. The reason for separating the two is that organisms brought by the early Polynesians in voyaging canoes were few in kind, relatively infrequent in arrival, and generally benign in effects on Hawai'i's native flora and fauna. Most were domesticated introductions brought deliberately. Many of these early introductions were adapted to lowland areas cleared, or soon to be cleared, by the human settlers; and many were important enough for human survival to be cultivated or husbanded closely. In contrast, with the arrival of the ships from the continents, the kinds of introduced plants and animals increased dramatically as did the frequency of their arrival. A wider variety of organisms, many with broad environmental tolerances, were introduced for reasons other than basic needs, and many accidental introductions occurred. Increased numbers of people and increased clearing and disturbance of native forests helped the new aliens to spread. Important alien groups that began to predominate included prolific weedy plants tolerant of conditions created by humans; mammals associated with humans, such as ungulates (hoofed mammals) and rats; various gamebirds and songbirds adapted to colder climates; and a number of invertebrates, diseases, and parasites to which native plants and animals were not adapted.

Alien species introductions continue in modern-day Hawai'i. New species enter the State despite precautions, new islands and habitats are reached by aliens (usually with inadvertent human help), and new circumstances or biological niches are created that favor the expansion of already-present invaders. Invasions can be sudden and pervasive. The spread of alien Japanese white-eyes, firetree, and western yellowjackets are but a few examples. Hawai'i is one of the best places in the world to observe serious alien species problems, to study processes and causation of invasion, and to observe the effects of invasions on native ecosystems.

ENDANGERMENT AND EXTINCTION

Studying native and alien species and the processes of evolution and biological invasion has value, but Hawai'i is much more than a laboratory for scientists. It has, unfortunately, become the leading state for both extinctions and Federally listed Endangered Species in the United States. Comprising only 0.2 percent of the nation's land area, the fourth-smallest state contributes about one-third of the plants and birds listed or considered for listing on the Federal Endangered Species list. Of all the plants and birds known to be extinct in the U.S., over two-thirds are from Hawai'i. Over half of Hawai'i's original bird species are known to be extinct, and most of the remainder are Federally Threatened or Endangered. Probably half the original land mollusks and arthropods are extinct, and at least 10 percent of the plants are known to be gone. A third of the remaining plant species or more may eventually be listed; the invertebrates are too poorly known to make assessments of status, but numerous species are candidates for Federal listing as Endangered Species.

The Federal Endangered Species Act of 1973 was designed to protect plant and animal species judged in danger of extinction (Endangered) or in danger of becoming so (Threatened). Species are initially considered "candidates" for Endangered Species status and then are "listed" according to set procedures. Listed species (or populations) are protected by Federal law after a process of information-gathering, publication of intent to list in the *Federal Register*, and public and agency comment. Habitat essential to species survival can also be defined in the listing process. Recovery plans and recovery teams can be created for listed species, to ensure active attempts to bring about downlisting or delisting of species. (The State of Hawai'i has also drafted a list of organisms considered at risk in the State.) The cost and time required to list individual species are considerable and the bias toward more visible species in the listing process has been criticized, as has the idea of essential habitats, some of which may have been historically occupied but are no longer suitable for the species. In Hawai'i, where so many species are at risk, consideration of groups of species (rather than individual species) in the same vulnerable ecosystems seems a more efficient approach than considering species one by one.

MANAGEMENT AND RESEARCH
The extinction crisis in Hawai'i is very real, the loss of biological diversity is staggering, and the extent of alien invasions is discouraging. Simply setting aside a natural area (park or preserve) and doing nothing more to care for it results in further degradation and loss of native components over time. This is so because many remaining native species populations are small, fragmented, and thus subject to decline; and because aggressive alien species invade areas disturbed by natural events (such as hurricanes, windthrow, and fire) and human-caused events (such as fire, road construction, and forest fragmentation and loss). Important changes occurring in areas contiguous to natural areas can affect plants and animals within the protected areas, particularly if forests continuous with those inside the protected areas are destroyed or degraded, or if aggressive alien plants or animals are introduced and encouraged.

Researchers and managers responsible for maintaining Hawai'i's biological heritage spend considerable time and money in efforts to protect and encourage native species and ecosystems, especially through control and removal of alien species. They work closely together to understand what needs to be done to protect the natural resources, to use the most effective methods to do so, and to evaluate the results. The programs are not cheap, but the results have been remarkably effective, particularly when the most ecologically valuable areas are studied and managed incrementally. Not enough money and personnel are available to restore everything to a near-native state, especially all at once. But one can still find native species and communities in many areas of Hawai'i, including Hawaii Volcanoes National Park.

WHAT CAN YOU DO?
The concern of visitors and residents, including landowners of areas near parks and preserves, is vital. Without everyone's active interest, natural areas will become increasingly isolated islands (surrounded by other much modified lands), with continuing native species loss and alien species invasion.

Many people have a difficult time understanding the fact that plants and animals out of place (weeds) can cause endangerment, extinction, and considerable trouble and expense. A beautiful plant seen near a resort area in Honolulu may be a severe threat to native species in a park. An otherwise useful and tasty animal like the domestic pig can destroy a plant and animal community in a natural area. It is difficult to associate individual human actions with such problems. Yet "we the people" introduced pigs and goats, guavas, mosquitoes that carry bird diseases, and innumerable other invasive species to Hawai'i. We can't take back what has been done, but what we do from here on also counts. Here are a few things for which people can take responsibility.

1) Don't release cats, birds, rabbits, reptiles (lizards, etc.), aquarium snails and fish, or other unwanted pets. The Humane Society is the proper place to take unwanted animals. It is illegal to abandon animals in Hawai'i. 2) Report observations of these and other alien species in natural areas to the appropriate State, County, or Federal land managers. 3) Neuter cats (and dogs) not used for breeding, so that those that escape will not be able to produce unwanted offspring to populate our few remaining wild areas. 4) For landscaping, use native plantings or alien species that are not known to be readily dispersed invaders of natural areas. Encourage others to do the same. 5) Clean boots and clothing after hiking trips in lowland areas infested with alien plants, especially on other islands; this is vital prior to hiking in natural areas. 6) Obey quarantine laws and treat forms issued on incoming airlines seriously. Do not deliberately transport plants or animals from island to island or place to place without obtaining Department of Agriculture clearance. 7) Report all sightings of snakes to the Department of Agriculture. 8) Support management programs on natural areas selected by the people for these values, despite objectives that might be in conflict with land uses on private or public lands elsewhere.

PURPOSE OF THIS BOOK
This book was written to tell the stories of some native and alien species found in the Park. We have chosen those species or groups that are most likely to be seen by Park visitors, those that seem most interesting or important to know something about, and those that provide some idea of the diversity of life to be found in the Park. Pencil and prose sketches combined should provide a flavor of the biota of the Park.

If you are aware you might understand; if you understand you might appreciate; if you appreciate you might be concerned, and if you are concerned you might help protect and pass on to future generations a beautiful part of the world.

THE PARK

Hawaii Volcanoes National Park is the largest area in the State in which predominantly native ecosystems are protected and managed. Established in 1916 as a part of Hawaii National Park (with what is now Haleakalā National Park on Maui), Hawaii Volcanoes covers nearly 10 percent (240,000 acres) of the largest island in the Hawaiian Archipelago, and it is one of the few protected areas that include continuous lands from sea level to mountain summit (13,677 ft at the top of Mauna Loa). The summit areas of two active volcanoes, Mauna Loa and Kīlauea, are included in the Park, and their flows through the years and across altitudinal and climatic zones have created substrates of different ages, textures, and chemical composition for the establishment of plant and animal communities.

The Park has been designated an International Biosphere Reserve (1980) and a World Heritage Site (1987), both of which signify value to a worldwide community and a special obligation to manage wisely and well in conjunction with surrounding land use. Even though the Park is large, it does not provide sufficient habitat for the survival of many species and biological communities within its boundaries. To preserve species and biological communities for the long term, Federal and State agencies and private landowners must work together to protect the remaining natural areas, irrespective of administistative boundaries.

Seven ecological zones (seacoast, lowland, mid-elevation woodland, rain forest, upland forest and woodland, subalpine, and alpine/aeolian) are included within the boundaries of the Park. Distinct plant and animal communities occur within each of these zones and are described herein. A special "multizonal" section is included for those species or groups that are readily found in several or all zones.

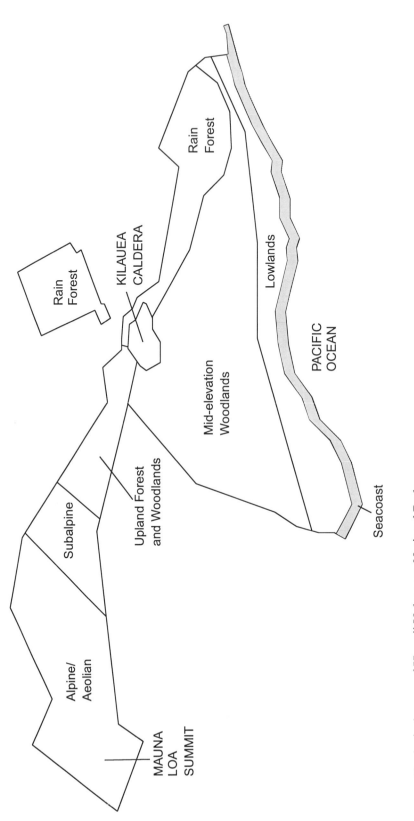

Ecological zones of Hawaii Volcanoes National Park.

MULTIZONAL

Some plants and animals are found in a wide range of ecological zones spanning elevational, temperature, and precipitation gradients. Often, these tolerant species are alien or introduced, successful because of their "generalist" tendencies. However, some native species -- for example, 'ōhi'a (*Metrosideros polymorpha*), 'io or Hawaiian hawk (*Buteo solitarius*), and Hawaiian bat or 'ōpe'ape'a (*Lasiurus semotus cinereus*) -- are also adapted to variable conditions and can be found in many places in the Park in similar abundance. Some special systems, with unique plant and animal communities, may also be found in many areas of the Park; lava flows and caves are two prominent examples that span many ecological zones.

Several species, groups, or systems difficult to assign to any one zone are treated as multizonal. Other species, though occurring in more than one zone, are covered under the zones in which they are more typical or likely to be seen.

'Ōhi'a or 'Ōhi'a Lehua (*Metrosideros polymorpha*)

Myrtle family (Myrtaceae)

Endemic to the Hawaiian Islands

Distribution in the Park: Coast to tree line on Mauna Loa

The 'ōhi'a is the most abundant and widespread native tree in the Hawaiian Islands. It is dominant or codominant in every ecological zone (except the coastal and alpine/aeolian zones) and almost every vegetation type within the Park. 'Ōhi'a trees form the uppermost canopy of the Park's rain forests and are the primary trees in dry lowland, mid-elevation, and subalpine woodlands. Even where other species make up the dominant vegetation cover, such as in the koa woodlands and upland forests of Mauna Loa, the 'ōhi'a remains an important and conspicuous component.

A member of the myrtle family, the 'ōhi'a is closely related to species of similar appearance in the South Pacific. New Zealand, in particular, is a center of distribution for the genus *Metrosideros*, with more than a dozen species including the showy pohutukawa (*M. excelsa*) and the northern and southern rata (*M. robusta* and *M. umbellata*). Some of these attractive New Zealand *Metrosideros* have been planted as ornamentals in California and, to a lesser extent, in Hawai'i. Formerly, the common 'ōhi'a of Hawai'i was considered to be the same species as that found in Tahiti (*M. collina*), but the most recent taxonomic treatment recognizes this and all other Hawaiian representatives of the genus (five species) as distinct and endemic to the Hawaiian Islands.

A morphologically variable species, 'ōhi'a has eight varieties, of which four occur in the Park. All are trees with gray shaggy or flaky bark and gray-green to yellow-green foliage. Leaves are simple, unlobed, and arranged opposite one another on stems. All varieties bear clusters of pompom-shaped flowers with many colorful stamens and small, inconspicuous petals. Flowers are usually red but may be yellow, dull pink, or orange. Some flowers may be seen on individual 'ōhi'a trees throughout the year, but there are usually two peak flowering periods in the Park, one in winter and one in mid-summer. 'Ōhi'a flowers (lehua) produce large amounts of sweet nectar and are a critical food source for several Hawaiian honeycreepers, such as the 'apapane, common 'amakihi, and 'i'iwi. 'Ōhi'a fruits are small three-chambered, top-shaped capsules, which split when dry and release many miniscule linear seeds. These seeds are very light in weight and are dispersed by wind. Many 'ōhi'a trees in the Park, particularly those in areas that have received cinder fall from volcanic vents, bear clusters of reddish aerial roots hanging from main branches. These aerial roots often form when trees are damaged by falling cinders or receive blows from falling trees.

'Ōhi'a varieties may usually be distinguished by the shape, size, and hairiness of their thick-textured leaves. Two hairy-leaved varieties of 'ōhi'a are common in the Park: var. *incana* has round to ovate leaves with undersides covered by short white hairs; var. *polymorpha* has rounded leaves with heart-shaped bases and undersides covered by dense, gray, wooly hairs. Both of these pubescent, or hairy, varieties are physiologically adapted to grow on new lava flows and in dry areas. Variety *incana* is the most common type in the Park and is abundant in the Kīlauea Caldera region, along the East Rift, and in the Park lowlands; var. *polymorpha* is common in the Park's upper reaches, particularly the subalpine woodlands of Mauna Loa. The reflective white or gray hairs on the leaves of these two varieties may help reduce leaf temperatures and prevent water loss to 'ōhi'a plants in sunny, dry sites. The denseness of the matted hairs (particularly in var. *polymorpha*) may serve to trap moist air near the leaf and reduce desiccation in dry and windy conditions. Throughout the world, many plant species adapted to deserts exhibit similar leaf characteristics. The two smooth-leaved varieties of 'ōhi'a are seen most often as rain forest trees. Variety *macrophylla* has large, broad leaves with a few hairs along the midrib, and bark that peels in strips; it is a common component of forests of 'Ōla'a and the East Rift of Kīlauea. Variety *glaberrima* has smaller, completely hairless leaves and inflorescences and is found in mid-elevation rain forests and high-elevation woodlands.

'Ōhi'a seedlings (generally of hairy-leaved varieties) are among the first flowering plants to colonize new lava flows and are preceded as pioneer plants only by algae and ferns. If water is not limiting and there is a source of wind-borne seeds nearby, 'ōhi'a seedlings will appear in cracks and crevices of pāhoehoe flows within about four years. In the Kīlauea region, young 'ōhi'a trees are prominent components of pioneer lava flow vegetation along with native ferns, shrubs, and lichens. In areas of high rainfall, 'ōhi'a trees may be well established within 20 years, and a mature multilayered rain forest may develop from bare lava in as little as 400 years. In closed forests, the shade-intolerant 'ōhi'a seedlings are usually found growing epiphytically on other trees or logs.

Because new lava flows are quickly colonized, the 'ōhi'a forests that subsequently develop on these substrates may be relatively even-aged stands or "cohorts." Mature stands of forest may decline or die synchronously in the space of a few years, a process known as 'ōhi'a dieback. Large stands of 'ōhi'a forest on the windward slopes of the island of Hawai'i declined and died during the 1960s and 1970s, leading many foresters and botanists to search for plant diseases or insect infestations to explain the sudden loss of trees. No causative plant pathogens or insects were found, and today vegetation ecologists recognize 'ōhi'a dieback as a natural successional phenomenon. The "trigger" for decline or dieback may be some climatic instability, such as a drought, an exceptionally wet year, or a strong windstorm. In many areas free of fast-growing alien plants, the dead or dying 'ōhi'a canopy is replaced by a new stand of young 'ōhi'a trees, already present as seedlings but previously prevented from growing by the heavy shade of the canopy. In forests already invaded by alien plants, canopy dieback often results in the proliferation of sun-loving weeds and the conversion of the native forest to one dominated by aliens.

The Park's 'Ōla'a Forest exhibits a different type of 'ōhi'a dieback known as "displacement dieback;" most of the large canopy 'ōhi'a have died, but the dense cover of tree ferns has prevented large-scale regeneration of shade-intolerant 'ōhi'a seedlings. Where feral pigs have disrupted the tree fern layer, alien plants have become prominent.

Dead 'ōhi'a trees or snags remain important elements in forests that have undergone dieback. Snags are used by native birds as perches, sites for territorial displays, and sometimes as nest sites. Dead wood is critical for the larval stage of many native insects. Snags are also important substrates for dozens of primarily epiphytic species of ferns and herbs. Even predominantly terrestrial tree species are often seen growing as epiphytes on large ‘ōhi‘a snags.

‘Ōhi‘a dieback has important implications for preserve designers and land managers of natural areas in Hawai‘i, who must consider the ages of tree stands and substrates within park or preserve boundaries to ensure the preservation of mature closed-canopy rain forest stands, so important as habitat for native birds, invertebrates, and shade-loving understory plants.

'A'ali'i (*Dodonaea viscosa*)

Soapberry family (Sapindaceae)

Indigenous to the Hawaiian Islands

Distribution in the Park: Widely distributed from sea level to above tree line on Mauna Loa

One of the most abundant native shrubs in Hawaii Volcanoes National Park, 'a'ali'i is found in every ecological zone except rain forests and the alpine desert near Mauna Loa's summit. 'A'ali'i is perhaps most characteristic of lowland shrublands, mid-elevation woodlands, and the mountain parkland and subalpine shrublands of Mauna Loa. While typically a shrub in lowland and subalpine habitats, 'a'ali'i is an understory tree in montane koa groves and mid-elevation 'ōhi'a forests.

Both tree and shrub forms of 'a'ali'i have narrow leaves, widest at the tips or middle. Leaf tips are variable, either pointed or rounded, and the leaf surface may be smooth, hairy, or rough. Often young leaves and branch tips are covered by an uneven shiny coating. Flowers of the 'a'ali'i are small, clustered at the ends of branches, and lack showy petals. Individual plants usually have only male or female flowers; male flowers are those with the pollen-bearing stamens, and female flowers have a central pistil, which if pollinated will eventually develop into the fruit. Sometimes male plants will also have some flowers that have both sexual parts together. The dry fruits, or capsules, that develop on female plants are about 0.5 in. long, with two to four papery wings. These persistent capsules may be straw colored but are usually conspicuously red- or purple-tinged and are valued as lei-making material.

The tree form of 'a'ali'i characteristically has a single trunk and upright habit, larger, thinner leaves than the shrub form, and somewhat flattened capsules with only two wings. Because of differences in form and size, the tree and shrub forms of 'a'ali'i were previously considered distinct species. *Dodonaea sandwicensis* was the name given to the tree form, and the shrub forms were known as *D. eriocarpa* and *D. spathulata*. The most current treatment of the genus considers these plants to be one species, which is also found in other tropical and subtropical regions of the world.

'A'ali'i is one of only a few Hawaiian plant species that respond favorably to fire. While individual shrubs may be killed when a fire passes through a community, others resprout from their bases after a low-intensity fire. Also, fire appears to stimulate the germination of 'a'ali'i seeds. Along Chain of Craters Road in many areas burned during recent eruptions, 'a'ali'i has become the dominant plant in open forests and shrublands. A considerable increase in 'a'ali'i was noted after a fire in the lower part of Mauna Loa Strip, where the plant has now become much more abundant than the fire-sensitive pūkiawe.

A small percentage of 'a'ali'i in Hawaii Volcanoes displays symptoms of a "yellows disease," which causes elongated deformed branches, yellowing of leaves, and eventual withering of the entire plant. Two possible causes have been discovered by plant pathologists, a virus and a mycoplasma-like organism (MLO). Diseased 'a'ali'i shrubs are particularly noticeable along Mauna Loa Strip Road in the upland woodlands. While diseased plants apparently do not recover, the yellows disease currently afflicts relatively few individuals of this widespread species.

Both 'a'ali'i and koa are important hosts for the colorful iridescent koa bug and the small blue-gray to green Blackburn butterfly. Both these native insects may be found on 'a'ali'i in the koa groves and open shrublands of Mauna Loa Strip. The butterfly may also be found on 'a'ali'i in lower-elevation woodlands where koa does not grow.

Pūkiawe (*Styphelia tameiameiae*)

Epacris family (Epacridaceae)

Indigenous to the Hawaiian Islands

Distribution in the Park: Coast to 10,000 ft elevation on Mauna Loa

One of the most widespread and common of Hawai'i's native plants, pūkiawe grows in many habitats, including dry windswept coasts, deserts, rain forests, bogs, and nearly barren, frost-prone mountain slopes above tree line. Usually a shrub, pūkiawe may become a small tree in closed moist or wet upland forests. In the Park, pūkiawe occurs as a low-growing compact shrub near the coast, in the Ka'ū Desert, and in 'ōhi'a woodlands of middle elevations. In rain forests of Kīlauea Caldera and 'Ōla'a, infrequently-occurring pūkiawe shrubs are taller and more spindly with lax, spreading branches. The species reaches its greatest size and dominance in the shrub communities of the koa parkland and subalpine woodlands of Mauna Loa Strip, where it may form large, nearly impenetrable thickets more than 10 ft tall. Here the multiple stems of pūkiawe grow densely packed and intertwined. The small twigs are brittle, but the large stems have hard, reddish wood and are covered with shaggy, charcoal gray bark.

The only member of the epacris family native to Hawai'i, pūkiawe has its closest relatives in Australia and New Zealand. In some older books, pūkiawe is referred to as an endemic plant, restricted to the Hawaiian Islands, but today the Hawaiian *Styphelia* is considered to be indigenous; it is the same species as a plant found in the Marquesas, an island group far to the south of Hawai'i.

Pūkiawe leaves vary in size and shape but are usually small, thick textured, and awl shaped. The tips of the leaves end in sharp points, which makes pūkiawe brush very difficult to walk through. The undersides of the leaves are light bluish gray; this silvery hue is particularly pronounced in the young growth at stem tips. Flowers of pūkiawe are white and tiny, only about 0.1 in. long; they are borne inconspicuously among the leaves near branch tips. Pūkiawe fruits are small (about 0.25 in. long) and round. Varying in color from red to pink to white, they are often mottled with two colors. The flesh of pūkiawe fruits is white, rather dry and spongy, and covers a stony-hard center containing several seeds. Pūkiawe fruits are readily eaten by the nēnē or Hawaiian goose, and pūkiawe seeds are a conspicuous component of nēnē scats (droppings) in dry areas such as Ka'ū Desert.

Pūkiawe shrubs are sensitive to fires and are killed unless the fire is of low intensity. Resprouts are only observed on pūkiawe stumps after very "cool" fires. Because of sensitivity to fire, burned shrublands typically have greatly reduced pūkiawe cover. Eventually pūkiawe recolonizes burned areas by seeding in from unburned sites.

Hawaiian Hawk or ʻIo (*Buteo solitarius*)

Eagle and Hawk family (Accipitridae)

Endemic to the island of Hawaiʻi. **Federally listed Endangered Species**

Distribution in the Park: Sea level to tree line (8,500 ft)

'Iolani Palace in Honolulu was named for this "royal hawk," favored by Hawaiian ali'i (chiefs). Fossil records tell us that the 'io was formerly present on other Hawaiian islands, although it now is found only on Hawai'i Island. Fortunately, this Endangered Species (proposed for downlisting to Threatened) is adaptable to alien vegetation and prey, and up to 2,500 birds may be found over most of Hawai'i Island. Females are somewhat larger (16-18 in. body length) than males (15.5 in.) and are able to capture larger prey. 'Io foods include an assortment of native and alien birds, small mammals (female 'io take small Indian mongooses occasionally), insects such as the praying mantis, and some aquatic animals such as crayfish.

Dark- and light-phase birds (apparently at a 2:1 ratio), and immature plumages of each, present some challenges in identification. Adult dark-phase birds have yellow ceres (fleshy area above the bill), legs, and feet and are dark brown above and below. Dark-phase birds less than three years old (first year and subadult) have blue-green ceres, legs, and feet and are mottled on the breast with buffy and light brown feathers. Light-phase adults have dark heads and backs but are white beneath; extensive dark markings occur on breast and throat. Younger light-phase birds have white to rusty heads and breasts. Age differences in cere, leg, and foot color are similar to those of dark-phase birds.

Home ranges of radio-collared 'io average over 1,000 acres, and birds can often be seen soaring overhead. (Hawaiian owls or pueo also soar in the daytime and can be confused with 'io, although they are usually seen closer to the ground.) 'Io generally nest from March to September, but not all individuals nest every year. One bluish egg in a bulky stick nest is the rule. Incubation takes about 38 days, and young birds remain in the nest for two months. Adults feed young for five to eight months after they leave the nest, which probably explains why adults are not ready to nest again the following year.

This easily seen and tame hawk has been subject to harassment and shooting in the past, and it is still disturbed and even killed by thoughtless or ignorant humans, especially around nest sites. Destruction and alteration of Hawai'i's forests have also taken a toll, although hawks are quite adaptable. Predation by cats, rats, and mongooses; avian diseases; and environmental contaminants are all considered of minor importance in limiting 'io numbers at present. However, a species that has such a low reproductive potential and comparatively low total numbers can quickly decline. The fact that 'io are comparatively long-lived birds counteracts reproductive failure, if not prolonged.

Survival of this conspicuous species can be assured by public education, adequate long-term monitoring of populations (and potential limiting factors such as contaminants, disturbance, and habitat degradation), and enforced penalties for harassment. We should implement or continue all these conservation measures and learn as much as we can about the majestic 'io.

Pacific Golden Plover or Kōlea (*Pluvialis fulva*)

Plover and Dotterel family (Charadriidae)

Indigenous; migratory winter visitor from the Arctic

Distribution in the Park: Sea level to 10,000 ft elevation

When this large (11 in.), long-legged shorebird arrives in Hawai'i in August, it is in drab winter plumage -- a mottled brown and gold above and below, with a buffy brown stripe above the eye continuing to the back. Head and breast are lighter brown than back and wings. By the time of departure in late April, most male kōlea have assumed the dramatic breeding plumage (see inset) of black face, throat, breast, and crown and white question-mark-shaped stripe reaching from above the eye to under the wing. The large head and erect posture are further guides to identification, and kōlea run in short, quick bursts as they search for invertebrates in open grassy areas. Kōlea often whistle a loud, clear, two-toned, "kleeip" when they begin their rather erratic flight.

Pacific golden plovers are easily seen in grassy or other open areas in Hawaii Volcanoes. Creation of pasture on ranchlands around the Park has probably allowed a larger wintering population than was present before introduction of domestic animals. A good place to see kōlea at close quarters is Kilauea Military Camp within the Park.

The migration of kōlea is one of the most difficult known -- a distance of about 3,000 mi at an elevation of 20,000 ft, where navigation by sun and stars is possible. Probably about 50 to 60 hours are needed to reach Hawai'i from the breeding grounds on the Siberian and Alaskan tundra. Some Pacific golden plovers winter as far south as coastal areas of northeastern Africa and New Zealand. The closely related American golden plover (*P. dominica*), formerly considered the same species as the kōlea, breeds mostly to the east of *P. fulva* and winters in South America (usually in inland areas). Studies have shown that plant seeds from digestive tracts of kōlea and other shorebirds remain viable upon arrival in Hawai'i. Seeds stuck to feathers or embedded in mud on the feet of migratory birds are another important means of plant dispersal to Hawai'i.

Kōlea are strongly territorial on wintering grounds in Hawai'i, returning to the same patch of ground each year. Yet some kōlea, apparently of both sexes, tolerate other strange kōlea at close quarters. Territory size defended by more aggressive birds can be ten times that defended by less aggressive individuals. The degree of attachment to a territory can be so strong that birds may starve if denied access. At night, kōlea leave their territories to roost in groups in open areas. In Honolulu, they may roost on rooftops, but in Hawaii Volcanoes kōlea are sometimes startled by car lights from their roosting sites along roads.

J. YOSHIOKA

Common Myna (*Acridotheres tristis*)

Starling and Myna family (Sturnidae)

Alien; introduced from India in 1865

Distribution in the Park: Sea level to about 8,000 ft elevation, in
all areas except forest interiors; most commonly in disturbed areas such
as roadsides and pastures and dry open areas at lower elevations
(below 5,000 ft)

Noisy, pugnacious, social, comical, ubiquitous -- all these adjectives describe the common myna. Introduced in 1865 to control army worms, mynas certainly eat their share of insects. And this short-tailed, brown and black, 9-in. bird with white wing patches and bright yellow bill, eyepatch, and legs is easy to observe; it is often perched conspicuously on a tree branch or wire, strutting in an open area, or flying with others of its kind. Common mynas are well adapted to people and their activities, to livestock, and to a variety of habitats in Hawai'i. Mynas also provide some degree of roadside sanitation and can often be seen in small numbers cleaning up carrion or garbage created by humans.

But there is a down side. In the late 1800s, these birds were common even in deep forests, where they nested in cavities, perhaps in direct competition with cavity-nesting native birds (such as the now-extinct 'ō'ō) on several islands. Competition may have extended to insect foods; social species such as mynas can easily dominate other birds in areas where insects are especially abundant. Mynas and other introduced birds are known to harbor parasites and diseases, such as avian malaria and pox, to which native species are not adapted because of long isolation in Hawai'i; and they spread seeds of alien plants in most areas where they occur. Also, mynas prey on eggs and nestlings of other birds. In common with many invasive species, a decline in numbers may have been partly related to depletion of readily available (native) prey. The past effects of common mynas on native Hawaiian species will never really be known.

Male common mynas court females in the spring by presenting feathers, cigarettes, cellophane, or other nest materials. Quivering, bowing, head and neck feather erection, and singing of sorts precede mating, which probably occurs year round and maintains the pair bond. Both sexes build the nest in a cavity, and two to five blue-green eggs are laid. Both sexes incubate for about 13 days, and young leave the nest a month or so after hatching. The immediate area around the nest is defended strongly. Both sexes brood and feed the nestlings and fledglings. The same nest may be used twice or more in a season by the same pair, and the same nest site may be reused in subsequent seasons.

Although more likely to attract attention in Waikīkī or Kailua-Kona than in rural areas, communal myna roosts are characteristic of the species in Hawai'i. The noisy, bubbly sounds of large groups of birds at dusk and dawn and the thick deposits of "whitewash" or guano under roosting trees are signs that mynas are spending the night. Because it is possible to contract a lung disease transmissible from birds to humans in bird roosts, it is best not to linger in these areas unless protected with respirator and immunization. To visitors and residents alike, the conspicuous common myna is now a memorable part of the Hawai'i experience.

J. YOSHIOKA

House Finch (*Carpodacus mexicanus*), House Sparrow (*Passer domesticus*), and Nutmeg Mannikin (*Lonchura punctulata*)

Finch family (Fringillidae), Cardueline Finch subfamily (Carduelinae);
Old World Sparrow family (Passeridae);
Waxbill, Mannikin, and Parrotfinch family (Estrildidae)

Alien. House finch introduced from California before 1870 (native to U.S. Mainland); house sparrow introduced from New Zealand in 1871 (native to Europe and Asia); nutmeg mannikin introduced from Southeast Asia about 1865

Distribution in the Park: House finch in open areas from sea level to shrubland high on Mauna Loa; house sparrow at lower elevations, especially around human habitations; nutmeg mannikin from sea level to alpine scrub

House finches or linnets and house sparrows are small (5.5-6 in.), brown, thick-billed birds that are often seen around houses, farmlots, and open woods. Female house sparrows (upper illustration) have no streaking below, while female house finches are streaked all over. Male sparrows (lower illustration) have gray crowns, black bibs, and grayish cheeks, while male finches usually have pink, red, or yellow foreheads, bibs, and rumps. Finches of both sexes have dark legs, whereas sparrows of both sexes have pale legs. Nutmeg mannikins, also found in the Park, are much smaller (4-4.5 in.), more gregarious birds with dark brown heads and throats, and grayish breasts and sides marked with small dark crescents. Large flocks of mannikins are often found in grassy areas.

House finches eat fruits and insects; in Hawai'i they are also known as "papaya birds" because of their preference for this fruit. They build nests in various alien and native plants in Hawai'i. In Hawaii Volcanoes National Park, house finch numbers have increased in recent decades, based on counts made in study plots over the years. This may have resulted from an increase in ranching and associated water availability over a large area. More likely, however, increasing abundance of alien plants such as firetree, introduced grasses, and banana poka has provided more finch food. House finches lay three to five greenish blue, lightly speckled eggs; they breed from February to August.

House sparrows, sometimes called English sparrows, survive in towns in many parts of the world by eating garbage, seeds, and bread put out by people. They nest in buildings as well as in various native and introduced plants in Hawai'i. House sparrows lay two to four whitish eggs blotched with brown and gray, and breed year round. House sparrows characteristically utter flat, persistent chips and twitters. (House finches have a more musical double-noted call, a distinctive twitter, and a canary-like warbling song with a "burr" at the end.)

Ancestors of the Hawaiian honeycreepers were cardueline finches, the same subfamily to which house finches belong. It is difficult to imagine how two groups of such colonizers, perhaps looking something like the relatively drab seed-eating house finch, evolved into over 50 kinds of honeycreepers (subfamily Drepanidinae), including species that became nectar sippers, insect chasers, caterpillar catchers, and "woodpeckers." Hawai'i can truly be a magic place!

Japanese White-eye or Mejiro (*Zosterops japonicus*)

White-eye family (Zosteropidae)

Alien; introduced from eastern Asia

Distribution in the Park: Ubiquitous -- deep forest to residential areas

This small (4.5 in.) olive-green bird with yellowish to buff throat and breast and a prominent white eye-ring was first released on O'ahu in 1929 by the Territorial Board of Agriculture and Forestry. At least 252 birds were introduced on Hawai'i Island in 1937. A favorite cage bird in Japan, the species is used there in singing competitions. A strong flyer, often found far out at sea, it has now spread on its own. White-eyes are present on all eight main islands of the Hawaiian Archipelago in most habitats and are likely the most abundant bird in the Islands.

In the Park, the frequency of occurrence of this species on census plots increased from 23 percent in the period 1940 to 1944 to 50 percent in 1948 to 1949 and to nearly 100 percent in 1975 to 1980. A 1936 Park checklist did not mention the species. White-eyes are most abundant in moist koa-'ōhi'a forest on Mauna Loa and least abundant in rain forests. Densities in Park woodland, savannah, and scrub habitats are high.

White-eyes often occur in flocks but are difficult to see because they are small and in continual motion. Their scolding twitters and thin "tseets" are often heard, but they also deliver a soft, high-pitched, complex song, something like that of the house finch. They often imitate other birds and are similar in size and color to native honeycreepers such as the common 'amakihi. White-eyes frequently feed on 'ōhi'a lehua blossoms and other flowers but are omnivorous, taking insects, nectar, and fruit. Nesting has been recorded from February to November. Nests are tidily woven cups of fiber and grass (often with a lining of moss), with three to four whitish eggs. Incubation is by both sexes for 11 days, and nestlings fledge in 9 to 10 days.

Although white-eyes are found in nearly all habitats, numbers generally are lower in closed, undisturbed forest than in open forest. A survey conducted by the U.S. Fish and Wildlife Service showed that mejiro populations were higher along forest edges than in forest interiors on several islands in several forest types. Forest edges seem to act as avenues along which Japanese white-eyes disperse. Areas cleared of native 'ōhi'a and koa are colonized by white-eyes and other alien birds in higher numbers and more rapidly than by native species.

An introduced species as numerous and widespread as the white-eye might be expected to have affected native birds. Although competition is difficult to study in wild species, scientists believe that white-eyes have negative impacts on species that feed on similar foods. These include the endemic 'elepaio, common 'amakihi, and Hawai'i creeper, as well as other introduced birds in the lowlands. As white-eye numbers increased explosively in Hawaii Volcanoes from the 1940s to the 1960s, several native honeycreepers decreased. The relationship may or may not have been cause and effect; response to general native forest deterioration and disturbance caused by other alien animals and alien plants may have affected both white-eyes and honeycreepers. For example, white-eyes are definitely attracted to the nectar and fruit of the alien banana poka vine, spread by feral pigs and alien gamebirds.

Recent studies of white-eyes have shown that they can affect entire ecosystems. They are the main dispersal agent of faya tree seeds in natural areas of Hawaii Volcanoes. Together, white-eyes and faya have converted over 30,000 acres of native forest in the Park from largely native to largely alien species since 1961. Alien firetrees can often be seen growing beneath native 'ōhi'a trees, probably because white-eyes and other birds have rested in the 'ōhi'a and defecated seeds. Removal of faya trees in ecologically important areas is possible, but there is no known way to remove Japanese white-eyes at their present stage of abundance in Park forests. Perhaps, like the common myna, once a common invader in rain forests, white-eye populations will someday decline naturally.

House Cat (*Felis catus*)

Cat family (Felidae)

Alien; introduced shortly after the arrival of Europeans (1778)

Distribution in the Park: Sea level to at least 9,500 ft on Mauna Loa

Hawai'i is a paradise for cats as well as people. Partly domesticated at best as pets, house cats readily survive in wild areas on a varied diet including rodents, birds, insects, seafood, garbage, and fruits, depending on availability. Increasing numbers of people in Hawai'i will undoubtedly mean increasing numbers of cats in natural areas, either as pets out for a short hunt or unwanted animals abandoned in some remote place. Established populations of cats reproduce in the wild and add to the feral (domestic animals gone wild) population. Feral cats come in all colors and sizes, but reversion to the ancestral gray "mackerel tabby" form with black markings is not uncommon. Short-tailed cats (with Asian Manx ancestry) are also common. But long tailed or short tailed, white, black, or calico, cats in the wild are larger and more aggressive than most house cats.

Feral house cats are solitary, nocturnal hunters that come together briefly for mating. After a gestation period of about two months, a litter of four to six helpless young are born. Males move considerable distances in hunting forays (covering up to 8,600 acres in a few weeks) and in search of females, and a nightly 5-mi journey in coastal to mid-elevation (4,000 ft) areas of the Park may not be unusual. Presumably cats range just as far or farther on the more severe upper slopes of Mauna Loa.

Because feral house cats are large, far-ranging, nocturnal hunters, they pose a tremendous threat to ground-nesting birds. Their tree-climbing abilities also make them a danger to tree-nesting species. In Hawai'i, the characteristic and unsettling evidence that cats have found a seabird colony is a pair of wings near most bird burrows. In the Park, cats prey on alien gamebirds, nēnē or Hawaiian geese, dark-rumped petrels or 'ua'u high on Mauna Loa, and forest birds. The significance of predation by cats in preventing bird increases, reducing numbers of rare birds, or precluding reestablishment of nesting in a given area is unknown, but it could be considerable. Predation on hawksbill turtle hatchlings may also be important in limiting the reproductive success of this Endangered Species.

Control of feral house cats has been accomplished in different areas around the world by shooting, live or kill trapping, introducing feline diseases, and using toxicants. Diseases such as feline enteritis or leukemia seem risky because pet house cats would also be vulnerable. No toxicants are registered for cat control in the United States. Live trapping in remote areas usually means that cats must be dispatched; the ferocity of most of these animals, the difficulty of carrying captured individual animals out, and the need for efficiency in use of tax dollars are arguments for this. Kill trapping with various kinds of traps is difficult because nontarget species such as nēnē could conceivably be injured. In less remote areas, feral cats captured alive can be taken to Humane Society shelters.

Unfortunately, in the absence of effective management action, cats have become abundant in most backcountry areas of the Park. Unwanted house pets should be taken to Humane Society shelters by their owners, rather than abandoned in the Park or elsewhere. All pets should be neutered as a rule. Cat owners cause unnecessary expenditures and the deaths of native species and cats alike when they behave irresponsibly.

Small Indian Mongoose (*Herpestes auropunctatus*)

Civet and Allies family (Viverridae)

Alien; introduced in 1883 from Jamaica (introduced there from India)

Distribution in the Park: Sea level to about 7,000 ft on Mauna Loa; in general, most abundant in lowland areas and least abundant in wet forests and high elevations

The mongoose named Rikki-Tikki-Tavi achieved heroic stature in a Rudyard Kipling story by protecting a British household in India from the "evil" cobras. In actuality, cobras are rather slow compared to rattlesnakes in the American Southwest; the raised head of the cobra falls toward the victim when it strikes, whereas the rattler strikes more rapidly from a coiled position. Who knows how Rikki might have fared in Texas! In Hawai'i, where no native land snakes are found, Rikki would have had no worries! Small Indian mongooses were introduced to Hawai'i to control rats in sugar cane fields. We now know that this early experiment in biological control did not work because mongooses sleep at night when rats are most active, and because many other sources of food are available to this adaptable predator. Sugar cane damage by rats is currently as high on Hawai'i Island, where mongooses are plentiful, as on Kaua'i, where they either have not yet established or are present in very low numbers.

Known simply as "mongoose" (plural mongooses) in Hawai'i, the scientific name of this animal means "gold-spotted creeper." Mongooses are often seen scurrying on short legs across roads or open areas, with a tail as long as the body extended behind. When mongooses are excited, tail hairs become erect and the tail appears to be nearly the diameter of the body. The local name "Hawaiian ground squirrel" is likely based on fluffy-tailed animals. When the tail hairs are relaxed, however, the tail seems much smaller, and mongooses can look somewhat like rats from a distance. But as noted, rats are rarely abroad in daylight hours.

Male small Indian mongooses can weigh nearly 3 lb, but females are smaller, seldom exceeding 1.3 lb; animals are about 2 ft long including the tail. Mongooses inhabit overlapping "home ranges" but shift activity areas at times, and radio-collared animals have moved over 2 mi in 24 hours to exploit abundant food. Home ranges of mongooses are larger during the breeding season (500 acres) than during other times of the year (125 acres). Females produce two to five (usually three) helpless young, usually in February through September, after a gestation period of seven weeks. Some females have two litters per year. Older animals in the lowlands of Hawaii Volcanoes often have several toes missing (presumably from catching them in cracks in the lava) and teeth that are extremely worn (probably from abrasive foods such as shellfish and cockroaches).

Mongooses are opportunistic, largely solitary predators, taking mice and rats in some areas, large numbers of cockroaches and other insects in others, and crabs at other times and places. Berries and other plant foods are also consumed. Garbage dumps, fish-cleaning sites, campgrounds, and other "enriched habitat" can be concentration points. Mongooses are known to prey on Endangered hawksbill turtle hatchlings on the Park seacoast and undoubtedly do so elsewhere. But to managers of natural areas in Hawai'i, predation on the eggs and young of ground-nesting birds is the most disturbing habit of this small predator.

Endangered ground-nesting species at risk to mongooses include the nēnē or Hawaiian goose, koloa maoli or Hawaiian duck, dark-rumped petrel or 'ua'u, Newell's shearwater or 'a'o, wedge-tailed shearwater or 'ua'u kani, black-necked stilt or ae'o, Hawaiian gallinule or 'alae 'ula, and Hawaiian coot or 'alae ke'oke'o. 'Alalā or Hawaiian crow nestlings often leave arboreal nests prematurely and, while flightless and on the ground, are vulnerable to predation. Reduction of mongooses at places and times when nesting birds are concentrated is especially important. The mongoose may be one of the main limitations to colonial nesting seabirds that once nested abundantly on many islands. Newell's shearwaters and wedge-tailed shearwaters now nest only on Kaua'i, where mongooses are probably absent.

So far, much mongoose control has been accomplished by trapping animals during bird-nesting season, but an anticoagulant toxicant has recently been registered to better protect nesting birds from this predator in key areas. In Hawaii Volcanoes, the chemical may be used to protect nēnē in lowland nesting sites and (with feral house cat control) even possibly to encourage reestablishment of colonies of seabirds such as dark-rumped petrels, Newell's shearwaters, and band-rumped storm petrels or 'akē'akē high on the slopes of Mauna Loa.

Rats:

Black Rat (*Rattus rattus*), Polynesian Rat (*R. exulans*), and Norway Rat (*R. norvegicus*)

Old World Rat and Mouse family (Muridae)

Alien (black and Norway rats). **Polynesian introduction**
(Polynesian rat). Polynesian rat introduced by humans from central
Pacific Islands as early as 400 AD; Norway rat probably introduced
after 1825 from European and American stocks; black rat arrived in
numbers after 1870, of European ancestry

Distribution in the Park: Norway rat generally near human
habitations at lower elevation but ranges to 4,000 ft elevation in the
Park; Polynesian rat in lowland forests and scrub, in suitable habitat
to about 5,000 ft in small numbers; black rat from sea level to
about 9,000 ft

Polynesian or Pacific rats (lower right illustration) are the smallest of the three species of rats found in Hawai'i. Brownish above and white to gray below, they weigh from 1.5 to 3 oz. The tail is about the same length as the head and body, and ears are small compared to those of the black rat (lower left illustration) and Norway rat (upper illustration). Polynesian rats in the Park feed on invertebrates and plant material on the ground and under leaf litter and are not often found in trees or shrubs; thus they generally do not threaten native birds and fruits in Hawai'i's forests. However, Polynesian rats can be serious predators on some kinds of rare insects and on ground- or burrow-nesting seabirds. Polynesian rats, like the other two rat species, are active mainly at night.

Black rats, also known as roof rats, weigh between 3 and 4 oz, whereas Norway rats (the ancestor of the white laboratory rat) weigh up to 13 oz. Black rats have tails that are longer than head and body and large ears that, when pulled gently down, cover their eyes. Black rats have three distinct color phases: uniform smoky gray above and below; brownish gray above and gray below; and brownish gray above with white below. Black rats predominate in mid to low elevations in wet to dry forests and scrub and in gulches near sugar cane fields. They occupy a wider range of habitats than either of the other two rats, wider perhaps than that occupied by the introduced house mouse. Norway rats are most abundant in wet areas, and the Hawaiian name, 'iole po'o wai, means "water-diving rat." They have tails that are much shorter than their bodies, smaller ears than black rats, and white feet.

Studies of black rats in the Park suggest that densities of up to seven animals per acre are likely in moist forests and that movements up to 1,700 ft occur in short periods, although most movements are less than 350 ft. Black rats breed year round, but pregnancy peaks vary from winter in the lowlands to summer higher on Mauna Loa. Although invertebrates are consumed and diets reflect opportunistic feeding, black rats usually eat more seeds, fruits, and other plant material than Polynesian rats. Some of the plants they prefer are rare and must be protected if plant reproduction is to be successful. In the Northwestern Hawaiian Islands, black rats were important culprits in the near-extinction of the Laysan finch and the extinction of the Laysan rail. Because they are arboreal, black rats are also a threat to many species of snails and forest birds. Black rats commonly use holes in trees for nesting and resting, thus competing with and preying upon cavity-nesting birds such as the 'ākepa.

Studies of black rat reduction with toxicants in certain areas of the Park should help researchers determine whether rare plant and bird survival can be enhanced during critical reproductive periods. Persistent use of rodenticides in sugar cane fields in Hawai'i has favored the increase of the more resistant Norway rats at the expense of Polynesian rats. Rats eventually reinvade poisoned areas, and there is currently no hope of completely eliminating them. However, fewer black rats at certain times and in certain places will favor native plants and birds in the Park.

House Mouse (*Mus domesticus*)

Old World Rat and Mouse family (Muridae)

Alien; introduced before 1816

Distribution in the Park: Ubiquitous (except in rain forest),
from sea level to high on Mauna Loa (probably to 13,000 ft),
but most abundant in lowland habitats

These small (0.5 oz) mammals were called 'iole li'ili'i or "little rats" by the Hawaiians. They are usually present wherever humans have been, throughout the world. In Hawai'i, house mice live in a wide variety of habitats, some of which are far from human habitation. They are eaten by small Indian mongooses, feral house cats, both species of owls (pueo or Hawaiian owl and common barn owl), and the Hawaiian hawk or 'io. House mice are omnivorous but primarily eat invertebrates and small seeds. They are the only mice in Hawai'i.

House mice are pale grayish brown, and they are extremely prolific. Females may have one litter per month, each with 5 to 13 young, and breeding begins when mice are only six weeks old. At that rate it is easy to see why, under favorable conditions, and especially in dry lowland habitats, numbers can build up rapidly at times, and mice can be seen almost everywhere, even in daylight hours. Such "plagues" have occurred in recent years on Kaho'olawe, Maui, and the kona (leeward) coast of Hawai'i Island. Generally, outbreaks occur during the fall months. Research in the Park suggests that peak breeding seasons of mice are similar to those of rats (but less restricted) at different elevations, with pregnancy peaking in winter months in lowland areas and in the summer at higher elevations, especially above 5,000 ft on Mauna Loa and in the 'Ola'a rain forest (4,000 ft elevation).

Like rats, house mice can transmit several pathogens to humans. Diseases caused by rodent-borne pathogens in Hawai'i include sylvatic (bubonic) plague (now considered eradicated), typhus, leptospirosis, and salmonellosis (gastroenteritis). The incidence of leptospirosis (a flu-like disease caused by bacteria) in Hawai'i is the highest anywhere in the U.S. The Hawaii Department of Health monitors rodent populations for diseases so that humans will be forewarned if diseased animals increase in wild populations. Because plague is often fatal and other rodent-borne pathogens may cause serious illness, it is best to avoid handling rodents found dead in the wild, or those brought home by a pet cat.

Hawaiian Bat or ʻŌpeʻapeʻa (*Lasiurus cinereus semotus*)

Common Bat family (Vespertilionidae)

Endemic at subspecies level to the Hawaiian Islands;
  Federally listed Endangered Subspecies

Distribution in the Park: Sea level to 10,000 ft

The Endangered Hawaiian bat is the smallest (3-5 in. long) of three subspecies of the hoary bat; the other two subspecies are widely distributed in North America and in Central and South America. The wing-span of this bat is about 13 in., yet males weigh only about 0.5 oz; females are slightly heavier. The bat may be gray or reddish, sometimes without the hoary or whitish tips to the hairs on the back that help characterize the species.

The 'ōpe'ape'a is the only native land mammal in Hawai'i, and the only extant (surviving) bat established here. (The other bats native to Hawai'i are now extinct.) It has been observed in small numbers from sea level to 10,000 ft elevation, flying over most vegetation, whether alien or native, except deep, wet forest. Hawaiian bats fitted with tiny radio transmitters have been found to travel as far as 8 mi from their roosting sites to forage for insects.

Hawaiian bats are solitary except for a brief mating period and when individuals sometimes gather to feed on abundant insects. They roost singly in trees (both alien and native) or crevices and sometimes blunder into lava tubes, where they may be trapped and die. Not much is known about how many 'ōpe'ape'a exist, but one guess is a few thousand in scattered populations, including those on Kaua'i, Maui, and Hawai'i. Currently, efforts are increasing to census bats with "bat detectors," instruments capable of changing the bat's ultrasonic echo-location frequencies to sound audible to humans. Some Hawaiian moths can detect sonar in the frequency range emitted by bats and thus are able to avoid them.

In the Park, Hawaiian bats occur along the Kalapana coast, high on Mauna Loa, and in between. Bats are best seen at dusk or in car headlights, and from August to November when young are on the wing. Some evidence exists that they are inactive in the winter (December-March). 'Ōpe'ape'a feed on a broad range of insects (both alien and native), and they are often found where insects are most abundant -- near water and in the lowlands. Bats can also sometimes be seen chasing insects around street lights in towns. The best time and place to see Hawaiian bats in numbers on Hawai'i Island is in the fall along Highway 11 on the kona (leeward) coast from the Ka Lae (South Point) turnoff to the road to Pu'uhonua o Hōnaunau National Historical Park.

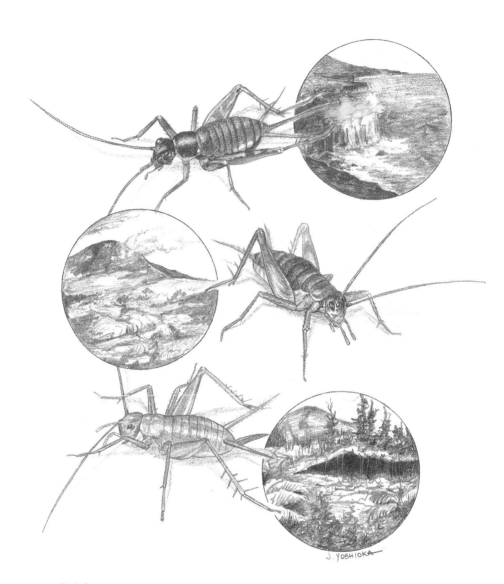

J. YOSHIOKA

Crickets:
  Hawaiian Splash Zone Cricket (*Caconemobius* sp.),
  Dark Lava Flow Cricket (*C. fori*), and
  Big Island Cave Cricket (*C. varius*)

Cricket and Katydid order (Orthoptera), Cricket family (Gryllidae)

Endemic (species discussed here) to the Hawaiian Islands

Distribution in the Park: Splash zone, new lava flows, lava tubes

Hawai'i has many species of crickets, including three native groups (swordtail, tree, and ground or rock [caconemobius] crickets) and a number of introduced forms. The chirps made by males of some of these species, which attract mates in the forest both day and night, were once thought by the Hawaiians to be made by native tree snails or "singing shells." Newcomers to Hawai'i today often confuse cricket songs (made by rubbing forewings together) with the calls of small frogs during breeding season. But the three species of caconemobius crickets discussed here are wingless and do not "stridulate" (rub one body part against another to produce sound). They are "crickless" crickets, according to local naturalist Bill Mull.

These mute midgets are endemic to Hawai'i and are confined to wet rock habitats, including ocean splash zones, lava flows, and caves. A recently discovered coastal species, the Hawaiian splash zone cricket (upper illustration), feeds on flotsam stranded in rocky areas. This species is strongly nocturnal and sometimes the most abundant animal on wet boulders at night. Since it tolerates salt water, this cricket (or a similar species) may have been the initial caconemobius colonizer, arriving on "rafts" of debris from distant shores. It is found on all main Hawaiian Islands. Another form, even more recently discovered, is found near anchialine pools away from the splash zone. It may also prove to be a new species.

The dark lava flow cricket (middle illustration) appears to be more closely related to the Big Island cave cricket (lower illustration) than to the Hawaiian splash zone cricket. Dark lava flow crickets are known to colonize new pāhoehoe lava flows within a month of solidification. This wingless black species lives in cracks during the daytime and emerges at night to feed on windborne debris (plant and animal) concentrated in cracks and surface irregularities. Sometimes meals are even steam heated or broiled on the spot by nearby hot lava! As vegetation fills in the cracks on lava flows, lava flow crickets, which must depend on moisture in deep cracks to withstand desiccation, can no longer survive. They are not found on lava flows over 20 to 100 years old (depending on local conditions and type of flow).

Big Island cave crickets live in the lava tubes formed in past eruptions and have evolved in less than a few hundred thousand years from surface-dwelling ancestors. True troglobites (species restricted entirely to caves), these crickets are blind, lack body pigmentation, and are omnivorous. They share the silent darkness with other crickets evolved from surface tree crickets (*Thaumatogryllus*) and a number of other fascinating invertebrates. Like many animals, they communicate by pheromones (odor-producing chemicals).

Although the casual visitor will probably not spot these small inhabitants of many ecological zones, careful observation may be rewarded with a glimpse of these and other inconspicuous residents of the Park.

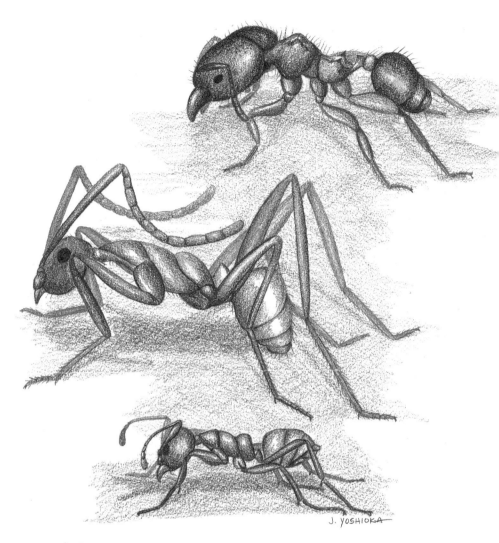

Ants:
 Big-headed Ant (*Pheidole megacephala*),
 Long-legged Ant (*Anoplolepis longipes*), **and**
 Argentine Ant (*Iridomyrmex humilis*)

Ant, Wasp, and Bee order (Hymenoptera), Ant family (Formicidae)

Alien (probably all ants in Hawai'i)

Distribution in the Park: Big-headed ant from sea level to
 about 2,500 ft; long-legged ant from sea level to about 4,000 ft;
 Argentine ant predominantly 4,200 to 8,000 ft

Ants are among the most widely distributed and abundant of land animals, and many ant species eat animals, especially other invertebrates. Humans have introduced at least 40 species of ants to Hawai'i, of which less than 10 have been recorded in the Park. All ants found in Hawai'i are social animals to some degree; those most dangerous to native species generally live in large colonies. A few species may have arrived in canoes of early voyagers to the Islands, but numbers of species most certainly increased dramatically after European people landed. Three species that are especially harmful to native Hawaiian animals are found in the Park.

Big-headed ants (top illustration) were first recorded in Hawai'i in 1886 and are believed largely responsible for the disappearance of most native insects and spiders, and possibly some native birds in lowland areas of the State. This species has been recorded in 'ōhi'a canopies as well as on the ground at elevations up to 2,500 ft. Although it has been the most abundant ant of the Park lowlands for nearly 50 years, dominant ant species change over time, and big-headed ants are now absent where long-legged ants (center illustration) are present in many areas of Hawai'i. Big-headed ants are not especially tolerant of cold, nor of extremely low or high humidity. They are brown with a spine on the thorax (middle section), and soldiers have proportionately enormous black heads and jaws. Workers are about 0.1 in. long, but queens can reach about 0.3 in. Nests are generally underground or beneath various objects, and mating flights (with winged queens and males) provide a means of dispersal.

Long-legged ants, originally native to Africa, were first reported in Hawai'i in 1952 and first seen in the Park in 1982 at Waha'ula. The species has since been observed (one individual) in Nāmakani Paio Campground at about 4,000 ft elevation, no doubt carried there by humans. Fortunately, long-legged ants prefer moist lowland areas, and a queen and social system would likely be necessary for establishment in the uplands. Long-legged ants are especially troublesome to immature native insects such as damselflies (order Odonata) that frequent areas around streams, ponds, and anchialine pools. Even nonnative cockroaches (order Blattaria), the only other arthropod common in some lowland areas, must remain active to avoid capture by these ants.

The aggressive Argentine ant (bottom illustration) is considered by many to be the world's worst ant pest. This small (about 0.1 in.) blackish brown ant dominates throughout northern and temperate zones of the globe and at higher elevations in the tropics. It was first reported from Honolulu in 1940 and reached Hawaii Volcanoes only in 1967. In Hawai'i, where much of the remaining native terrestrial biota is found at higher elevations, Argentine ants prey on native insects, which are important as pollinators of native plants, as food items for native birds, and as members of unique biological communities. Like the big-headed ant, Argentine ants are found high in forest canopies, often in large numbers, and they likely cause problems for nesting native birds and native arboreal invertebrates.

Argentine ants are especially fond of sweets and survive well in human habitations and refuse sites. They are characteristically very active when one turns over something and exposes a group of them (usually 100+). Ground nests are typically found in the soil, from which individuals forage out along scent trails in search of food.   Eggs are small, pearly, and elliptical in shape.   Queens are flightless, so the species must spread by walking, thus slowing invasion rates and making control feasible.   In Haleakalā National Park on Maui, where rare high-altitude native insects have been better studied than in Hawaii Volcanoes, Argentine ant colonies have been temporarily controlled in localized areas with an insecticide. Since ants pass attractive foods rapidly through the colony in a process called trophallaxis, they are especially vulnerable to poisoned baits carried home by foraging workers. Removal or reduction of one alien animal species (small or large) to protect many unique native species is often necessary in Hawaiian natural areas.

SPECIAL MULTIZONAL SYSTEMS

LAVA FLOWS

On Hawai'i Island, recent lava flows can still be found from the top of Mauna Loa to the edge of the sea. Such flows provide unique opportunities to study the arrival and establishment of new life as barren substrates cool. Flows of known ages that encompass considerable ranges in elevation and/or span large temperature and rainfall gradients provide especially useful areas where biologists can determine effects of these variables on colonization patterns of plants and animals without worrying about differing ages of substrates. And when different-aged but otherwise similar lava flows are compared side by side under otherwise similar conditions, the effects of time alone on plant and animal communities can be seen.

One surprising discovery in studies of life on new lava flows is that animals often arrive before plants. Invertebrates that feed on wind-borne debris may colonize pāhoehoe lava flows within a month after an eruption ceases. Algae may take six months or so to establish themselves, probably depending on the accumulation of enough nutrients; algae, mosses, and ferns can still be largely limited to edges of the flow a year after eruption ceases. Extensive variations in temperature, humidity, and wind on these barren, black "neogeoaeolian" surfaces (new wind-blown substrates) must make life difficult for both plants and animals, but discontinuities in the lava surface that moderate temperature and humidity and encourage accumulation of wind-borne nutrients are the key to survival.

Early animal colonizers on lava flows include the wingless nocturnal dark lava flow cricket (*Caconemobius fori*) and a large endemic wolf spider (*Lycosa* sp.). Other animals found well away from the edges of cooled flows include a number of alien arthropod scavengers. Among the plants, algae, ferns, 'ōhi'a (*Metrosideros polymorpha*), lichens, and mosses establish early, usually in that order. Alien plants often arrive late in this harsh habitat; they are not as well adapted to it as natives. Slow-to-cool areas such as cinder falls might show little sign of life even after three years, but most surfaces are colonized much sooner by at least some life forms. By nine years after eruption, some cracks and crannies are crowded with plants, but other similar areas are strangely barren. Distances from seed sources and effects of prevailing northeast trade winds also influence establishment.

Survival of 'ōhi'a trees on older flows seems to depend on the depth of ash or lava deposited and nutrient availability. Alien plants that do manage to colonize early are sometimes outcompeted by better-adapted natives with the passage of time. Dark lava flow crickets usually abandon a lava flow when it becomes covered with vegetation (within 20-100 years). Wolf spiders are apt to be found on older, more hospitable substrates as well as on early flows. Even at the top of Mauna Loa (13,677 ft elevation), a stone desert with extreme temperatures and precipitation often falling as snow, lichens, mosses, and over a dozen species of resident arthropods can be found on lava flows of widely varying ages. In such alpine/aeolian areas, many invertebrates such as wolf spiders, wēkiu bugs (*Nysius wekiuicola*), and various flies scavenge or prey upon other invertebrates blown on upslope winds and numbed by cold to which they are not adapted.

CAVES OR LAVA TUBES

Lava tubes originate when cooling crust forms over underlying molten lava streams. The crust insulates moving lava, but eventually the sources of the flow cease and tubes empty of molten material. Once cooled, such "caves" can support life adapted to limited food sources such as tree roots from the surface, slime consisting of organic material leached from above, bacteria and fungi that live on the slime, and other cave colonizers. Connections among tubes and cracks under the earth's surface may allow colonization of newly formed tubes from other older areas.

Animals that were able to survive these dark, cold, humid environments (many of which contain lethal gases) primarily evolved by adaptive shifts from ancestors in surface forest, lava flow, or seacoast environments. It might seem that underground species have had more time to evolve on the older islands than on the comparatively young island of Hawai'i (800,000 years old), but much underground habitat on the older islands has collapsed; diversity of life in lava tubes is really correlated more closely with size of subterranean habitat than with age of island. Cave-adapted, and indeed obligate (cave-restricted), forms in the Park include a blind species of wolf spider (*Lycosa howarthi*); several insects including a mute or "crickless" cricket (*Caconemobius varius*), a blind terrestrial water-treader (*Cavaticovelia aaa*), a thread-legged bug (*Nesidiolestes ana*), planthoppers (*Oliarus polyphemus* and related species), a blind earwig (*Anisolabis howarthi*), and springtails (order Collembola); and white millipedes (order Diplopoda). Reduction of eyes, wings, pigments, cuticle thickness, and spines are characteristic adaptations. Longer, thinner appendages and reduced numbers of young are also frequently found. Behavioral and physiological adaptations include slow or little movement, increased tolerances to considerable moisture and unusual gases, increased parental care of young, and increased sensory structures.

Caves are zoned habitats for plants and animals, with different communities found in each zone. Entrances may be protected habitats for rare plants and nesting or roosting sites for owls, petrels, and other birds. Rats and other surface forms may forage beyond this area into a transition zone where surface influences of moisture and gas exchange are felt, but generally not into the deep cave zone with its relatively stable air mass saturated with water vapor. Cave-adapted species are largely restricted to deep (stagnant air) zones. Birds and bats and other smaller surface creatures may fall through vertical cave entrances and become trapped and fossilized in caves. Indeed, some of the most exciting discoveries in recent years in Hawai'i have been the amazing variety of extinct Hawaiian birds discovered in sink holes and lava tubes.

Hawai'i's caves are also sites of unique geological formations, and some were once used by early Hawaiians for burials, shelter, water collection, and artistic expression in petroglyphs. Combined biological, geological, paleontological, archaeological, and cultural values mean that considerable knowledge is necessary to avoid causing damage to these resources even during brief visits. Because exploration of most of this subterranean area in the Park remains for the future, a conservative approach to cave use has been taken by Park managers. Several laws mandate caution, both for resource protection and for visitor health and safety. Permits are necessary to enter all lava tubes except the lighted portion of Nahuku (Thurston Lava Tube), and a classification system currently puts most caves off limits except to those with an approved designated scientific purpose and considerable expertise. Some recreational caving in the Park may be possible once a better knowledge and inventory of natural, cultural, and geological resources has been obtained. In the meantime, several well-known caves exist outside Park boundaries for recreational use by island visitors.

KĪPUKA

Kīpuka are islands of older vegetation surrounded by lava flows or by less-developed plant and animal communities. Park kīpuka such as Kīpuka Puaulu and Kīpuka Kī in the upland forest and woodlands zone and Kīpuka Nēnē in the mid-elevation woodlands zone are large and accessible enough to be named on maps and experienced by many visitors. Other kīpuka of various sizes (up to several thousand acres) and shapes, many of which remain unnamed, are scattered throughout the Park.

Because kīpuka are usually separated by less hospitable terrain, distinct plant and animal forms may develop in different kīpuka over time. Like islands surrounded by water, these areas are important in the process of evolution, especially for less mobile forms. In fact, some lava tubes may have been colonized long ago by kīpuka species, which gradually (after isolation) developed into new species now confined to lava tubes. Unfortunately, some of these oases of greenery have been used in the past for logging, planting of alien grasses for livestock, and grazing.

Kīpuka are pleasant places for people to visit, not only because of the richness of native plant and animal life, but because many are less disturbed by alien plants and animals than less-isolated areas. Alien plants, unable to disperse across fairly large expanses of lava, and feral pigs (*Sus scrofa*), which are at least slowed by rugged 'a'ā flows, are less evident in remote kīpuka than elsewhere. However, rats (*Rattus* spp.) and small Indian mongooses (*Herpestes auropunctatus*) seem to reach even the most distant and isolated kīpuka over time.

One beautiful remote kīpuka, composed primarily of lowland rain forest and now covered by lava from the Pu'u 'Ō'ō eruption, was seemingly less frequented by mosquitoes than the nearby forest. Fewer mosquito breeding sites were available there because pigs seldom crossed the lava to create them; exposure to breezes blowing across the barren landscape may have also reduced mosquito immigration. This large (175-acre) Kīpuka had a denser canopy than nearby forest and less exposed ground surface as measured in comparable vegetation plots. The total number of native species was similar in both areas, but more species of fragile native ferns were found in the Kīpuka. Perhaps because of the thick forest canopy, the Kīpuka showed somewhat less native species cover near the ground than the adjacent forest, and no alien grasses or herbs were found there. Only half as many alien plant species (all woody plants) were found in plots in this Kīpuka as compared with adjacent rain forest plots.

Kīpuka are being formed during the Pu'u 'Ō'ō eruption but will likely contain a greater number of introduced plants than kīpuka formed in the past. This is so because more aggressive alien species are present now and are becoming more widely distributed in the Park.

THE SEACOAST

The seacoast zone of Hawaii Volcanoes National Park, like much of the seacoast of the rest of the island of Hawai'i, is exceedingly rugged; isolated white-sand beaches and tide pool areas inhabited by various kinds of marine life are accessible only to the more adventurous visitors who care to hike through the hot, dry lowlands of the Park to reach geologically older shoreline areas. Hawai'i Island is young and growing, and the shoreline within the Kalapana area of the Park continues to be covered and redelineated by lava flows entering the sea. Erosion of active basaltic flows, deposition and stabilization of the eroded material into permanent beaches, and subsequent colonization by plants and animals of cooled coastline lava flows and newly formed beaches are long-term, ongoing processes.

Although some shoreline within the Park still exhibits the sea cliffs, tide pools, and lava benches formed in prehistory, more recent lava flows entering the sea from Kīlauea Volcano have produced the inhospitable, barren, seemingly lifeless coast of the Kalapana Extension of the Park that is seen by most visitors. Even areas that have so far escaped being overrun by lava have been drastically altered by the eruption. Less than 10 years ago, this shoreline of the Park consisted of sea cliffs plummeting some 50 ft to the ocean. Since the current eruption began, black sand, formed by the explosion of molten lava as it meets the water, has been deposited along the bases of the sea cliffs by ocean currents. Extensive beaches have formed, nearly burying the rocky cliffs that were once habitat for seabirds such as the black noddy or noio *(Anous minutus melanogenys)* and various shellfish and other marine creatures. These black-sand beaches will disappear and reappear with changes in tides, currents, wave action, and further eruptive activity.

Along the older sections of the Park's seacoast, terrestrial plants and animals continue to thrive on or near rocky cliffs, lava benches, tide pools, and occasional beaches of white sand, contrasting with the stark coastal lava fields of more recent volcanic activity. Rocky cliffs subjected to the surge of waves are often pinkish, due to coralline algae *(Porolithon* spp.) that encrust them. In addition to the coralline algae, sea lettuce or limu pālahalaha *(Ulva* spp.), limu 'aki'aki *(Ahnfeltia concinna)*, and other limu (seaweeds) grow firmly attached to the substrate. The roiling, turbulent habitat also supports a variety of animal life. The hā'uke'uke *(Colobocentrotus atratus)* or shingle urchin is found in this zone along sections of the shore where the full force of surf and wave action occurs. The flattened, broad-based shape of this sea urchin is an adaptation for survival in this type of environment, as is the similar shape of mollusks known as 'opihi or limpets *(Cellana* spp.). Another conspicuous inhabitant of the surge zone, the large, flat-bodied grapsid crab known as the 'a'ama or rock crab *(Grapsus tenuicrustatus)*, skitters along the face of the cliff just out of reach of the crashing surf.

Horizontal surfaces of ancient lava flows form benches at or just above mean tide level along older coastline. While the seaward faces of these benches are much the same as the sea level faces of rocky sea cliffs, crevices and depressions in the benches form tide pools, providing varied saltwater environments (depending on degree of exposure to air or water) for plants and animals. Greatest fluctuations in temperature, salinity, and submergence occur in those pools farthest from the sea; blue-green algae, mollusks, grapsid crabs, gobies, and blennies are characteristic plants and animals of these more inland saltwater tidal pools. (Anchialine pools are discussed elsewhere.) In the more stable marine environment of tide pools on the seaward edge of the lava benches, plant and animal communities include various seaweeds and worms, mollusks (snails, etc.), crustaceans (crabs, shrimps), and echinoderms (sea urchins, sea cucumbers, starfish).

Several species of shorebirds, which migrate to Hawai'i during the winter months, can be spotted foraging on the lava flats for small invertebrates and limu. The wandering tattler or 'ūlili (*Heteroscelus incanus*) is the subject of a favorite Hawaiian song, "'Ūlili E"; bristle-thighed curlews or kioea (*Numenius tahitiensis*) and ruddy turnstones or 'akekeke (*Arenaria interpres*) can also sometimes be observed in relatively undisturbed coastal areas in the Park.

Small beaches of white sand occur at 'Āpua Point, Keauhou Landing, Halapē, and "Boulders" in the Park, and also landward of some of the older lava benches, where the remains of coral animal skeletons, seashells, and coralline algae have been crumbled and deposited by the sea. This material has been entrapped in the irregular shoreline to form more or less permanent habitat for other forms of marine life such as ghost crabs or 'ōhiki (*Ocypode ceratophthalmus, O. laevis*). Ghost crab presence is evidenced by well-defined mounds of sand formed by mature male crabs as they dig spiral burrows into which they attract females for mating. Female hawksbill turtles (*Eretmochelys imbricata*) also use the isolated, undisturbed sandy beaches in the Park to come ashore and lay their eggs. "Tractor tracks" indicate that turtles have recently been present, and it is necessary to minimize human disturbance to protect this Endangered Species. Naupaka kahakai (*Scaevola sericea*) and pōhuehue or beach morning glory (*Ipomoea pes-caprae* subsp. *brasiliensis*) are characteristic plants along the older shoreline; both stabilize the sand into safe havens for other life. Occasional coconut palms or niu (*Cocos nucifera*), some planted by modern-day humans, also dot the landscape and provide oases of shade and additional habitat for various animals such as geckos and invertebrates.

Recent lava flows, both rough 'a'ā and smoother pāhoehoe, from several major vents along the East Rift of Kīlauea Volcano have flowed downslope and added new coastline to the Park between 'Āpua and Ka'ena points. These flows originated from the Mauna Ulu eruption series of 1969-1974, and at present (1994) from vents at the base of the Pu'u 'Ō'ō cone. The flows from Pu'u 'Ō'ō and Kūpaianaha destroyed the entire village of Kalapana, to the east of the Park, in 1990, as well as the Park's Waha'ula Visitor Center (1989) and Kamoamoa Campground (1992). The heiau at Waha'ula, one of the most famous heiau or temples of Hawai'i Island, is now surrounded by lava from the ongoing eruption. Waha'ula Heiau was built about 1100 A.D., reputedly by Pā'ao, a famous kahuna (priest) from Tahiti.

Many Hawaiian villages dating from the pre-European contact period existed along the Puna and Ka'ū coasts, including the part of the coastline now within Hawaii Volcanoes National Park. These villages were concentrated on the wetter shores of Puna corresponding to the eastern part of the Park. Settlements in the western lowlands were primarily small fishing villages, but those of the east were farming communities as well, as evidenced by various archaeological remains. In addition to Waha'ula Heiau, the area contained house sites, a portion of cobblestone trail, sweet potato pits, and petroglyphs or rock carvings, all evidence of thriving Hawaiian communities. These cultural resources were mapped and studied by Park archaeologists before lava from the current eruption covered most traces of former human habitation. Federal and State laws protect the cultural resources of the Park from vandalism and collection (including excavating, removing, desecrating, or otherwise disturbing) any archaeological sites or remains.

The seacoast of Hawaii Volcanoes is a hostile land of rugged beauty, to be treated with respect. Volcanic hazards in the Kalapana Extension area and rough terrain preclude casual visits to most of the remote seacoast of the Park. The privilege of taking any type of marine life from the eastern Park boundary southward to 'Āpua Point, by fishing, gathering, or any other means (including the harvesting of shellfish and crabs), is extended only to residents of Hawaiian ancestry residing in the Kalapana area.

J. YOSHIOKA

Niu or Coconut Palm (*Cocos nucifera*)

Palm family (Arecaceae)

Polynesian introduction

Distribution in the Park: Coastal groves at ʻĀpua Point, Keauhou
Landing, and Halapē; Kalapana coast where spared by eruption

To many people, the coconut palm symbolizes the vegetation of tropical islands, and this plant is often depicted in photographs and drawings of coastal Hawai'i. Yet the coconut (called niu by the Hawaiians) is not native to these islands but was brought here by the voyaging Polynesians who first populated Hawai'i. An immensely useful plant, the niu provided the Hawaiians (and other Polynesians) with food and oil (flesh of fruit), utensils (shell), fiber for cordage (husks), thatching and basket-making material (leaves), and posts for structures (trunk). It is hardly surprising that coconuts would be brought along on ocean voyages, particularly by people intent upon settling a new island group. The coconut was planted less widely in Hawai'i than in other islands of the South Pacific, perhaps because it was less important as a food here. Coconut oil was not valued as highly as kukui (candlenut) oil by Hawaiians.

The place of origin of the coconut is not known but is thought to be somewhere on the shores of the Indian Ocean. The plant was widely distributed in the Old World tropics in ancient times and was carried throughout the tropical Pacific. The fruit of the coconut palm (the coconut itself) does float and is capable of surviving in seawater for about four months. Therefore, once the coconut is brought to an island group and planted, the species can spread unaided from island to island.

The niu or coconut is typically tall and single-trunked, and at maturity it can attain a height greater than 100 ft; dwarf forms also exist, and these are frequently cultivated. The trunk of the coconut palm is relatively slender, with a swollen base and characteristic rings, which are marks left after leaves detach and fall. Like most palms, the sturdy leaves are borne only at the top of the trunk; they may be as long as 18 ft and are pinnately compound (shaped like a feather), with perhaps 100 narrow leaflets arranged along a central stalk.

Flowers are small and dull colored in large, branched clusters, which emerge from the leaf bases. Most of the several hundred flowers of a cluster are male, bearing only the pollen-producing structures or stamens. Female flowers are found near the base of the branched flower clusters; these are the flowers that, when fertilized, form the fruit of the palm, the coconut. The coconut (which is not actually a nut but a fruit type called a "dry drupe") takes more than a year to develop and consists of a fibrous husk surrounding a hard inner shell, within which is the edible coconut "meat" and watery liquid.

The coconut palm is not widespread or common in Hawaii Volcanoes, but it does occur at several coastal localities, including the sites of old Hawaiian villages. A few scattered individuals may be seen growing on Hōlei Pali, more than 500 ft above sea level, where they were undoubtedly planted. Until the area was covered by lava from the ongoing eruption, the Park's most accessible sites with coconuts were Kamoamoa and Waha'ula, where tall palms graced the shore and surrounded the popular picnic area and Hawaiian village site.

J. YOSHIOKA

Hala or Screwpine (*Pandanus tectorius*)

Screwpine family (Pandanaceae)

Indigenous to the Hawaiian Islands; also native to many Pacific islands, Australia, New Guinea, the Philippines, and Indonesia

Distribution in the Park: Kalapana coast where spared by eruption

The hala (or pū hala), formerly known as *Pandanus odoratissimus,* is a tree characteristic of wet to moist coastal forests in windward Hawai'i. Hala are relatively small trees, rarely exceeding 30 ft in height. They are typically much branched, with slender, ringed trunks. One of the most striking characteristics of the hala is the numerous overlapping prop roots, which support the relatively weak-stemmed plant. Hala plants are unisexual, bearing either male or female flowers; the trunk of the male hala is considerably harder than that of the weak-cored female tree. The fragrant male flowers (hīnano) are borne in large, pendent clusters protected by large, yellow bracts (leaf-like structures). Tiny female flowers occur in round clusters at branch tips; these later develop into large, globose, collective fruits containing many (perhaps 50) fruitlets or "keys" (inset). When ripe, these keys are brightly variegated yellow, orange, or red and may be strung into colorful leis. In ancient times, the dried fibrous fruitlets were useful as paint brushes; the flesh of ripe fruit could also be eaten, although because of irritating crystals and unpalatability, this was done only in times of famine. While the aggregate hala fruit superficially resembles a pineapple (a nonnative plant), the two species are in different plant families and are not closely related.

The leaves of hala (lau hala) are long, narrow, and drooping and in mature plants are clustered at branch tips. In younger plants, the leaves are spirally arranged along the stem. The most pronounced feature of hala leaves is the row of sturdy prickles found along the margins and midrib. Although spiny, the leaves of hala are the most useful part of the plant to Hawaiians, who prepare the leaves by stripping off the prickles, then plait the lau hala into mats, baskets, and many other everyday objects. In ancient times, lau hala were used to make sails for outrigger canoes. In some areas without pili grass, the leaves were important as thatching material for houses.

The hala is thought by some to have been intentionally introduced to Hawai'i by Polynesian settlers, and there is no question that hala was propagated and planted near Hawaiian homes and villages. Its fruits readily float, however, and the species may have colonized Hawai'i without the help of humans. Once here, the floating fruits of hala allowed dispersal to shores throughout the Islands. Recently discovered "fossil" remains of hala from Kaua'i indicate that the plant has been in Hawai'i for a million years.

While hala trees are abundant in undeveloped wet seacoast and lowland areas of Hawai'i Island, particularly in the Puna District, expanses of hala forest do not occur in Hawaii Volcanoes, where little suitable habitat exists. Hala trees were a component of some of the lowland forests of Waha'ula near the Park's Kalapana District Visitor Center, but that entire area was covered by lava in 1989-91. Until 1992, hala could still be seen at Kamoamoa Campground and Picnic Area, but because of the ongoing eruption from the Pu'u 'Ō'ō and Kūpaianaha vents, well-developed stands are now best viewed in coastal areas outside the Park.

Milo (*Thespesia populnea*) **and Hau** (*Hibiscus tiliaceus*)

Mallow family (Malvaceae)

Indigenous to the Hawaiian Islands; both occur throughout tropics

Distribution in the Park: Scattered coastal sites

The mallow or hibiscus family contains more than 20 species native to Hawai'i, including two shrubby trees seen most often near the coast, milo and hau. Hawaiians had many uses for both these plants, and some believe they are Polynesian introductions rather than native species.

Milo (inset) is a small tree, and because of its attractive flowers and foliage it has been planted as an ornamental in some lowland towns and parks. Older specimens are usually single-trunked with dark scaly, furrowed bark. Milo leaves are shiny, dark green, and prominently heart shaped, with rounded bases and elongated, pointed tips. Large yellow flowers with dark red or purple centers are much like those of hibiscus, but they are more cup shaped and do not open widely. The dry fruits of the milo are flattened, five-ridged, brown capsules; these are numerous during the late winter and spring. Extremely salt tolerant, this tree may be seen along the coast mixed with hau and hala, where it is often sharply wind-sculpted from strong on-shore breezes. During the winter, salt spray from high surf may partially defoliate the canopy of milo trees, but they survive and regain their foliage in the spring or summer. Milo is also a component of the vegetation surrounding several shallow brackish anchialine pools near Halapē and Keauhou Landing. Hawaiians fashioned bowls from the beautiful wood of the milo; modern woodworkers also use milo for bowls and carvings. The young leaves of milo are edible, and parts of the tree were used for dye and medicine in old Hawai'i.

Hau (main illustration) is a more shrubby, spreading species than milo, and in wetter seacoast areas it may form dense thickets. Hau was formerly abundant in the coastal forest at Waha'ula and scattered in the Kamoamoa area, but its natural habitat in the easternmost part of the Park's seacoast and lowland zones has been largely covered by lava from the ongoing eruption. It may still be seen in the Park near headquarters and Volcano House, where it was planted. The leaves of hau are much broader than those of milo and are typically more rounded than heart shaped. They are somewhat shiny on their upper surface and covered with matted white hairs beneath. Newly opened flowers are large, yellow, and often have a dark red center; throughout the day the yellow flowers darken to orange or dull red. Hau fruits are dry capsules, but unlike milo, these split open into five sections when mature. Hau was an extremely valuable plant to Hawaiians, and it was often propagated near Hawaiian villages. Its wood is light and buoyant and was used for canoe outriggers, fishing net floats, and adz handles. The inner bark of the hau provided fiber for making cords, ropes, and fishing nets; hau fiber is still valued by some lei makers who prefer to use native or Polynesian plant materials to braid and weave (haku) or wind (wili) flowers and foliage.

Naupaka Kahakai (*Scaevola sericea*)

Goodenia family (Goodeniaceae)

Indigenous to the Hawaiian Islands

Distribution in the Park: Restricted to several coastline sites

One of the most conspicuous plants of undisturbed coastlines is naupaka kahakai or beach naupaka (formerly known as *Scaevola taccada* or *S. frutescens*), a robust shrub with thick, bright green, succulent leaves. Naupaka leaves are usually about 8 in. long or smaller, with prominently rolled margins. Tufts of soft white hairs are found in leaf axils, and the leaf blades may be softly hairy or smooth and hairless. The 1-in. long flowers are white and often streaked with purple; they are irregularly shaped and appear to be split with half the flower missing. Several species of Hawaiian naupaka have a similar "half flower," although flowers of the nine Hawaiian species vary in shape, size, and color. One Hawaiian legend explaining the unusual shape of naupaka flowers recounts a story of a young Hawaiian woman who tore the flower in half when angered by her unfaithful lover. The fleshy fruits of the naupaka kahakai are white, globose, about 0.5 in. long, and crowned with the remains of the withered flower. A related species, the Kīlauea naupaka (*S. kilaueae*), is described in the mid-elevation woodlands zone.

Of all the naupaka species in Hawai'i, the beach naupaka is the only one that is not restricted to the Hawaiian Islands; it is indigenous to other island groups and continental shores. Beach naupaka fruits may float in seawater for more than a year without losing viability, which explains why this species is distributed throughout the Pacific on tropical and sub-tropical shores. Seed or fruit dispersal of many other common coastal plants (*e.g.*, the coconut palm, hala, and beach morning glory) also occurs via ocean currents. In general, coastal vegetation has propor-tionally fewer endemic plant species than other vegetation types in Hawai'i, perhaps because of the relative ease with which the buoyant seeds and fruits of beach plants are dispersed from island to island.

Naupaka kahakai is one of the dominant plants of native coastal shrublands in Hawai'i and may be found on both windward and leeward shores. In the few relatively undisturbed coastal areas of the main Hawaiian Islands, it is often abundant on both sandy and rocky substrates. Particularly on undeveloped beaches and dunes, naupaka shrublands may contain a diversity of other native shrubs and vines. In Hawaii Volcanoes National Park, naupaka kahakai occurs on the rocky shore near Kamoamoa, Keauhou Landing, and Halapē. Since the loss of Waha'ula to new lava flows, the most extensive and well-developed naupaka shrubland of the Park is at 'Āpua Point, a dramatic coastal site also notable for its population of a rare shrub in the pea family, the red-flowered 'ōhai. Naupaka was severely impacted in the past by feral goats all along the Puna and Ka'ū coasts, but since the removal of these browsing, nonnative animals in the early 1970s, naupaka has partially recovered at many Park sites.

Morning Glories:
Pōhuehue (*Ipomoea pes-caprae* subsp. *brasiliensis*),
Pā'ū o Hi'iaka (*Jacquemontia ovalifolia* subsp. *sandwicensis*),
and Koali 'Awa (*Ipomoea indica*)

Morning Glory family (Convolvulaceae)

Indigenous to the Hawaiian Islands; found throughout tropics;
Endemic subspecies (Pā'ū o Hi'iaka)

Distribution in the Park: Pōhuehue and pā'ū o Hi'iaka on
sandy beaches; koali 'awa in lowlands to 4,000 ft

Three native morning glories may be frequently seen in the Park coastal areas and lowlands. The pōhuehue or beach morning glory (<u>illustrated</u>) is restricted to coastal sites and primarily grows on or near sandy beaches. This robust vine often forms thick mats of trailing reddish stems just above the high-water mark. Its leaves are thick, 2 to 4 in. broad, and prominently two-lobed with a central indentation. (The specific name *pes-caprae* means "goat hoof.") Large five-parted, funnel-shaped flowers may be seen throughout the year and are bright pink or light purple with a deeper purple interior. The fruits of the pōhuehue are dry, globose, papery capsules, which contain several brown, hairy seeds. In Park sites where sea turtles nest, this vine, along with beach naupaka, sometimes impedes the seaward march of newly hatched turtles, although this cause of mortality is likely less important than the depredations of small Indian mongooses and feral house cats.

Another vine in the morning glory family, pā'ū o Hi'iaka, is far less common than pōhuehue. Like the pōhuehue, pā'ū o Hi'iaka is restricted to sandy beaches. An endemic subspecies of a more widespread species, pā'ū o Hi'iaka has slender spreading stems, small, rounded, silvery, hairy leaves, and delicate, pale blue or white, cup-shaped flowers. The plant's Hawaiian name means the skirt of Hi'iaka (the younger sister of the volcano goddess Pele).

A third native morning glory, the koali 'awa or koali 'awahia (formerly known as *I. congesta*), has a much wider distribution in the Park than either pōhuehue or pā'ū o Hi'iaka. A more slender vine than pōhuehue, this morning glory has softly hairy, heart-shaped leaves with very pointed tips. Its showy, funnel-shaped flowers are a light sky blue with a paler interior when they open in the morning, but they fade to a delicate pink as the day progresses. The koali 'awa occurs sporadically throughout the coastal lowlands, where it sprawls on the ground among nonnative grasses or climbs over shrubs. Although primarily a lowland species, the vine is abundant in Kīpuka Puaulu of the upland forest and woodlands zone, where it grows high into the canopy of native trees and trails large ropy stems in the forest understory. Although it is a native plant, the koali 'awa must sometimes be cleared from trails, walls, and archaeological sites in the lowlands, because its viny growth form may be destructive to important cultural resources.

All three of these native morning glories have been used medicinally by Hawaiians. Koali 'awa is still used in Hawaiian folk medicine as a poultice to treat wounds, aches, and strains.

Black Noddy or Noio (*Anous minutus melanogenys*)

Jaeger, Gull, and Tern family (Laridae); Tern subfamily (Sterninae)

Endemic (subspecies) to Hawai'i; species breeds on islands in the tropical Atlantic and Pacific

Distribution in the Park: Rocky coastal areas, especially pali (cliffs)

Also known as the white-capped or Hawaiian noddy, this tern is the only common bird that flies just offshore of Park pali or cliffs. About 14 in. long, noio have lighter caps that extend farther back on the head and a faster, more "fluttery" flight than the larger (nearly twice as heavy) noio kōhā or brown (common) noddy (*A. stolidus pileatus*), which nests on offshore islands. The Hawaiian population of black noddies has yellow-orange feet and legs, unlike populations elsewhere, and is considered an endemic subspecies. Noio have stronger, steadier wingbeats than most other seabirds and use their long, sharp bills to catch small fish near the sea surface. These same lethal instruments are also sometimes used to eat Endangered hatchling hawksbill turtles as they travel to the sea after emerging from underground nests on Park beaches.

Noio nest on rocky cliffs or in caves on the main Islands. They can live 16 to 18 years and first breed between three and four years of age. Egg-laying peaks in December and January but continues to June, especially if weather destroys winter nests. Nests are often just above high-water surge, and nesting tends to be colonial. Black noddies build nests of twigs, pine needles, algae, and feathers, and cement them with guano. Females lay a large single egg, which requires 34 to 36 days of incubation. Hatchlings are brooded for a few days and average 28 days from hatching to first flight. Parents feed young for several weeks after they begin to fly. Black noddies forage close to shore and eat almost any small fish available.

The name "noddy" comes from the nodding and bowing typical of males feeding fish to females before egg laying. The scientific name *Anous* is Greek for "unmindful," probably because the birds are easily approachable in nesting colonies, a characteristic that makes them vulnerable to humans. Eggs and young were eaten by Hawaiian people in the past. Noio have long suffered from other predators such as rats, feral house cats, small Indian mongooses, common mynas, and probably ants (several species). As a result, most nesting colonies of this species on the main Islands are now confined to inaccessible cliffs and caves. Overfishing by humans could further jeopardize the survival of the species, as noio need large fishes to drive the small fishes upon which they feed to the surface of the sea.

J. YOSHIOKA 1991

Humpback Whale (*Megaptera novaeangliae*) and Other Whales

Fin-back Whales (Balaenopteridae) (Humpback); Dolphins (Delphinidae)

Indigenous; humpback winters in Hawai'i, summers in North Pacific waters
Federally listed Endangered Species (Humpback)

Distribution in the Park: Offshore waters

Swallows always return in the spring to Capistrano in southern California, and kōlea or Pacific golden plovers consistently arrive in Hawai'i in August to spend the winter months. Such recurring events are useful cues in places where seasonal changes are subtle. Come November in ocean-oriented Hawai'i, it is difficult to ignore the return of humpback whales from the North Pacific to calve and breed. Hawai'i's official State Marine Mammal spends most of its time where it can be observed, in warm offshore waters less than 600 ft deep. Whales are most often seen near breeding grounds off Maui and Moloka'i but are usually first spotted on their return along the kona (leeward) coast of Hawai'i Island, at South Point, or even along the Kalapana coastline of the Park.

From November to February, when whale numbers peak in the Islands and young are born, and again from March to May, when the large mammals head north, look for wide spouts (exhaled air), raised white fins and flukes (tails), knobby heads, and breaching (leaping) animals offshore. These moderately large whales (about 50 ft long and weighing 40 tons, much smaller than the blue whale [*Balaenoptera musculus*], the largest animal ever, at 100 ft and 150 tons) seem common at times. However, this is because over half (about 1,000 animals) the entire population of the Pacific Ocean may be concentrated in Hawaiian waters at once.

Humpbacks (order Mysticeti) are notable for large flippers (*Megaptera* means "large wing"), which are up to 30 percent of the body length; for unique flukes by which individual animals can be identified; and for beautiful, everchanging, and haunting underwater songs sung on breeding grounds. Humpbacks are social animals year round, although -- as one expert puts it -- large baleen whales really live in "heards" rather than herds, distantly tied to others by underwater communication rather than visual contact. In Hawaiian waters, humpbacks do not feed, but in the North Pacific they consume vast quantities of schooling fishes and planktonic animals (krill) by lunge feeding or by ascending from beneath the potential meal while concentrating prey within a tubular net of bubbles.

Toothed whales (order Odontoceti) found in Hawai'i include the sperm whale (*Physeter macrocephalus*), up to 60 ft long, and about 15 species of smaller whales (14-20 ft long) and (smaller still) dolphins or porpoises. The most commonly seen dolphins are probably bottlenose dolphins (to 9 ft long) and smaller spinner dolphins (to 7 ft long). Both species spend morning hours in groups close to shore but swim several miles offshore to feed at night.

All whales or cetaceans (the order Cetacea is used by many authorities) are protected by the Marine Mammal Protection Act of 1972, which prohibits "hunting, pursuit, and harrassment." Approaching whales within 100 yds is considered harrassment. Some species, including the humpback, are also protected by the Federal Endangered Species Act, and a humpback whale sanctuary has been established on the breeding grounds off the southern coast of Maui. If our ever-expanding, inquisitive, and exploitive human species is to continue to enjoy whales, such protection is vital.

Green Turtle (*Chelonia mydas*) **and**
  Hawksbill Turtle (*Eretmochelys imbricata*)

Sea Turtle family (Cheloniidae)

Indigenous. Federally listed Threatened (Green) and **Endangered**
  (Hawksbill) **Species**

Distribution in the Park: Offshore waters, coastal beaches

Green and hawksbill turtles, collectively called honu in Hawaiian, both nest in Hawai'i, the former largely on the Northwestern Hawaiian Islands and the latter on the main Islands. The giant (up to 1,500 lb) leatherback sea turtle (*Dermochelys coriacea*) is often seen in the open ocean in Hawaiian waters, where it feeds on jellyfish, but it does not come ashore.

The green turtle (main illustration), Federally listed as a Threatened Species, feeds largely on pastures of algae, or limu, growing on coral and rocks near the main Hawaiian Islands. It is the most commonly seen turtle and can be distinguished from hawksbills by the nonoverlapping scutes (plates) and smooth edges on the carapace (upper shell). Before their breeding season from May through August, these reptiles migrate up to 800 mi to nest mainly on French Frigate Shoals in the northwestern part of the Hawaiian chain. Adult females breed every two years at most, and only about 100 to 350 females nest each year. French Frigate Shoals is one of the few areas in the world where male and female turtles haul out of the water to bask on beaches, probably to increase body temperature, rest, and avoid sharks. Hawaiian green turtles average 150 to 400 lb. Hawksbills average 75 to 150 lb.

Probably fewer than 200,000 mature female green turtles survive in the world, where once tens of millions of turtles existed. These animals likely take up to 40 to 50 years to reach sexual maturity. Hawaiians ate green turtle meat, and fishing crews once exploited turtles in large numbers. Green turtles are still taken illegally, and additional animals are accidentally caught in fishing nets, killed by eating marine debris including plastics, and affected by habitat destruction including water pollution. Over 50 percent (49-92% at different sites) of the animals are affected by fibropapilloma (tumors), some of which are life threatening. The cause of this disease is unknown.

The hawksbill turtle or honu 'ea (inset) can be recognized by the pointed beak (probably an adaptation to feeding on sponges) and by serrated edges and overlapping scutes on the carapace. The species nests primarily on eastern beaches of Hawai'i Island, and two nesting areas are located in Hawaii Volcanoes National Park. Nesting season is from July to November, during which time females periodically come ashore at night to lay several clutches of eggs. Rear flippers are used to dig a cavity in which eggs are deposited, and then to cover the eggs with sand. During the extended incubation period (about two months) eggs are in danger of being dug up by feral house cats, small Indian mongooses, dogs, and humans. Some hatchlings are also eaten by mammals and birds, and others become caught behind rocks and vegetation in rugged Park beaches, preventing them from reaching the sea.

Interference with nesting hawksbill turtles by visitors in the Park, including compaction of sand, unauthorized campsites in protected nesting areas, and campfire lights, which disorient both nesting females and hatchlings moving to the sea, can also be a problem. Park managers are working to educate the public and to solve these problems in order to increase the nesting success of this Endangered Species in Hawaii Volcanoes.

73

Crabs:

A'ama or Rock Crab (*Grapsus tenuicrustatus*),
Hermit Crabs (several species and genera), and
'Ōhiki or Ghost Crabs (*Ocypode* spp.)

Class Crustacea; Grapsid Crab family (Grapsidae),
Hermit Crab family (Paguridae), and Ghost Crab family (Ocypodidae)

Indigenous to the Hawaiian Islands; found throughout the Indo-Pacific

Distribution in the Park: Rock crabs along older rocky seacoast;
hermit crabs in tide pools and shallow water; ghost crabs on established
sandy beaches

Conspicuous to explorers of rocky shorelines is the dark greenish black 'a'ama or rock crab (lower illustration). Members of the family to which this species belongs are typically found along rocky shores, occurring in shallow water or intertidally; 'a'ama frequently leave the water and clamber over the rocks, scurrying into concealment in narrow crevices when threatened. These crabs are inconspicuous when immobile against the dark rock background. The bodies of 'a'ama are up to 2.75 in. wide -- a delectable meal for would-be predators, including those humans who use them as bait or eat them whole and raw at luaus (Hawaiian feasts). 'A'ama were used medicinally by the Hawaiians, and they were also a sacred food for certain kahuna (priests).

'A'ama are well adapted to life in their wave-battered environment; the flat body and flattened, wide, long legs with spines on the tips enable these animals to withstand the force of the waves. The species has relatively small pincers, which reduce the body weight that must be moved quickly in response to danger. While 'a'ama can be seen during the day, more animals emerge from concealment at night to scavenge on the rocky substrate; when a flashlight beam shines on them, they "freeze" in position.

Several genera and species of hermit crabs, pāpa'i iwi pūpū or unauna, inhabit empty mollusk shells in the tide pools and shallow waters of the Park. The abdomen of hermit crabs is soft, without apparent segments, and is modified for holding the animal in its mobile home. One chela, or pincer-like claw, of the hermit crab is often larger than the other and functions to close off the shell opening when the crab withdraws for protection into the shell. To determine whether a seashell is "alive," look for the soft body with retractible, soft eyestalks and "stomach foot" of the living gastropod mollusk; crab legs, pincers, and rapid locomotion indicate that the mollusk has died and the empty seashell is now inhabited by a hermit crab. The drawing of mollusks (next account) shows a hermit crab living in a nerite (marine snail) shell.

Isolated sandy beaches within the Park are habitat for ghost crabs or 'ōhiki (upper illustration). *Ocypode ceratophthalmus*, the larger and more conspicuous of the two species found in Hawai'i, occurs throughout the entire Indo-Pacific region and is, in fact, one of the most widespread Indo-Pacific crabs. The other 'ōhiki, *O. laevis*, is known only from the Hawaiian Islands and possibly the Line Islands, Johnston Island, and Raratonga. The two species are difficult to tell apart; however, patient observers may identify *O. ceratophthalmus* by the presence, on mature adults, of an elongation of their gray-green eyes, whereas *O. laevis* has yellow eyes and no eye elongation. Both species possess a stridulating organ on the inner surface of the palm of the large chela; this ridge of comb-like teeth can be scraped against the uppermost segment of the appendage to produce a rasping sound, which is thought to be either a warning to crabs venturing into another's territory, or a mating call of males to attract females.

'Ōhiki are well suited to life on the beach. They have exceedingly long legs, which enable rapid movement on sand. These crabs are efficient sand burrowers, with the end segment of their legs sharp, slightly broadened, and bristly to carry sand, and with short, flattened pincers for effective digging. Ghost crabs are primarily nocturnal, but larger adults of both species may emerge from their burrows on overcast or rainy days, especially in the late afternoon. Normally the color of coralline sand, chromatophores (pigment cells) within the crab change the body color to match the background; thus, 'ōhiki are camouflaged even on sandy beaches composed of fairly large amounts of ground-up lava (black sand) mixed with coralline material.

Ocypode ceratophthalmus is primarily intertidal and capable of withstanding prolonged submersion, whereas *O. laevis* is less tolerant of submersion and lives above the high tide line. *Ocypode ceratophthalmus* is an aggressive species and has been observed in combat, dismembering and even cannibalizing others of its own species as well as exerting heavy predation pressure on the smaller, more docile *O. laevis*. The aggressive behavior of *O. ceratophthalmus* presents a problem in mating, which has been solved by the development of a definite zonation pattern of burrows dug by males and females of different ages. Crabs of both species construct different-shaped burrows at different distances from the mean water level according to their sex and age. Male *O. ceratophthalmus* advertise the location of their burrows by enlarging the entrance and heaping the excavated sand into definite mounds. Female and juvenile *O. ceratophthalmus* (and *O. laevis*, which must remain inconspicuous to their aggressive neighbors) scatter the excavated sand or dump it in a low, loose mound just outside the burrow entrance, and often plug their burrows with loose sand to minimize contact with other crabs.

'Ōhiki forage over the entire width of the beach during the night, although the debris line in the intertidal zone, containing the most food items, is the area most frequented. Because mature females of each species live higher on the beach than do the mature males, the females must pass through the male zone to reach intertidal feeding areas. During daylight hours, almost all crabs are actively engaged in burrow construction, and very little feeding occurs. Younger, smaller crabs less than 0.5 in. in body width can be readily observed in daytime, but larger individuals emerge only fleetingly to repair burrows or furtively dash toward the lapping waves.

Small Indian mongooses and feral house cats, both unwelcome aliens in natural areas of Hawai'i, prey upon 'ōhiki; on numerous beaches around the State, sand-dwelling crabs are dug from their burrows by humans and their dogs. 'Ōhiki are used by Hawaiians as live bait for some types of fishing, and like the 'a'ama, they are a gourmet treat in local cuisine.

The Hawaiian word for crabs in general is pāpa'i. The different groups of crabs were often further designated (*e.g.*, pāpa'i iwi pūpū, hermit crabs), and the more useful or notable species had their own "specific" Hawaiian names.

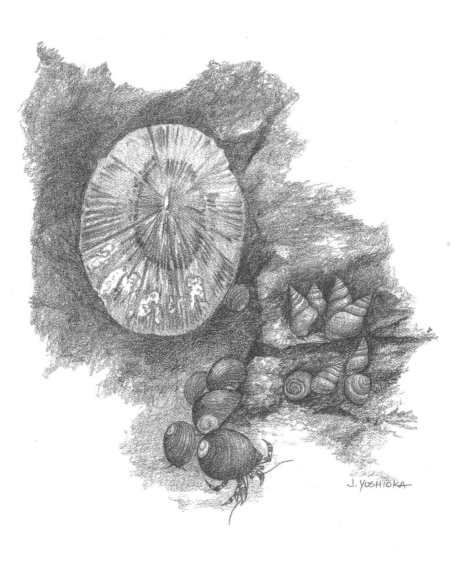

J. YOSHIOKA

Gastropod Mollusks:
Periwinkles, Nerites, and Limpets

**Class Gastropoda (Stomach-footed Mollusks); Periwinkle family
(Littorinidae), Nerite family (Neritidae), and Limpet family (Patellidae)**

Indigenous (Periwinkles and Nerites); **Endemic** (Limpets)

Distribution in the Park: Rocky seacoast

Several gastropod mollusks, or "seashells," can be observed in the coastal areas of Hawaii Volcanoes. As with most of the intertidal marine plants and animals, these relatives of terrestrial slugs and snails are more common along the geologically older coastal areas of the Park than in the shoreline areas impacted by recent volcanic activity.

Periwinkles (*Littorina pintado*, right in illustration) are found in occasional clusters of individuals on rocks high above the high tide level and splash of the waves. These marine snails occur throughout the tropics in the high shoreline zone. They seal themselves into their shells with an operculum (a "trap door" composed of horny material on the end of the foot) and glue themselves to the rocks with mucus as protection against desiccation. Even though periwinkles can live out of water for as long as a year, they rely on the ocean for development of eggs and larvae. Periwinkles feed on algae and detritus, which they scrape from the surface of the rocks with their radulae, or rasp-like "teeth." They follow the ebb and flow of the tides as they feed, and this rhythmic movement persists even if they are removed from the shoreline. Hawaiians called periwinkles pūpū kōlea or pipipi kōlea, and they were one of several small intertidal species of marine snails used for food.

Small, grooved, black nerites (*Nerita picea*, bottom of illustration) are found lower on the rocks, from the splash zone to the high-water mark, just below the periwinkles, often in groups under ledges or in depressions in the rock. These snails, like the periwinkles, move vertically with the tide as they browse on microscopic algae. The Hawaiian name for nerites is pipipi, a general name for small mollusks with habits and habitat similar to nerites. Pipipi do not hide during the day but may be found on the rocks day and night. The soft parts of the animals were -- and are still -- used for food, and the shells are used for leis. One of the pipipi shells illustrated here is inhabited by a shallow-water hermit crab, or unauna (see Crabs account); the empty shells of pipipi, periwinkles, and other gastropod mollusks provide portable homes for several species of these crustaceans. The black nerite is found in other areas of the Pacific as well as in Hawaiian waters.

Two of the four species of limpets endemic to the Hawaiian Islands may be noticed on sea cliff areas along the shoreline of the Park. The conical shape of these low-profile, broad-based limpets (upper left in illustration), known as 'opihi in Hawai'i, is ideal for withstanding the powerful wave action in their habitat, and the strong muscular foot firmly attaches the animal to the substrate with a suction difficult to break by even the most determined 'opihi collector. 'Alinalina, or yellow-foot limpets (*Cellana sandwicensis*), are typically found at and below the zero tide mark, usually on coralline algae in the surge zone. Their shells are often tufted with clumps of the algae growing in that environment. The makaiauli, or black-footed limpet (*C. exarata*), is found higher in the intertidal zone and is not generally found where the waves crash continuously. Both species, however, may be found intermingling at the transitional areas of their preferred habitats.

'Opihi move about, as do all gastropod or "stomach-footed" mollusks, by means of a single large, muscular foot. They feed by scraping algae off the rocks, sometimes moving randomly and not necessarily returning to the same place after a day of grazing. Often, though, they create "home scars" of heavily grazed spots from which they forage outward and to which they return when not feeding. All 'opihi feed on coralline algae, but makaiauli also eat diatoms and blue-green algae. 'Opihi populations appear susceptible to unfavorable environmental conditions such as extended periods of sunny weather and calm seas, which cause the algae on which they feed to burn and die back and vulnerable young 'opihi to dry out and die. 'Opihi are a highly prized delicacy, and regulations by the state of Hawaii are enforced to protect this Hawaiian-style escargot from being overharvested.

**SPECIAL SEACOAST SYSTEM:
ANCHIALINE POOLS**

Close to the ocean in lava bedrock and elevated fossil coral reefs around the world, rare small bodies of water with unique characteristics can be found. These pools have a subterranean connection with the sea, and they exhibit measurable salt content and tidal fluctuations. In Hawai'i, many of these anchialine (pronounced ank'-i-a-line) "near the sea" pools were used by early Hawaiians for drinking water, bathing, and fishponds. Many have been modified for and by these uses. Most of the 650 or so pools on the island of Hawai'i are located on the kona (leeward) coast, and many still contain unusual animals.

In Hawaii Volcanoes National Park, at least 22 pools exist, distributed in at least eight sites. Most pools in the Park are somewhat lower in salt content (6 parts per thousand) than most kona coast pools (15 parts per thousand), but both are considerably lower than ocean water (35 parts per thousand). Most rare animals are found in saltier pools, so fewer rare species are found in the Park than are found in leeward pools. Park pools are also smaller than those on the kona side of the Island, but there is good structural diversity (*e.g.*, caves, cracks, and open pools). The Park contains most of the pools found on the windward side of the Island. They can probably be protected more readily in the Park than in other locations, especially where hotel development threatens.

Seven species of fish, nine crustaceans (shrimps, prawns, etc.), and one mollusk (a snail) occur in Park pools. Fishes such as kūpīpī, āholehole, and pāpio (young ulua, crevalle or jack -- *Abudefduf sordidus, Kuhlia sandvicensis, Caranx* sp.) were probably introduced into the pools from the ocean by humans, for use as food. Another introduction, the large, blue Tahitian prawn (*Machrobrachium lar*), is known to displace and prey on native prawns and shrimp. Both species of native shrimp, 'ōpae 'ula (*Halocaridina rubra*), a minute, red, herbivorous shrimp, and a larger shrimp that also preys upon it (*Metabetaeus lohena*), are characteristic of Park anchialine pools. Two species of small native 'o'opu or gobies (family Gobiidae) prey on crustaceans, and native waterbirds probably prey on the fishes. Many pool animals are most active and most readily observed at night. In the dark, the eyes of native prawns reflect a golden glow by flashlight and look like tiny moving jewels in the pool depths.

Anchialine pool plants include various algae -- single-celled and fila-mentous green, blue-green, and calcareous red -- plus emergent vegetation such as native sedges and 'ākulikuli or sea purslane (*Sesuvium portula-castrum*). Dense stands of introduced sourbush *(Pluchea symphytifolia),* native milo (*Thespesia populnea*), and sedges, as well as thick mats of algae, contribute to early aging or senescence of the pools.

Slowing the unnatural senescence of anchialine pools, through reduction of problem vegetation, and increasing populations of native species of animals by removing introduced prawns and fishes are jobs for Park resource managers. Use of these unique areas (which often look like little more than cracks in the lava) as sources of water for fighting fires, for trash and chemical disposal, for wishing wells, and for bathing with soap must be avoided if the Park is to preserve pristine examples of these rare coastal pools.

LOWLANDS

The lowland zone of Hawaii Volcanoes National Park is a long and narrow belt bounded on the southern, or seaward, side by the seacoast, which is under the direct influence of salt spray and other maritime conditions; on the northern or landward side the lowland zone is bounded by the steep Hilina and Hōlei pali (cliff) systems. Hilina Pali, 1,000 ft from top to base, is a fault scarp, the result of seaward slumping on the south flank of Kīlauea Volcano. Slumping is due to magma intrusion and solidification within the volcano, which pushes the unsupported south flank toward the sea. The tops of Hilina and Hōlei pali reach an elevation of 1,500 to 2,000 ft, while elevations at the cliff bases range from 600 to 1,000 ft. The lowlands stretch between the western boundary at Kīlauea's Great Crack of the Southwest Rift zone and the eastern boundary near Waha'ula, recently covered by lava from Pu'u 'Ō'ō and Kūpaianaha vents.

Substrates in the lowlands are a mosaic of different ages, ranging from lavas of the current eruption downslope of Pu'u 'Ō'ō to ancient lava flows exposed on the steep face of Hilina Pali, estimated to be 20,000 to 100,000 years old. Ash deposits as much as 25,000 years old are exposed on the tops of Pu'u Kapukapu and Pu'u Kaone, hills that rise above the coast near Halapē and Ka'aha. These cliff lavas and ash pockets are the oldest exposed substrates anywhere on Kīlauea Volcano. The next-oldest substrates of Kīlauea (1,500 to 10,000 years old) are also found in the lowland zone, in two kīpuka just above and immediately below Hilina Pali, as well as at a site in the remote western corner of the Park. Recent flows are particularly conspicuous in the eastern half of the lowland zone, directly downslope of the active middle section of Kīlauea's East Rift. The Mauna Ulu series of flows (1969-1974), originating from a lava shield along the Chain of Craters, is massive and reached the sea in the early 1970s, adding new coastline to the Park between 'Āpua and Ka'ena points. These flows are primarily smooth pāhoehoe; most still glisten with a glassy sheen and support little vegetation. Even more recent are the flows, both rough 'a'ā and smoother pāhoehoe, that continue (as of 1994) to emerge (sometimes through subterranean tubes) from vents at the base of the Pu'u 'Ō'ō cone on the Park's eastern boundary. These flows have covered many thousands of acres of forest and shrubland. In the central and western Park lowlands, ash deposits of various ages cover many old flows. In some areas, the dark sandy ash was deposited in a thick layer, which has been subsequently sculpted into dunes by the wind. Rocky soils have gradually developed and accumulated beneath the eastern lowland forests, the result of decomposing organic matter from plants.

Much of the lowland zone is hot and dry. The mean annual temperature is greater than 72°F, with lower temperatures recorded during the winter months. Rainfall in sections of the lowlands is the lowest of any Park zone except the summit of Mauna Loa. Average annual rainfall ranges from more than 60 in. in the eastern section of the lowlands to less than 20 in. in the western part. Summer drought conditions often occur.

The combination of relatively recent substrates and dry, hot conditions limits the development of vegetation in much of the lowlands. Sparse vegetation is seen in the remote southwestern section of the Park, where the landscape is dominated by bare lava flows and rocky or shallow ash substrates supporting scattered alien grasses (particularly Natal redtop, *Rhynchelytrum repens*) and the hardy native shrub 'uhaloa (*Waltheria indica*). Deeper ash soils of the western lowlands have been heavily invaded by the alien, fire-stimulated molasses grass (*Melinis minutiflora*). The central coastal lowlands are covered by alien grasses, primarily bush beardgrass (*Schizachyrium condensatum*), thatching grass (*Hyparrhenia rufa*), and Natal redtop. A few grasslands here are dominated by the native pili (*Heteropogon contortus*). Scattered shrubs, both native and alien species, are seen in the central section, but trees are restricted to steep pali slopes and rough 'a'ā. The paucity of trees and shrubs is an unnatural condition, caused by the former presence of large numbers of feral goats (*Capra hircus*) and the past use of fire by the original Hawaiian inhabitants. It is only in the wetter eastern lowlands of the Park that woody vegetation is abundant.

The extreme eastern end of the Park lowlands includes wet and moist forests of 'ōhi'a (*Metrosideros polymorpha*) and lama (*Diospyros sandwicensis*), often mixed with other native trees and Polynesian introductions such as kukui (*Aleurites moluccana*). Shrubland vegetation dominated by native species (sometimes called lowland scrub) is also well represented in the eastern lowlands. The most abundant shrub species in unburned sites are the native 'ākia (*Wikstroemia sandwicensis*), 'a'ali'i (*Dodonaea viscosa*), and 'ūlei (*Osteomeles anthyllidifolia*), but Polynesian introductions such as noni (*Morinda citrifolia*) and alien shrubs such as lantana (*Lantana camara*) and Christmas berry (*Schinus terebinthifolius*) are also common. Often several species of grasses are mixed in with the shrubs in this vegetation type, typically bush beardgrass, pili, and broomsedge (*Andropogon virginicus*). Just west of the lowland forests and shrublands are rocky pāhoehoe flows with scattered 'ōhi'a trees and a ground cover of grasses, both native and alien. In its descent of Hōlei Pali, Chain of Craters Road passes primarily through this type of vegetation and crosses numerous recent flows sparsely colonized by young 'ōhi'a trees.

Wildlife of the lowland zone consists of a variety of birds, invertebrates, and introduced mammals. Alien birds are common in the open vegetation of most of the lowlands; most often seen are common mynas (*Acridotheres tristis*), Japanese white-eyes (*Zosterops japonicus*), and spotted doves (*Streptopelia chinensis*). In the native forests of the extreme eastern lowlands, native forest birds may be found at unusually low elevations. 'Apapane (*Himatione sanguinea*) and common 'amakihi (*Hemignathus virens*) have been observed at 50 ft elevation near Kalapana. Upslope, at about 1,000 ft elevation, the Hawai'i thrush or 'ōma'o (*Myadestes obscurus*) and 'elepaio (*Chasiempis sandwichensis*) may be occasionally heard. The Endangered Hawaiian hawk or 'io (*Buteo solitarius*) is a rarely seen inhabitant of the lowland zone. The scarcity of most native forest birds at low elevation is thought to result from avian pox and malaria, introduced diseases spread by the night-flying southern house mosquito (*Culex quinquefasciatus*).

Insects and spiders are abundant in the Park's lowlands; most are alien species. Exceptions are native crickets and wolf spiders (*Lycosa* spp.) well adapted to life in the harsh environment of recent lava flows. Most other native lowland insects have been decimated by aggressive introduced big-headed ants (*Pheidole megacephala*) and other species. It is impossible to gauge the amount of damage to native invertebrates done by these and other introduced insects. Today, insects most often seen in the lowlands are cockroaches, abundant in areas frequented by visitors, particularly campsites, picnic areas, and roadside turnouts. The most commonly seen mammal is the alien small Indian mongoose (*Herpestes auropunctatus*), found throughout the zone. Black rats (*Rattus rattus*), feral house cats (*Felis catus*), and feral pigs (*Sus scrofa*) are rarely seen by visitors but are widespread in the Park lowlands.

The lowland zone of the Park, like most of the Hawaiian Islands below 1,500 ft elevation, was impacted to some degree by the native Hawaiian people, who inhabited this region in relatively large numbers for hundreds of years before the arrival of Europeans. The Hawaiian population appears to have been sizeable in late pre-European contact times, and such activities as clearing land for farming, burning vegetation to stimulate growth of pili used for thatching, and cutting trees for construction timber and firewood were undoubtedly significant disturbances to the original pre-human vegetation. Before recent lava flows covered many features, rock structures representing house sites, canoe sheds, walled enclosures, and agricultural sites abounded in the eastern section of the Park's lowlands, testifying to the thriving Hawaiian communities that once existed here.

Later uses of the Park's lowlands included goat and cattle ranching, which resulted in the loss of even more native trees and shrubs from browsing. Grasses introduced intentionally as forage or accidentally as weed seeds have spread widely in the lowlands, resulting in today's prevalent landscape of open grasslands. These alien grasses are extremely flammable; some alien grasses well adapted to fire increase in cover following each successive fire. Fire prevention and suppression are now extremely important elements in the Park's strategy to protect native vegetation.

Most of the Park's lowlands are certainly much changed from their original appearance, and the natural species composition of plants and animals can only be guessed. Nonetheless, the lowland zone is still a land of dramatic landscapes, vast empty spaces unpopulated by humans or their modern structures. The zone also contains significant examples of rare lowland forests and plants proposed for listing as Endangered Species. New lava flows continue to demonstrate the dynamic nature of Hawai'i's natural environment, and early succession of plants and animals on these flows proceeds, for the most part with native species. These recent lava flows, now barren, will support the lowland forests and shrublands of the future. Lowland areas, in which natural processes are allowed to continue unaltered by modern development, are extremely rare in the Hawaiian Islands.

Wiliwili (*Erythrina sandwicensis*)

Pea family (Fabaceae)

Endemic to the Hawaiian Islands

Distribution in the Park: Eastern lowlands

One of the most strikingly beautiful native trees still found at low elevations in the Hawaiian Islands, wiliwili (formerly known as *Erythrina monosperma*) has successfully survived the use of the lowlands for cultivation by Hawaiians, extensive and repeated fires, cattle grazing, the depredations of feral goats, and the wholesale invasion of alien plants.

A small to medium-size tree in the pea family, wiliwili usually grows no taller than 20 to 30 ft. The trunks of mature wiliwili trees are typically short and thick, with light-colored, furrowed bark. The trees usually branch low on the trunk, and the thick, spreading branches and stout twigs have distinctive smooth, yellowish orange bark. Leaves are compound, with three rounded leaflets that are broader than long and extend to a rounded tip. Light green above, wiliwili leaflets are covered with soft brown hairs on their undersides. Curved pea-like flowers about 2 in. long are clustered on stout stalks at branch tips. They vary in color and may be red, orange, yellow, white, or even green, but most trees in the Park bear bright red-orange flowers. Pods 2 to 3 in. long develop from the flowers and when mature are gray-brown and constricted between the seeds. Mature pods are rather dry and split open to reveal one to three bright red seeds. These colorful seeds have been used by lei makers to make decorative string necklaces.

One of the few native trees that is strongly deciduous, wiliwili drops most of its leaves in the fall and winter, then leafs out again in the spring. Leaf-drop usually coincides with blooming, resulting in a dramatic display of bright flowers unobscured by foliage.

The wood of wiliwili is light and pithy and of little use for construction or farming implements. The lightness of the wood was much appreciated by Hawaiian fishermen and canoe builders, who used wiliwili for canoe outrigger and fishing net floats.

While not uncommon in the Hawaiian Islands, wiliwili trees have become rare in the Park since lava covered the Wahaʻula area. Formerly, wiliwili was an important component of Wahaʻula forests, where it grew mixed with kukui, hau, lama, and hala. Today, wiliwili trees are found occasionally on old ʻaʻā flows near Kamoamoa, and a few individuals remain on the steep slopes of cliffs to the west toward Hilina Pali.

Kukui or Candlenut (*Aleurites moluccana*)

Spurge family (Euphorbiaceae)

Polynesian introduction; possibly native to Malaysia

Distribution in the Park: Wet and moist forests of the eastern lowlands

Although it is the State Tree of Hawai'i, the kukui is not indigenous to the Hawaiian Islands; it was brought here by Polynesian settlers. Because of its long residence in Hawai'i, kukui has spread widely along the lower windward slopes of most of the Hawaiian Islands and is the dominant or codominant tree in many areas. In the Park, kukui is found in mixed stands with 'ōhi'a, lama, or hala.

Before lava flows covered Waha'ula in 1989, kukui was a prominent component of the coastal forest there, where it grew with hala, wiliwili, and hau. Most of the kukui remaining in the Park grows in forests near the Park's eastern boundary, up to an elevation of 2,000 ft. Kukui also grows in groves scattered along Hōlei Pali, where it is a spreading tree more than 50 ft tall with grayish white bark. Even from a distance, kukui can readily be identified in these groves by its pale silvery green foliage, composed of large, three- to five-lobed leaves. On close inspection, the light green leaf surface is seen to be covered with a rough, mealy pubescence. Young leaves are ovate and unlobed and when they first appear are often tinged with pink. Small flowers are found in large clusters at branch tips; individual flowers have five creamy white or pinkish petals and are either male or female. Kukui fruits are large, irregularly rounded, about 2 in. wide, with an outer green fleshy covering over an inner stony fruit wall, which encloses one or two seeds. Kukui reproduce well on steep slopes and cliffs, because being rolled or washed downslope over rocks helps to break down the hard covering over the seeds and probably enhances germination.

Hawaiians found numerous uses for the kukui. Fruits, commonly called "nuts," were perhaps the most useful part of the plant. The meat of the seed is edible when roasted and is still used to make a relish called 'inamona. Because of the high percentage of oil within the kernels, the dried nuts could be burned and were strung together and used as lights or torches in old Hawai'i. The extracted oil was used in lamps. After curing and polishing the hard shells, kukui "nuts" were strung into shiny black leis, which are still popular today. Other parts of the tree were also useful. The soft wood was made into fishnet floats and, occasionally, canoes. Dyes were obtained from bark, roots, fruit, and the ash of burned "nuts." Leaves, flowers, milky sap, and raw kernels are still used medicinally.

Kukui may be seen in the distance along the lower part of Chain of Craters Road and the coastal highway. The tree also grows near Lae 'Āpuki and has been planted in Kīpuka Puaulu in the upland forest and woodlands zone.

Lama (*Diospyros sandwicensis*)

Ebony family (Ebenaceae)

Endemic to the Hawaiian Islands

Distribution in the Park: Lowland forests, woodlands, and shrublands; also scattered on several pali (cliffs)

A member of the tropical ebony family, lama (formerly known as *Diospyros ferrea*) is closely related to the familiar persimmon tree of the eastern United States (*D. virginiana*), as well as to the larger-fruited oriental persimmon or kaki (*D. kaki*). A relatively short tree with a wide-spreading canopy, the lama is a common component of dry and moist forests of the Hawaiian lowlands. The species is found on all the main Hawaiian Islands except Ni'ihau and Kaho'olawe, and in some remaining forests and woodlands below 2,000 ft elevation it is the dominant tree.

Leaves of the lama are drab green and thick, usually 1 to 3 in. long. Young leaves growing at the tips of branches are often conspicuously red, at least during part of the year. The undersides of young leaves are covered with silky hairs, and slender young twigs are densely clothed with reddish hairs. Flowers are tiny and easily escape notice, but with a hand lens or magnifying glass fine details may be seen. Only 0.25 in. long, flowers are three parted with overlapping sepals (green leaflike structures) tightly overlapping the buds. The delicate corolla (fused flower petals) is creamy white to shell pink in color, and like the green sepals, is covered outside with golden, silky hairs. By contrast, lama fruits are showy and bright orange to red. Ovoid and about 0.5 to 1 in. long, the edible fleshy lama fruits are most abundant during late summer, fall, and winter. Spherical finely branched growths often seen on lama twigs and branches are formed by tiny mites.

Since the arrival of humans, the lowlands of Hawai'i have been greatly disturbed by burning, farming, grazing, feral ungulates, and, most recently, urban development. Because of these factors, lama forests are far less widespread than they would have been a thousand years ago. Within Hawaii Volcanoes, one of the most accessible lama forests was near Kamoamoa Campground, until it was covered by lava from the Pu'u 'Ō'ō eruption. The tree is also prominent in more remote forests upslope to an elevation of about 1,500 ft. Lama is the dominant tree in the Nāulu Forest remnants surrounded by the 1969-74 Mauna Ulu lava flows on Hōlei Pali; these kīpuka are visible from Chain of Craters Road below the hairpin curve at about 1,000 ft elevation. Lama, often mixed with the more abundant 'ōhi'a, occurs as scattered individuals along Hōlei, Hilina, and other pali (cliff) faces of the Park's dry lowlands. Many years of feral goat browsing have unfortunately reduced the number of lama trees in the lowlands, but these destructive animals were eliminated from much of Hawaii Volcanoes in the 1970s, allowing increased regeneration of native woody species in deforested areas. A recent study of coastal woodlands in the eastern section of the Park showed that lama was reproducing, and many young trees were found on sites with rough 'a'ā substrates.

Alahe'e (*Canthium odoratum*) **and**
 'Ahakea (*Bobea timonioides*)

Coffee family (Rubiaceae)

Indigenous (alahe'e) and **Endemic** ('ahakea) to the Hawaiian Islands

Distribution in the Park: Eastern coastal lowlands to forests above
 1,500 ft elevation

Alahe'e (illustrated) is a small tree in the coffee family, a group that includes more than 50 native species in Hawai'i (5% of the flora). An important understory component of many of the remaining lowland forests of Hawai'i Island, alahe'e is found on most of the major Hawaiian Islands as well as on islands of Micronesia and southern Polynesia.

An attractive tree with glossy, dark green leaves and smooth white bark, alahe'e rarely grows taller than 20 ft. Flowers are borne in clusters at branch tips and are sweetly fragrant when the tree is in full bloom during the summer. Individual flowers are small, white, and tubular. These develop into irregularly grooved, flattened, fleshy fruits, which are shiny green when immature and black when ripe. The hard wood of alahe'e was used by Hawaiians to make agricultural tools.

In the Park, alahe'e is most abundant in forests of lama near Kamoamoa, but the tree is also scattered in drier 'ōhi'a woodlands on and above the major fault cliff systems or pali that loom above much of the lowlands.

A much rarer member of the coffee family, the 'ahakea (*Bobea timonioides*) grows in a few of these pali forests. A larger tree than the alahe'e, the 'ahakea has a pale, straight-boled trunk. Like other plants of this family, its leaves are opposite each other on the branches, but unlike the alahe'e, they are ovate, dull textured, and have prominent veins and red leaf stems. Flowers are small, and fruits are not often noticed. The causes of 'ahakea's rarity are not known but may include loss of lowland forest habitat or past use of its yellow wood to make canoe paddles and to trim the sides of Hawaiian canoes. A candidate for Endangered Species status, the 'ahakea is not restricted to Hawaii Volcanoes National Park but also occurs in forests of lower Puna and South Kona on the Big Island, and in dry forests of leeward East Maui.

Common Guava (*Psidium guajava*)

Myrtle family (Myrtaceae)

Alien; from tropical America

Distribution in the Park: Coast to 4,000 ft elevation

Although much used by the Hawai'i visitor industry as an example of tropical Hawaiian fruit, guavas are not native to Hawai'i but were introduced in the late 18th and early 19th centuries from tropical America. The common guava, like its near relative in the rain forest, the strawberry guava or waiawī (*P. cattleianum*), probably became established as a wild plant in Hawai'i soon after its introduction.

Far less abundant in Hawaii Volcanoes National Park than strawberry guava, common guava is most often seen in the lowlands and the lower reaches of rain forest on Kīlauea's East Rift. In open dry grasslands and woodlands, guava is a low-growing shrub with sparse foliage, but in wet forests the species may be a tree greater than 30 ft tall. Whether a shrub or tree, guava has a distinctively multi-hued, smooth bark, which peels off in thin sheets. Guava leaves are arranged opposite one another on angular branches and are dull green, elliptic to oblong, and leathery textured with conspicuous lateral veins. The flowers of guava are white with five petals and many stamens clustered like a pompom in the center. Usually less than an inch in diameter, guava flowers are borne close to the stem in the axils of leaves. The fruits that develop from these flowers are large (1-4 in. diameter) yellow berries. The exterior of the fruit is bumpy or dimpled, and the remains of the flower persist at the tip opposite the stem. The interior of guava fruit is pink (sometimes white) and juicy with many seeds embedded in the pulp. Guava is commercially valuable for its fruits, which are used to make juices, jams, jellies, and candies.

Despite its crop value, the common guava is a problem weed in many areas, and the abundant fruits of wild trees harbor a large population of alien fruit flies, which are serious agricultural pests. Wild guava trees are particularly numerous in river valleys and near streams, where they may displace native vegetation. In Hawaii Volcanoes, common guava occurs primarily in lowland areas previously disturbed by ancient Hawaiian agricultural practices and later grazing activities. The tree (unlike its cousin the strawberry guava) is not a serious invader of closed-canopy native forests.

Noni or Indian Mulberry (*Morinda citrifolia*)

Coffee family (Rubiaceae)

Polynesian introduction

Distribution in the Park: Seacoast and lowlands

The noni is a conspicuous element in the dry grasslands and moist shrublands below Hōlei Pali in the eastern section of the Park, where it grows from cracks in old pāhoehoe flows, usually near sites formerly inhabited by Hawaiians. In this area noni is a shrub and rarely reaches heights greater than 10 ft, but in wetter areas or under cultivation, the plant can grow into a small tree. Leaves of the noni are large and broad, dark glossy green, and have prominent, light-colored veins. Like other members of the coffee family, the leaves are opposite on the stem and have small but noticeable leaflike structures (stipules) at their bases.

Flowers of the noni are borne in round clusters near branch tips and are small, white, and five parted. The fruit of the noni is unusual in that it develops from the ovaries of many flowers fused together. Noni fruits are several inches long, irregular in shape, and bear a pattern of many polygons representing the individual flowers from which the fruit developed. When ripe, fruits are yellowish white, soft, and have an unpleasant odor.

Introduced by the Polynesians who settled Hawai'i, noni was an important medicinal plant for the ancient Hawaiians, who used the ripe fruit pulp as a poultice and the juice to make a tonic and to treat several illnesses. The leaves and bark of the noni were also processed for medicine. The plant is still used today for home remedies. Despite its strong smell, noni fruit may also have provided emergency food for Hawaiians in time of famine. Other parts of the plant, such as the roots and bark, were used to make a red or yellow dye.

Noni is native to Southeast Asia and Australia and is not indigenous to the Hawaiian Islands. It was carried throughout the Pacific because of its usefulness to humans. A related species, called noni kuahiwi (*M. trimera*), is endemic to several Hawaiian Islands but does not occur on the island of Hawai'i.

J. YOSHIOKA

ʻŪlei (*Osteomeles anthyllidifolia*)

Rose family (Rosaceae)

Indigenous to the Hawaiian Islands

Distribution in the Park: Eastern lowlands to mid-elevation woodlands

Few members of the typically temperate rose family are native to Hawaiʻi; one strawberry (*Fragaria chiloensis* subsp. *sandwicensis*), two raspberries (*Rubus hawaiensis* and *R. macraei*), a rare bog plant (*Acaena exigua*), and the relatively common ʻūlei are the only species of the rose family that naturally occur in the Islands. ʻŪlei is a sprawling woody vine or shrub and is most often seen in moist to dry lowland vegetation. It occurs outside the Park in subalpine shrublands and upland woodlands above 6,000 ft elevation. Indigenous to Hawaiʻi, ʻūlei also occurs in the South Pacific on the Cook Islands and Tonga.

One of the most beautiful plants of the Park lowlands, ūlei is distinguished by shiny, pinnately compound leaves; open, white flowers; and clusters of round berries that ripen from green to white and bear the star-shaped remains of the withered flowers throughout their development. Flowers are most abundant during the winter and early spring months, when large white clusters at branch tips make ʻūlei conspicuous even when mixed among other shrubs. While flowers have a faint odor, they are not sweetly fragrant. Ūlei flowers or foliage are sometimes seen in leis made of native plant materials; they were a popular lei-making material in old Hawaiʻi. Hawaiians also used the wood of ʻūlei for implements and the supple viny branches for weaving fish traps and baskets.

Today ʻūlei is common near Lae ʻĀpuki, where it grows with other native shrubs and trees such as ʻākia, ʻaʻaliʻi, and lama. Here the plant forms low, spreading mats of arching branches, which, coupled with uneven rocky terrain, make walking through the native shrublands difficult. Because this region is subjected to lava flows from the East Rift of Kīlauea and has been invaded by nonnative grasses that readily carry fire, the primarily native lowland shrublands are occasionally burned. ʻŪlei is an example of a native shrub that can often survive fire and resprout from stem bases.

ʻŪlei is also a component of ʻōhiʻa woodlands of the mid-elevation zone, where it typically grows more upright as a shrub. Areas where ʻūlei may be readily found include the former ʻĀinahou Ranch, Hilina Pali Road, Chain of Craters Road, Keʻāmoku Lava Flow near Kaʻū Desert Trail, and the region between Hawaiian Volcano Observatory and Kīpuka Puaulu.

Lantana (*Lantana camara*) **and**
 Christmas Berry (*Schinus terebinthifolius*)

Verbena family (Verbenaceae) and Mango family (Anacardiaceae)

Alien

Distribution in the Park: Coast to approximately 3,000 ft elevation

Native to the West Indies, lantana (<u>illustrated</u>) was an early post-contact introduction to the Hawaiian Islands, arriving in the middle of the 19th century. Probably introduced as an ornamental, the shrub became a pest after the introduction of alien fruit-eating birds such as the common myna. These birds spread lantana seeds widely, and lowland pastures as well as native forests and shrublands were heavily invaded.

Varying in size from 2 to more than 10 ft tall, lantana is capable of forming dense, impenetrable thickets. Woody, much-branched stems bear numerous sharp, down-curved prickles. Lantana leaves are ovate and 1 to 2 in. long with toothed edges, prominently impressed veins, and a rough, sandpapery texture. The tubular flowers are individually small but are borne in dense, showy terminal and axillary clusters more than 1 in. across. Flower color varies from bright yellow to orange to pink or rose within a single cluster. Fruits are small, round, and fleshy and are purplish black when ripe. While edible for birds, lantana fruits are poisonous to humans and other mammals. Flowers and fruits are most abundant in the spring and summer. The entire shrub, particularly the foliage, has a pungent odor, which is more pronounced when the weather is sunny and hot.

Because of its poisonous properties and its ability to displace forage plants on ranches, lantana was an early target for biocontrol efforts. Starting in 1902 and continuing for about 60 years, more than 20 insect species were introduced to Hawai'i to combat the spread and intensification of lantana. Leaf-feeding moths, stem-boring beetles, gall-forming flies, and leaf miners were introduced from tropical countries all over the world; some became established and began to attack lantana. While complete control has not been achieved even after 90 years, lantana cover has been greatly reduced in many lowland areas, and vast expanses of the shrub are largely a thing of the past on Hawai'i Island. In Hawaii Volcanoes National Park, scattered individual lantana shrubs may be seen throughout the lowlands and along Hilina Pali Road and the lower part of Chain of Craters Road. In only a few localities on steep slopes and pali faces are sizable thickets of lantana encountered. Lantana remains an important component of dry lowland vegetation on Kaua'i, where large, nearly impenetrable thickets still exist in remote valleys.

In the eastern lowlands near Kamoamoa in the Park, lantana grows mixed with native shrubs and another strong-smelling alien shrub or small tree, Christmas berry. Christmas berry has shiny compound leaves composed of many toothed leaflets, which have a turpentine odor when crushed. This species produces large clusters of small white flowers, with males and females borne on separate plants. Female flowers develop into shiny red fruits in the winter. These small, dry, berry-like fruits are attractive to birds, which eat them and disperse Christmas berry seeds. In some lowland areas of Ka'ū and Kona districts, Christmas berry is a serious invader of dry forests and shrublands, but the shrub remains relatively limited in distribution in the Park.

Pua Kala or Hawaiian Prickly Poppy (*Argemone glauca*)

Poppy family (Papaveraceae)

Endemic to the Hawaiian Islands

Distribution in the Park: Coastal lowlands, mid-elevation woodlands, and upland woodlands

The pua kala or Hawaiian prickly poppy is a notable exception to the general principle that endemic Hawaiian plants lack thorns, poisons, and other devices to deter browsing animals. This native poppy is covered with sharp, spiny prickles on its leaves, stems, and ovoid, ribbed seed pods. The only part of the plant lacking prickles is the showy, cup-shaped flower, which is composed of six white petals with a central cluster of many yellow stamens and a prominent three-part pistil (the female part of the flower). The pua kala is a large herb, often more than 3 to 4 ft tall. The plant typically is bluish green and slightly silvery, which makes it noticeable in its grassland habitats. The thick, bright yellow sap of the prickly poppy contains poisonous alkaloids, but the ancient Hawaiians used small quantities of this sap medicinally to treat aches and pains. The Hawaiian name for this poppy literally means "thorny flower."

While the Hawaiian prickly poppy is restricted to the Hawaiian Islands, the plant's closest relatives are species found in North and South America. One of these relatives, the yellow-flowered Mexican poppy (*A. mexicana*), has become established or naturalized on Maui, Oʻahu, and Kauaʻi but is not yet present on Hawaiʻi Island. Although the California poppy (*Eschscholzia californica*) has been planted in gardens of Park residences, it has not escaped in the Park, and the Hawaiian prickly poppy is the only wild poppy in Hawaii Volcanoes.

The endemic pua kala, although widely distributed in the Park, is by no means common. It is most often found in dry habitats, such as the grasslands and open ʻōhiʻa forests just above the extensive cliff or pali systems between 1,000 and 2,000 ft elevation. The trails to Halapē, Keauhou Landing, and Pepeiau cabin, as well as the road to Hilina Pali overlook, are localities where the prickly poppy may be seen. Poppies also grow in grasslands and rocky sites along Mauna Loa Strip Road, particularly near 5,000 ft elevation. It is not known if the poppy's relative rarity in the Park is a natural phenomenon; the scarcity may also be due to past depletions by feral goats or competition from the many nonnative plants now growing in its preferred habitat. Fire is probably not a serious threat to the pua kala, which has been frequently observed growing in previously burned grasslands and shrublands of the lowland and mid-elevation zones.

Kauna'oa Pehu (*Cassytha filiformis*) **and**
  Kauna'oa Kahakai (*Cuscuta sandwichiana*)

Laurel family (Lauraceae) and Dodder family (Cuscutaceae)

Status: Indigenous (kauna'oa pehu); **Endemic** (kauna'oa kahakai)

Distribution in the Park: Eastern lowlands (kauna'oa pehu);
  seashore (kauna'oa kahakai)

106

Kauna'oa pehu (<u>illustrated</u>) is a leafless parasitic vine native to the Hawaiian Islands but also found in many other tropical regions. Because it has little chlorophyll and no leaves other than a few minute scales, the yellowish green to orange-colored vine must depend on other plants for sustenance. Kauna'oa pehu manages to get nourishment by means of specialized sucking structures called haustoria, which attach to other plants and allow the vine to invade the tissue of the host. The flowers of kauna'oa pehu are small, dull colored, and three-parted with six tiny stamens. Flowers develop into small, pale, berry-like fruits, which retain the flower parts on the end.

Like any good parasite, kauna'oa pehu does not kill its host plant, which may be a tree, shrub, or grass. Kauna'oa pehu does not appear to be host specific and has been recorded on many plant species, both native and alien. This plant is conspicuous in the eastern lowlands of Hawaii Volcanoes, where it may be seen draping 'ōhi'a trees and native shrubs along Chain of Craters Road near Hōlei Pali. In some open shrublands, kauna'oa pehu vines grow interconnected as an open web matted over shrubs and grasses. It is almost impossible to walk through such areas, since multiple vines of kauna'oa pehu cannot be easily broken.

Similar in appearance is another native plant, the kauna'oa kahakai or true yellow dodder. It is an endemic member of the dodder family (Cuscutaceae), a small group of plants related to the morning glory family (Convolvulaceae). This vine is also a leafless parasite but has slender stems and is completely yellow-orange with no hint of green. Kauna'oa kahakai primarily parasitizes native shrubs and vines, such as naupaka kahakai, 'ilima, 'uhaloa, and pōhuehue, but the vine has also been recorded on grasses and nonnative shrubs. Kauna'oa kahakai vines are more common on the older Hawaiian Islands and are a popular lei-making material. Much rarer in the Park than kauna'oa pehu, the yellow dodder occurs primarily in sandy areas at the seashore, where it grows on both native and nonnative coastal plants.

Pili (*Heteropogon contortus*) **and**
Thatching Grass (*Hyparrhenia rufa*)

Grass family (Poaceae)

Indigenous (pili) to the Hawaiian Islands; also found in tropics
worldwide. **Alien** (thatching grass)

Distribution in the Park: Lowlands below Hilina and Hōlei pali

One of the few common lowland grasses thought to be native to Hawai'i, pili (<u>illustrated</u>) is widely distributed in the Park lowlands but is abundant at only a few sites.   At Ka'aha, Halapē, and a few sites below Hōlei Pali, this native grass seems to be holding its own in competition with several taller alien bunchgrasses.   Like these recent invaders, pili is adapted to fire and readily resprouts and germinates after its lowland habitat is burned.   Hawaiians took advantage of this trait and intentionally burned grasslands to stimulate pili, which they used for thatching material.   This activity undoubtedly altered lowland communities and reduced the cover of native forests and shrublands.   Because of its usefulness to Hawaiians, some botanists think that pili was brought to Hawai'i by Polynesian settlers.

Typically about 1 to 2 ft tall, pili is light bluish green when fresh and pinkish yellow when dry.   This grass is difficult to identify when mixed with other grasses and not in flower, but when flowering it is quite recognizable.   Pili flowers are borne tightly packed in two overlapping rows on a narrow inflorescence often nodding above the leaves of the grass.   Flowering stalks are conspicuous because of their dark brown bristles, or awns, 2 to 4 in. long, which are twisted about each other in the young inflorescence.   When the fruit or grain of pili is mature, the sharp-pointed awns readily detach from the inflorescence and easily work their way into the clothing or socks of hikers passing through stands of pili.

A recently introduced species from Africa, thatching grass or jaragua, has invaded many areas in which pili was common, such as Halapē and Ka'aha.   Thatching grass also has flowers with prominent twisted bristles, but inflorescences of this species are large, open clusters with wide-spreading branches.   One of the largest bunchgrasses in the Park, thatching grass usually ranges from 3 to 6 ft tall.   Leaf blades of this rank grass are often tinged with red, and drying foliage may be almost entirely purplish red.   This fire-adapted grass was introduced to 'Āinahou when this 6,324-acre area (incorporated into the Park in 1972) was operated as a cattle ranch.   It has been spreading in the Park lowlands for at least the last 20 years.   The eventual range of thatching grass may include much more of the Park, as it is now appearing on roadsides at 4,000 ft elevation.

J. YOSHIOKA

Fountain Grass (*Pennisetum setaceum*) **and**
 Natal Redtop (*Rhynchelytrum repens*)

Grass family (Poaceae)

Alien; both species from Africa

Distribution in the Park: Fountain grass in western lowlands;
  Natal redtop widely distributed in lowlands

Most biologists and land managers in Hawai'i consider fountain grass (illustrated) to be one of the 10 most disruptive alien plant species in the State. Introduced to the kona (leeward) side of Hawai'i Island in the first decade of the 20th century, fountain grass has spread widely and come to dominate vast acreages of pasture land, lava flows, and dry woodlands on the Island. While most abundant on the slopes of Hualālai, fountain grass is naturalized on three other islands (O'ahu, Lāna'i, and Kaua'i). Efforts are ongoing to prevent its establishment on Maui and its further spread on Lāna'i.

Fountain grass has little value as a forage plant and was introduced and subsequently planted in the Hawaiian Islands merely as an ornamental. Despite the tremendous damage to native ecosystems and loss of valuable pasturage caused by this grass, its seeds are still available in seed catalogs, and those who think it a beautiful ornamental grass may still purchase them. The grass has been declared a noxious weed by the Hawaii Department of Agriculture; this may slow its spread to currently uninvaded islands and districts.

A large bunchgrass often over 3 ft tall, fountain grass has narrow, wiry leaves, which are typically rolled up and appear round in cross section. Leaves arch outward from the base, which may be quite wide and massive in old plants. Fountain grass leaves are yellow green when fresh, but under dry conditions they fade to a pale straw color. The tiny flowers of fountain grass are borne in feathery red-purplish spikes well above the clump of leaves. These nodding inflorescences are found on mature grass clumps, and when the tiny fruits or grains ripen, they are probably dispersed by strong winds.

Although fountain grass is currently distributed over approximately 10 percent of the Park, most visitors to Hawaii Volcanoes will never see it. The grass was accidentally brought into the southwestern Park lowlands in the late 1960s, probably on the tires or underbody of a vehicle that had recently been in the infested part of Kona. Fountain grass was soon recognized as a serious invader of the Park, and systematic control was initiated in 1976.

After more than ten years of control efforts, fountain grass had not been eradicated from the Park, even though its density had been greatly reduced in the area of original infestation (approximately 1,000 acres). In the mid-1980s, surveys of the Park lowlands and subsequent distribution mapping revealed that fountain grass had spread over an area of more than 20,000 acres, where it grew scattered in low numbers in alien-dominated grasslands and sparsely vegetated lava flows. After fountain grass was found to be so widespread in the western Park lowlands, Park managers realized they could not control the grass over its entire range and changed from an eradication strategy to one of containment. To accomplish this, helicopter spotters and workers on the ground were used to systematically survey a buffer zone. Where it was found, the grass was removed manually, thus confining fountain grass to its already-disturbed lowland range. Along with periodic searches of lowland roads and trails, the confinement strategy has successfully prevented the further spread of fountain grass in the Park. As the alien plant control program has grown, Park managers have been able to focus more attention on the area of heavy infestation, and fountain grass is slowly being removed or reduced to very low levels in this remote, arid region.

Time and effort are being expended to control fountain grass in the Park lowlands because of the great potential for serious damage to many native ecosystems. Fountain grass is capable of invading not only disturbed grasslands, but also woodlands, open forests, and lava flows, where vegetation is primarily native. In these native systems, fountain grass may displace native plants and interfere with native tree reproduction; but more importantly, the grass provides a bed of continuous fine fuels, allowing fire to penetrate dry forests and other vegetation types formerly little affected by this perturbation. Since most native trees and shrubs are not well adapted to survive fires, the altered fire regime of repeated fires may result in the transformation of native vegetation to communities dominated by alien plants.

Another alien grass from Africa that has successfully invaded the Park lowlands is Natal redtop (formerly called *Tricholaena rosea*). This grass is much more widespread in the Park than is fountain grass, but its impact on native vegetation is far less severe. A low-growing, loosely branched grass, Natal redtop does not attain great height or grow into massive clumps. It is not strongly adapted to fire, although in wetter parts of the eastern lowlands redtop has increased noticeably following fires. Redtop is most abundant in dry, rocky sections of the Park lowlands; it is also a common roadside weed and may be seen on road verges from the coast to about 5,000 ft elevation on Mauna Loa. Natal redtop is most noticeable when in flower, usually in the spring and early summer. Inflorescences are about 6 in. long and pyramidal in shape. The eye-catching flowers are covered with dark pink or purple silky hairs; these fade to silvery white during the hottest part of the late summer.

J. YOSHIOKA

Laua'e (*Phymatosorus scolopendria*) and Other Lowland Ferns

Laua'e Fern family (Polypodiaceae);
  other fern families (Aspleniaceae; Nephrolepidaceae)

Alien (Laua'e); Indigenous and **Alien**

Distribution in the Park: Wet to moist lowland forests
  below 2,500 ft elevation

Laua'e (illustrated), formerly known as *Microsorium scolopendrium* and *Polypodium scolopendrium*, is the most abundant and conspicuous fern in coastal and low-elevation forests of lama in the moist eastern section of the Park. In many lama forests below 1,000 ft elevation, this fern is the dominant ground cover species. Primarily terrestrial, laua'e may also occur as an epiphyte. Varying from 1 to 3 ft tall, laua'e is composed of a stout, creeping, scale-covered rhizome and shiny green, erect fronds with sturdy, smooth, straw-colored stipes (leaf stems). Fronds are deeply lobed, and each lobe has a conspicuous yellowish vein branching from the prominent raised midrib. When fertile, fronds have many round yellow to brown clusters of spore-bearing structures on their undersides, and corresponding raised circles on upper frond surfaces.

Although laua'e is native to many other islands of Polynesia, it was not recorded from Hawai'i until the 1920s and is presumably a recent introduction. Laua'e fronds have a pronounced sweet smell, reminiscent of maile. Because of this quality, the fern is sometimes used for lei-making, usually mixed with flowers. Before the area was covered by lava from the current eruption, Kamoamoa and Waha'ula were localities where the laua'e fern could be readily seen in the Park. Now, the Park visitor must go to the forests upslope of Kamoamoa to find large stands of this fern. Scattered individuals of laua'e may still be found beneath trees and large shrubs in the remaining native shrublands near Lae 'Āpuki.

Other common ferns of the Park lowlands are the bird's nest fern (*Asplenium nidus*) and swordferns or kupukupu (*Nephrolepis* spp.). The bird's nest fern is a large showy fern, which is almost always epiphytic. Restricted to wet or moist lowland forests, this fern grows as a large cluster of long, unlobed, strap-shaped fronds forming a sort of bowl from which young fronds (fiddleheads) emerge. Bird's nest ferns were conspicuous in the recently destroyed coastal forest near Waha'ula; these epiphytes persist in less accessible forests upslope of Kamoamoa. Bird's nest fern is indigenous to Hawai'i but also occurs in many other tropical lands.

Two swordferns are common large terrestrial plants in lowland forests. One is an indigenous species (*Nephrolepis exaltata*; called *N. exaltata* var. *hawaiiensis* by some); the other, scaly swordfern (*N. multiflora*), an alien, was first reported in Hawai'i in the 1880s. Both species are robust ferns with narrow, erect, pinnately compound (shaped like a feather) fronds. The two species differ in the amount of scaliness present on frond surfaces (the alien species is much scalier) and are difficult to tell apart when they occur together. In some 'ōhi'a woodlands near Kalapana Trail, the alien scaly swordfern forms dense, nearly impenetrable stands over 6 ft tall. Scaly swordfern is an early colonizer of lowland lava flows, where it may be responsible for displacing native ferns.

Spotted Dove (*Streptopelia chinensis*) and Zebra Dove (*Geopelia striata*)

Pigeon and Dove family (Columbidae)

Alien; spotted dove introduced before 1880 from Southeast Asia; zebra dove introduced from Malaysia in 1922

Distribution in the Park: Spotted dove fairly common below 4,100 ft elevation, with small numbers to 8,000 ft; zebra dove in drier sites up to 3,000 ft elevation

Spotted or lace-necked doves (<u>lower</u> <u>illustration</u>) somewhat resemble, and are the same size (12 in.) as, the mourning dove of the U.S. Mainland and the leeward side of Hawai'i Island. However, adult spotted doves of both sexes have a white-spotted black patch on the back and sides of the neck. Immatures do not, but broad, rounded tails distinguish them from mourning doves, which have long, pointed tails. Smaller (8 in.), pale brown zebra or barred doves (<u>inset</u>) have rosy breasts with barring on sides and breasts, backs, and wings, and long, white-tipped tails. The skin around the eyes and bill is pale blue. Spotted doves utter three or four loud, low-pitched coos, whereas zebra doves give a staccato series of rapid, higher-pitched calls. Spotted doves fly strongly with rapid wingbeats, but zebra doves exhibit erratic flight patterns. The wings of doves, like some honeycreepers (subfamily Drepanidinae), make a whistling sound in flight, but the sounds are quite different. Wings of zebra doves also may make a clapping sound on takeoff, as do those of large (12 in.), stout rock doves (the common domestic, barnyard, or racing pigeon), also found in the Park.

Both spotted and barred doves build flimsy stick nests characteristic of their kind in trees and shrubs, lay two white eggs, and nest more than once each year. Nesting is year round in Hawai'i. Both species feed their young "crop milk," a sloughed-off lining of the crop produced by both sexes; males and females take turns incubating eggs and brooding young.

Spotted and zebra doves are seed eaters and feed on the ground. Spotted doves, like common mynas, are suspected of enhancing the spread of lantana, an undesirable lowland alien plant. Unlike most birds, doves can swallow water without tilting their heads back. Doves are conspicuous birds because they frequent areas humans also use, favor open places, habitually sit on wires, and pick up small stones along roadsides. The stones, held in the gizzard, serve as grit to help grind the hard seeds consumed by these birds. Both spotted and zebra doves are gamebirds in the State -- but not in the Park!

J. YOSHIOKA

Geckos and Skinks

Gecko family (Gekkonidae) and Skink family (Scincidae)

Alien and **Polynesian introduction**

Distribution in the Park: Usually below 2,000 ft, except for metallic
skink and house gecko (observed to about 4,000 ft on Mauna Loa)

The terrestrial "herpetofauna" (reptiles and amphibians) of Hawai'i
Island consists of five geckos, four skinks, an anolid lizard, a chameleon,
a blind snake, and three amphibians -- the marine toad, the green and black
poison-arrow frog, and the bullfrog. All 15 species are alien, although
some geckos and skinks arrived in early Polynesian times. Adult bullfrogs

have been observed in the Park at mid-elevation (4,000 ft), and poison-arrow frogs have also been reported from nearby (less than 1 mi) Volcano Village.

Geckos are small (2.5-5.5 in.), smooth-skinned reptiles with large toe pads for clinging to vertical surfaces. All species consume insects such as termites, cockroaches, ants, and moths in the lowland areas they inhabit. Geckos are largely nocturnal lizards that utter loud birdlike chirps in the night to advertise their territories. Some species are parthenogenic -- each individual is able to produce fertile eggs without breeding with another gecko. Tree geckos (*Hemiphyllodactylus typus*) are smaller (2.5-3.5 in.), less social, less common, less vocal, and less dependent on human habitations than the other four species. They may be recognized by two dark spots at the base of the tail and thin dark stripes from each eye to shoulder.

Geckos can change skin shade to varying degrees to match their backgrounds, so scale patterns and toe sizes must be used for certain identification. House geckos (*Hemidactylus frenatus*, upper illustration), Hawai'i's largest species (4-5.5 in.), often are off-white or pinkish when near lights at night and are the most common geckos in urban areas of Hawai'i. They have been recorded near buildings at up to 4,000 ft elevation in the Park.

The four species of skinks found in Hawai'i are small (less than 3-5 in.) lizards with smooth scales and streamlined bodies that taper gradually to long tails, which (like gecko tails) break off easily. (Tails regrow in a couple of months but are shorter and less colorful than originals.) Skinks are most active in daylight hours. They eat large numbers of insects and are adapted, with wedge-shaped heads, to burrowing in organic material such as leaf litter. Metallic or rainbow skinks (*Lampropholis delicata*, lower illustration) are the most common species in Hawai'i and are usually identifiable by a rusty sheen on the head, combined with a grayish blue sheen on the tail. (The less common azure-tailed skink [*Emoia cyanura*] has three prominent longitudinal white stripes and a brighter blue tail.)

Metallic skinks can be found up to mid-elevation (4,000 ft) in the Park. This skink, introduced to Hawai'i about 1900, is probably partly responsible for decreasing numbers of the three species of skinks that arrived with Polynesians -- the azure-tailed skink, the live-bearing moth skink (*Lipinia noctua*), and the snake-eyed skink (*Cryptoblepharus boutoni*). Snake-eyed skinks have immovable eyelids, making the eyes appear large and round, and two golden side stripes. They have been found in Park lowlands and in forests up to 3,200 ft elevation in Ka'ū Desert. It is likely that habitat destruction and predation by small Indian mongooses have played a part in the decline of small reptiles in many parts of Hawai'i, as they have elsewhere (*e.g.*, the Virgin Islands).

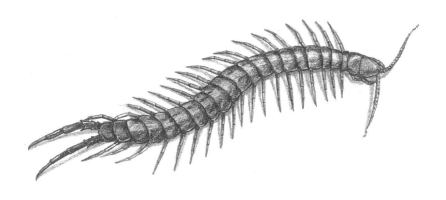

J. YOSHIOKA

Millipedes, Centipedes, Scorpions, and Pseudoscorpions

**Millipede order (Diplopoda); Centipede order (Chilopoda);
Scorpion order (Scorpiones); and
False Scorpion order (Pseudoscorpiones)**

Alien and **Native**

Distribution in the Park: Largely lowland areas, but some
millipedes found to considerable elevations

Millipedes, centipedes, and arachnids are all arthropods, but millipedes and centipedes have many more pairs of legs than insects, have no wings, and are cylindrical or more or less flattened. Arachnids, including spiders as well as scorpions and pseudoscorpions, have four pairs of legs, not six. Much remains to be learned about all these groups in the Park.

Millipedes (upper illustration) are fairly slow moving, roundish, and often roll up, but centipedes (middle illustration) are flatter and more active. Millipedes have two pairs of legs on most body segments, whereas centipedes have only one pair per segment. Millipedes feed on plant material, but centipedes are carnivorous, with chewing mouthparts and the first pair of legs modified into poison claws. Humans can suffer local pain, swelling, vomiting, dizziness, headaches, and an irregular pulse when bitten by larger centipedes. Millipedes emit a disagreeable odor when disturbed.

Twenty-five species of millipedes are currently known from Hawai'i. Nine are alien and 16 are endemic. *Trigoniulus lumbricinus*, the largest (up to 2 in.), is reddish brown and, when active, 90 pairs of orange-colored legs produce a wave-like motion. *Oxidus gracilis* is a common species with 20 legs, found to considerable elevations in natural areas. A blind native millipede lives in lava tubes in the Park.

The largest of 24 species of centipedes in Hawai'i, *Scolopendra subspinipes*, can reach a length of over 6 in. and has 20 pairs of walking legs. Like other centipedes, it is largely nocturnal and prefers dark areas. It preys on various insects, including cockroaches, and also eats earthworms. *Lithobius*, a mountain-dwelling centipede with 15 pairs of legs, is much smaller and faster than *Scolopendra*. A blind, pale *Lithobius* lives in lava tubes in the Park.

Scorpions look somewhat like small lobsters, with a pair of pedipalps (not true legs) modified as claws; a long "tail" held above the back terminates in a poisonous stinger. Claws or pincers are used to seize spiders and insects, and the stinger then paralyzes the prey. Young scorpions are born live and ride on the back of the female until first molt. Young of some species may take up to five years to reach adult size. A widely distributed alien species in Hawai'i's lowlands is the lesser brown scorpion *Isometrus maculatus* (lower illustration).

Pseudoscorpions are very small spider-like creatures (usually 0.4 in. long) without stingers. Many species have poison glands nonetheless, as well as silk glands on the jaws (unlike spiders, which carry them in the abdomen), used to construct nests. Although they are slow moving, pseudoscorpions prey on various insects and mites. Pseudoscorpions are known for "hitchhiking" by clinging to larger, flying insects as they move from place to place. These animals apparently occur in a variety of natural and man-made habitats in Hawai'i. *Tyrannochthonius howarthi*, a blind, long-legged species, occurs in a lowland lava tube in the Park.

Cockroaches:

  American Cockroach (*Periplaneta americana*),
  Harlequin Cockroach (*Neostylopyga rhombifolia*),
  German Cockroach (*Blattella germanica*), **and**
  Allacta similis

Blatellid Cockroach family (Blattellidae: German Cockroach and
  Allacta similis)**; Blattid Cockroach family (Blattidae:**
  American and Harlequin Roaches)

Alien

Distribution in the Park: Lowland areas. Some may be present in
  mid-elevation thermal areas and residential areas at higher elevations

121

There are about 3,500 species of cockroaches worldwide, of which 19 are found in Hawai'i. About 10 species have been recorded in the Park. Roaches are among the oldest winged insects (they appeared 350 million years ago in the fossil record) and one of the most adaptable. Cockroaches are one of the most persistent forms of life on earth. They have changed little from their initial forms of long ago and are, in fact, considered "living fossils" by scientists. Cockroaches usually scurry rather than fly and have flat, oval bodies and threadlike antennae. Most are nocturnal, and during the daytime they inhabit cracks or other places where their bodies are in contact with several surfaces at once. Cockroaches have chewing mouthparts and are related to grasshoppers and crickets. Metamorphosis is simple -- young cockroaches hatched from egg packets molt into larger and larger nymphs until adult size is reached.

American cockroaches (center in illustration) are large, common roaches (up to 2 in. long). They are a shiny reddish brown with yellowish edges and markings on the pronotum (area behind the head). The slender antennae are longer than the body. Adults fly well and are sometimes attracted to light. Nymphs take about 12 months to mature, and adults live about a year, feeding on organic matter of all kinds. These animals are common in Kalapana and many other lowland areas of the Park and provide food for ants (several species), small Indian mongooses, common mynas, and other species. The presence of cockroaches may, in fact, allow higher populations of some predators to exist than would otherwise be possible without such consistently abundant prey.

Harlequin cockroaches (bottom in illustration) are also large (1 in. long) roaches common in Park lowlands. This flightless species from Indo-Malaysia is irregularly marked with yellow and has shorter antennae than the American cockroach. First reported in Hawai'i in 1882, harlequins have habits similar to those of the American roach.

German cockroaches (top in illustration) are small (up to 0.6 in.), slender, pale to dark brown insects with two longitudinal brown marks on the pronotum. They are usually closely associated with humans. (The look-alike *B. lituricollis* is abundant in open lowland areas.) Female German roaches carry relatively large, partly extruded egg capsules for a month, then deposit them, whereupon two dozen or so nymphs emerge. Adult size is reached in four to six months. Like others of their kind, German cockroaches can produce several generations a year.

Allacta similis, the common forest roach in Hawai'i, is found in 'ōhi'a and koa forests in the Park from about 2,500 to 5,200 ft elevation, with peak numbers at about 4,500 ft. This small (0.4 in.), variable species from Australia (first recorded in the late 1800s in Hawai'i) can be recognized by a pronotum that is nearly twice as wide as it is long, and exposed cerci (sensory appendages) behind the wing tips. *Allacta* feeds on organic detritus and is active under bark, in foliage clusters, and in hollows in many species of plants; this species may provide food for some forest birds.

MID-ELEVATION WOODLANDS

MID-ELEVATION WOODLANDS

The mid-elevation zone of the Park is defined here as that area above Hilina Pali (2,000 ft elevation) and below Kīlauea Caldera (4,000 ft). This zone is bounded on the west by State lands of Ka'ū District and stretches eastward to rain forests and lava flows of Kīlauea's East Rift. Some writers have called this the "seasonal submontane zone." It includes the caldera (collapsed summit) of Kīlauea, Ka'ū Desert, the Southwest Rift zone, the upper Chain of Craters region, and numerous recent lava flows.

A diversity of substrates and lava flow ages occurs within the geologically active mid-elevation zone; many flows dating from the 20th century are found here. Kīlauea has been extremely active in historical times, with the latest eruption within the caldera in 1982. Kīlauea's most prominent feature is Halema'uma'u Crater, or "the firepit." This crater has been an important site of eruptive activity since the early 19th century and was Kīlauea's primary vent for more than 100 years, until the explosive eruption of 1924. For much of that time, the firepit contained a lake of molten lava. In 1924, the lava lake drained, a series of violent steam explosions occurred, and Halema'uma'u Crater doubled in size.

Earlier eruptions at Kīlauea's summit were even larger and more violent than the 1924 event. In 1790, a powerful explosive eruption occurred at the summit, which blanketed many square miles with ash. Near the caldera edge, the ash deposits from this event are 15 to 35 ft deep. The upper part of Ka'ū Desert is covered with ash to a depth of at least 4.5 ft, and ash deposits from 1790 are prominent for many miles downwind of Kīlauea Crater in the Park's mid-elevation zone. Of particular historical interest are the footprints preserved in hardened ash between Mauna Iki and Highway 11. These 200-year-old impressions are thought to be those of warriors of Keoua's army, caught unawares in the explosive eruption while marching to the kona (leeward) side of the Island to attack King Kamehameha I.

The Southwest Rift zone of Kīlauea has been far less active in historical times than the East Rift. The most recent Southwest Rift eruptions occurred in 1971 and 1974 and resulted in pāhoehoe flows near Mauna Iki and in the Ka'ū Desert. Mauna Iki, a small lava shield directly on the Southwest Rift, was formed during an eruption in 1919-20. Other prominent geological features of the Southwest Rift and Ka'ū Desert are the prehistoric Kamakai'a Hills, Cone Peak, Pu'u Koa'e, and pit craters along Ka'ū Desert Trail. The dry, windswept landscapes of Ka'ū Desert show only sparse vegetation but include drifting ash dunes, spatter cones, fault scarps, and broad vistas of distant Mauna Loa and the sea.

The eastern part of the mid-elevation zone is wetter and has denser vegetation than the western section. This area, traversed by the upper part of Chain of Craters Road and Hilina Pali Road, supports various vegetation types on substrates generally older than those of the western part of this zone. Old pāhoehoe flows of Kīpuka Nēnē and 'Āinahou dating from 750 to 1,500 years ago are prominent. The most striking geological feature of the eastern section is the line of pit craters of the upper East Rift zone (the Chain of Craters), stretching from Keanakākoʻi on the rim of Kīlauea Caldera to the shield of Mauna Ulu and its 20-year-old lava flows. Pit craters are thought to form when underlying magma drains away and causes the surface to collapse.

The climate of the mid-elevation zone shows a pronounced seasonal variation, with dry, warm periods typically occurring in the summer. Mean temperatures vary from 60°F near Kīlauea Caldera to 72°F at 2,000 ft elevation. Average annual rainfall ranges from 20 to 60 in., with higher precipitation occurring in the eastern portion of the zone and at higher elevation. The western section of the Park just above Hilina Pali receives only 20 in. of rainfall a year, because it is in a "rain shadow" created by the summit of Kīlauea Volcano and the east flank of Mauna Loa. Most of the precipitation in this area comes from moist air blown upslope by the northeast tradewinds, and this is partially blocked by Kīlauea's summit area. Kaʻū Desert, including a large portion of the Park's mid-elevation zone, is not a true climatic desert, as it receives up to 50 in. of rainfall annually, an amount sufficient to support forest vegetation. Most of the "desert" has only a sparse cover of drought-tolerant plants because of the youth and texture of its soils. Substrates of the desert are primarily young unweathered lavas and deep layers of porous ash and cinder, which allow rapid drainage and have little water-holding capacity. The forest stands that occur within Kaʻū Desert are usually on ʻaʻā substrates without deep ash cover. Desiccating strong winds also contribute to dry conditions, and the constant production of sulfur dioxide fumes and other toxic gases reduces plant growth in the area directly downwind of vents, such as those near Halemaʻumaʻu Crater.

Vegetation of the mid-elevation zone varies greatly with rainfall and substrate type. In much of the Southwest Rift zone and Kaʻū Desert, vegetation consists of scattered native shrubs and both native and alien grasses. ʻŌhelo (*Vaccinium reticulatum*), pūkiawe (*Styphelia tameiameiae*), ʻaʻaliʻi (*Dodonaea viscosa*), and ʻuhaloa (*Waltheria indica*) are most often seen, but rare native shrubs such as *Silene hawaiiensis* and Kīlauea naupaka (*Scaevola kilaueae*) also occur here. Where rainfall is adequate, relatively recent lava flows support scattered ʻōhiʻa (*Metrosideros polymorpha*), native shrubs, hardy ferns such as ʻamaʻu (*Sadleria cyatheoides*), the endemic ʻemoloa or lovegrass (*Eragrostis variabilis*), and a number of alien herbs and grasses.

Perhaps the most abundant vegetation type of the mid-elevation zone is an open woodland of ʻōhiʻa trees with an understory of mixed native trees and shrubs and ground cover dominated by alien grasses such as bush beardgrass (*Schizachyrium condensatum*) and molasses grass (*Melinis minutiflora*). This plant community is found primarily in the eastern section of the zone just above the pali (cliff) system delineating the lowlands. While extensive, the open ʻōhiʻa woodland has been much impacted by past feral ungulate browsing, cattle grazing, and wildfires. At higher elevations on the eastern side of the zone, along the upper Chain of Craters area, rainfall is greater, and all but very young substrates support an open forest of 'ōhi'a, with many associated native trees, shrubs, and uluhe or false staghorn fern (*Dicranopteris linearis*).

Native wildlife of the mid-elevation zone includes many bird species found in Park rain forests and upper-elevation woodlands. The 'apapane (*Himatione sanguinea*), Hawai'i's most common native bird, is found throughout the zone, wherever flowering 'ōhi'a trees occur. The mid-elevation zone provides habitat for these and other native nectar-eating birds, which is particularly important when flowering is sparse at higher elevations and when young birds disperse from breeding grounds in the late spring and summer. The common 'amakihi (*Hemignathus virens*) is also a characteristic denizen of the wetter forests and woodlands near the upper part of the Chain of Craters area and 'Āinahou. 'Io *(Buteo solitarius)*, the Endangered Hawaiian hawk, may be seen soaring over mid-elevation woodlands hunting for rodents or small birds. Grasslands and shrublands of the zone are critical feeding areas for the Endangered Hawaiian goose or nēnē (*Branta sandvicensis*), and Ka'ū Desert and 'Āinahou are important breeding and molting sites for this bird.

Alien birds are abundant in the mid-elevation zone. Small birds most often seen flitting from tree to tree in these woodlands are Japanese white-eyes (*Zosterops japonicus*) and nutmeg mannikins (*Lonchura punctulata*). Mannikins are particularly noticeable in grassy areas, where small flocks may be seen swaying atop grass inflorescences, feeding on seeds. The melodious laughing thrush or hwamei (*Garrulax canorus*) is a common but secretive bird of this zone, more often heard than seen. Common mynas (*Acridotheres tristis*) live near roads and areas regularly used by humans, such as campgrounds and shelters. Other alien animals of this zone include ubiquitous black rats (*Rattus rattus*), small Indian mongooses (*Herpestes auropunctatus*), and feral house cats (*Felis catus*). Feral pigs (*Sus scrofa*) also occur in mid-elevation woodlands, but drier habitats can support only low densities. A more important alien animal here is the feral goat (*Capra hircus*). Few if any goats are found in the Park today, but in the past large herds of feral goats roamed the mid-elevation zone, as well as the coastal lowlands, and did incalculable damage to the native plants there.

The mid-elevation woodlands are rich in invertebrate life. Many groups with numerous Hawaiian species are represented here, including the long-horned woodborers (*Plagithmysus* spp.), yellow-faced bees (*Hylaeus* spp.), oodemus weevils (*Oodemus* spp.), damsel bugs (*Nabis* spp.), and small moths of the genus *Udea*. Damsel bugs, especially *N. tarai*, may be found along Chain of Craters Road and on the road to Kīpuka Nēnē. Yellow-faced bees, important pollinators in most zones, are evident in open areas especially near native composite (sunflower family) flowers. Several species of lacewings in the genus *Anomalochrysa* may also be found in the zone. The related antlion (*Eidoleon* sp.) is characteristic and can be seen near Footprints Trail and from Namakani Paio to Kīpuka Nēnē. Unlike many continental antlions, this rare endemic predator neither builds pits nor eats ants. The alien western yellowjacket wasp (*Vespula pensylvanica*) is widespread in the mid-elevation woodlands and is locally abundant. Introduced spinybacked spiders (*Gasteracantha* spp.) are also prominent.

The most important management problem of the mid-elevation zone today is wildfire. Because of the invasion of fire-adapted alien grasses, fire is an all-too-frequent occurrence in the area; more than half of the zone's burnable vegetation has been subjected to fire since 1968. Ignition sources such as lava flows and lightning are impossible to control; during droughts cigarettes tossed from cars and untended campground fires are significant sources of fire. Since the establishment of alien grasses during the 1960s, fires at middle and low elevations in the Park have greatly increased in frequency and size. Before 1968, the average size of Park fires was less than 1 acre, but fires recorded from 1968 to 1993 averaged nearly 400 acres.

Of all the Park's major regions, the mid-elevation zone is the most accessible to the visitor. Important geological features of Kīlauea Caldera and upper Chain of Craters are reached by Crater Rim Drive and Chain of Craters Road. Ka'ū Desert and Kīlauea's Southwest Rift are traversed by the Ka'ū Desert, Mauna Iki, and Footprints trails. The Park's extensive open 'ōhi'a woodlands may be seen along Hilina Pali Road, Ka'ū Desert Trail to Pepeiau, the upper part of Halapē Trail, and portions of Kalapana Trail.

'Iliahi or Sandalwood (*Santalum paniculatum* var. *paniculatum*)

Sandalwood family (Santalaceae)

Endemic to Hawai'i Island

Distribution in the Park: Lower Mauna Loa Strip Road
and Kīlauea Caldera to eastern lowlands above Kamoamoa

Because of the history of overexploitation during the early 19th century, many people think that 'iliahi or sandalwood is rare or extinct. This is not the case on Hawai'i Island, and the sandalwood of Hawaii Volcanoes may still be found in considerable numbers. Botanists today recognize four species and several varieties of sandalwood in the Hawaiian Islands; one species (*S. ellipticum*) is relatively widespread on all the islands, one (*S. freycinetianum*) is found on most of the islands except Hawai'i, one (*S. haleakalae*) is limited to East Maui, and the fourth (*S. paniculatum*) is restricted to Hawai'i Island. Only one variety of sandalwood *(S. freycinetianum* var. *lanaiense)* is currently listed as Endangered; it is found only on Lāna'i and Maui.

One variety of one species of 'iliahi is found in Hawaii Volcanoes; this sandalwood largely escaped the ravages of the sandalwood trade because, in an era lacking roads, much of the Park was relatively inaccessible. This sandalwood is usually shrubby in growth form but may also be single-trunked and achieve the stature of a mid-size tree. Leaves are typically yellowish green with pale bluish white undersides. Young growth is often a prominent purplish red. Flowers are small, four-lobed, and yellow-green in color, fading to brown. They are fragrant, and in the summer when flowering is heavy, honeybees are attracted in great numbers to the trees. 'Iliahi fruits are fleshy, about 0.5 in. long, and are tipped with a conspicuous ring. When ripe, they are purplish-black. All sandalwoods are hemi-parasites, which means that they get some of their nourishment from other plants, although they are also capable of photosynthesis. The root systems of sandalwood trees invade the root vascular tissue of other plants and extract food. Apparently they do not specialize on any one species, but may parasitize 'ōhi'a, other trees, and grasses. Sandalwood trees may be readily viewed along Highway 11 near Mauna Loa Strip Road, where their yellowish foliage makes them conspicuous among the gray-green 'ōhi'a trees. The visitor may get a closer look at sandalwoods along Sandalwood Trail on the rim of Kīlauea Caldera and also in Kīpuka Kahali'i along Chain of Craters Road.

The collection of Hawaiian 'iliahi for trade was most intensive between 1815 and 1826. During this time vast quantities of the fragrant heartwood were shipped to China, where sandalwood was used to make carved objects, boxes, incense, and perfume. By the 1830s and 1840s, 'iliahi had been eradicated from many lowland forests, particularly on O'ahu. Some forests were destroyed by fire in an attempt to locate the last of the sandalwoods by their fragrant smoke.

While 'iliahi of upslope regions of Hawai'i Island generally escaped depletion during the 19th century, in recent years sandalwood logging has been revived on several ranches of South Kona. Large trees that escaped destruction by their inaccessibility can now be trucked or even helicoptered down the mountain for shipment to the Orient, where demand for the fragrant wood remains high. While lowland forests of 'iliahi and other native trees are largely gone and upland forests have been disturbed by grazing and logging, the sandalwoods of Hawai'i Island do not appear to be in danger of extinction. However, the cutting of large, slow-growing trees removes an important component of a scarce Hawaiian community type. Perhaps the economic value of sandalwood may encourage landowners to replant young trees in depleted forests and to remove cattle from open forests used as pastures.

J. YOSHIOKA

Firetree or Faya Tree (*Myrica faya*)

Bayberry family (Myricaceae)

Alien; native to the Azores, Canary Islands, and Madeira

Distribution in the Park: Widespread in eastern half of Park
between 2,000 and 4,000 ft elevation

Firetree, also called firebush and faya tree, is one of the most disruptive nonnative plants in Hawaii Volcanoes National Park. The common name firetree (preferred by Wagner *et al.*) is probably a corruption of the specific scientific name "faya." Native to the Azores, Canary Islands, and Madeira, which are volcanic islands off the coast of Africa, the tree was introduced to the Hawaiian Islands around the turn of the century, perhaps as a source of wood, for its waxy fruit, or simply as an ornamental. Because it grows rapidly, the tree was later used in reforestation and was planted in 10 forest reserves on three of the Hawaiian Islands.

Firetree varies in form with age and habitat from a shrubby, multi-trunked, small tree to a medium-sized, single-trunked tree with pale, unfurrowed bark. Young firetrees in open woodlands have a distinctive pyramidal shape. Leaves are shiny dark green, narrow, about 2 in. long, and prominently but irregularly toothed. Flowers are small and inconspicuous in axillary clusters or at the bases of small branches. Individual trees usually bear only male or female flowers, but some older plants have flowers of both sexes. Fruits of the firetree are small (less than 0.25 in. long) with a hard inner coat enclosing one to five seeds. Ripe fruits are reddish or purplish black and are covered by waxy plates.

An individual female tree may bear tens of thousands of fruits each year; fall is the time of greatest fruit production. Fruits are eaten and dispersed by birds, particularly the nonnative Japanese white-eye and the house finch, but possibly also by native fruit-eating birds. In some areas, feral pigs attracted to earthworms in soil beneath firetree stands also eat fallen fruit.

First noticed in the Park near Kīlauea Military Camp in 1961, firetree spread rapidly and invaded at least 9,000 acres within 16 years. Within another decade, the species had tripled its range in the Park and by 1985 was found over more than 30,800 acres of forest and woodland between 2,000 and 4,000 ft elevation. Firetree has been successful in the Park because it is capable of fixing nitrogen and can grow in nitrogen-poor soils of relatively recent volcanic substrates. It grows much faster than the native 'ōhi'a, and its litter adds nitrogen to the soil, which changes the natural nutrient balance and may encourage the invasion of other nonnative plants. In open woodlands heavily invaded by this species, almost every 'ōhi'a tree has at least one firetree growing beside or beneath it, a phenomenon related to the use of 'ōhi'a trees as perches by fruit-eating birds and to the suitability of cooler, shaded spots for seed germination. The woodlands of the mid-elevation zone are particularly suitable for firetree establishment because they provide shaded sites for seedlings, abundant sunlight for tree growth, and large populations of fruit-dispersing birds. Firetree is less successful as an invader of closed rain forests and grows slowly when shaded, but rain forests that have undergone canopy dieback or understory disturbance along the rim of Kīlauea Caldera are vulnerable to invasion.

In at least one spot in the Park, near Puhimau Crater, perhaps an early site of establishment, firetree has formed a closed canopy 50 ft tall mixed with only a few spindly 'ōhi'a trees. Almost no other plants are able to grow in the dense shade of this stand.

While this species cannot be controlled at present throughout its extensive range in Hawaii Volcanoes, the tree is being removed from the most intact and biologically diverse portions of the Park, called Special Ecological Areas. Using direct application of herbicides to freshly cut stumps of large trees and manual uprooting of saplings and seedlings, Park personnel have cleared more than 10,000 acres of this pest since 1985. Research is also under way to locate, propagate, and test insects and pathogens from the native range of firetree as biological control agents to combat the spread and intensification of this alien plant.

In 1986 Park resource managers first noticed dieback among invading firetree in the Hilina Pali area. Symptoms were chlorosis, defoliation, small leaf size, and, in severe cases, tree death. This dieback has now been documented from much of the tree's range in Hawaii Volcanoes, but it is most severe in a 200-acre area between the Hilina Pali and Chain of Craters roads. Concentric circles of less severe dieback surround a central area. Larger trees appear to be most susceptible to defoliation and decline. The cause of firetree decline is not known but is thought to be a plant pathogen, perhaps a mycoplasma-like organism spread by an insect such as the two-spot leaf hopper.

'Ākia (*Wikstroemia phillyreifolia* **and** *Wikstroemia sandwicensis*)

'Ākia family (Thymelaeaceae)

Endemic to Hawai'i Island

Distribution in the Park: Coast to 4,000 ft elevation

Few native Hawaiian plants are known to be poisonous, but the group of species known as 'ākia has a reputation for being highly toxic, and some species reportedly were used for executions and suicides in old Hawai'i. Toxicity probably varies among the dozen species found in the Hawaiian Islands, with some less poisonous than others; nonetheless, their fruit should not be eaten. 'Ākia growing near the shore was used as fish poison by Hawaiians. Leaves and stems were pounded, wrapped into packets, and placed in fish ponds or other still water. The poison caused the fish to float to the surface, where they could be easily gathered.

Two species of 'ākia are common in Hawaii Volcanoes National Park. One of these (*Wikstroemia phillyreifolia*, illustrated) is found from the open 'ōhi'a woodlands along Chain of Craters Road to the forests and shrublands of Kīlauea Caldera. This species also occurs in woodlands and shrublands near Ka'ū Desert and in the western section of the Park up to Kīpuka Puaulu.

This shrub is usually less than 4 ft tall, has shiny purplish brown bark, and bears small, ovate, dull green leaves about 1 in. long with whitish undersides. Flowers are small, tubular, and yellow and grow in clusters at branch tips. The small, fleshy fruits are orange and ovoid and contain only one seed. Care should be taken not to confuse 'ākia fruits with those of the edible 'ōhelo with which it grows. 'Ōhelo fruits may be distinguished from 'ākia by their many tiny seeds and round disk at the tip bearing the calyx lobes of the flower.

The second common 'ākia in the Park (*W. sandwicensis*) is a large shrub or small tree and is one of the dominant shrubs of the Park's eastern coastal lowlands. It is also a component of the understory in rain forests, particularly those below 3,500 ft elevation. In the dense shade of forests, this species is a single-trunked small tree. This 'ākia has dull green, ovate leaves, which are usually 1 to 3 in. long but may be much larger; leaf undersides are light green and show a conspicuous network of veins. Small yellow flowers and red-orange fruits are very similar to the other common 'ākia of the Park. This species has laterally flattened branches covered by smooth, purplish brown bark with a satin sheen and many small, white bumps called lenticels. The bark of this and other 'ākia species was important in Hawaiian days as a source of strong fiber for cordage. *Wikstroemia sandwicensis* can be seen in the shrublands near Kamoamoa and Lae 'Apuki, where it grows with lama, 'ūlei, and 'a'ali'i.

135

Kīlauea Naupaka or Huahekili Uka (*Scaevola kilaueae*)

Goodenia family (Goodeniaceae)

Endemic to Hawai'i Island

Distribution in the Park: Dry mid-elevation woodlands and upper edge of Ka'ū Desert

Unique to the island of Hawai'i, Kīlauea naupaka seems to be restricted to the Park and one area on the western slope of Mauna Loa, within the Hawaiian Ocean View Estates subdivision. The species was, until recently, a candidate for Federal listing as an Endangered Species; however, it was removed from consideration when more plants were found in existence than previously known. Nonetheless, Kīlauea naupaka has a relatively limited geographic distribution and is considered a rare plant in the Park.

A low-growing shrub rarely taller than 3 ft, Kīlauea naupaka has fleshy, yellow-green leaves 1 to 3 in. long with tiny marginal teeth. Its flowers, like other Hawaiian naupaka species, look like "half flowers" because the lobes are all on the lower side of the partially split floral tube. Often streaked with purple, these cream-colored flowers are borne in loose clusters at branch tips and are highly fragrant. The fleshy fruits are small and shiny purplish black.

Kīlauea naupaka can be most easily seen along Hilina Pali Road on substrates of pāhoehoe and ash. In this area, naupaka seems to be recovering from the effects of feral goats, which inhabited the Park in large numbers until the early 1970s.

Two other naupaka species are found in the Park but are unlikely to be confused with this one. The coastal naupaka kahakai (*S. sericea*) has much larger, thicker leaves than those of Kīlauea naupaka. Naupaka kuahiwi (*S. chamissoniana*), found in forests of Kīlauea Caldera rim and East Rift, is a small, upright tree with much larger, thinner, and more-prominently toothed leaves than Kīlauea naupaka.

Bamboo Orchid (*Arundina graminifolia*) **and Other Orchids**

Orchid family (Orchidaceae)

Alien (bamboo orchid); introduced from Asia, India, or Malaysia.
Other orchids **Alien** and **Endemic** to Hawai'i (three species)

Distribution in the Park: Abundant in lowlands and
mid-elevation grasslands and woodlands (bamboo orchid)

The orchid family is one of the largest of all the families of flowering plants, with perhaps as many as 15,000 to 20,000 species worldwide. Although orchids are notable components of many tropical areas, only three orchid species are native to the Hawaiian Islands. Many orchids require specialized insect pollinators; absence of suitable pollinators in Hawai'i may explain why more orchids have not been able to successfully colonize the Hawaiian Islands. Two endemic Hawaiian orchid species (*Liparis hawaiensis* or 'awapuhi a Kanaloa, and *Anoectochilus sandvicensis*) occur rarely in rain forests of 'Ola'a and Kīlauea's East Rift and are unlikely to be seen by visitors on established trails. Although tropical orchids are typically epiphytic (growing on another plant but not deriving food or water from it), the Hawaiian species are primarily terrestrial and have been severely impacted by the rooting and trampling of feral pigs.

Much more commonly seen are nonnative orchids, such as the bamboo orchid (illustrated, formerly known as *Arundina bambusifolia*). The common name of this large ground-dwelling orchid is derived from the resemblance of its leaves to those of bamboo. Flowers of the bamboo orchid are showy and about 2 in. broad; often only one or two flowers are present on an individual plant. Most of the petal-like structures of the orchid flower are white or lavender, but the specialized petal that is lowermost and largest in the flower (called the labellum) is usually purple with a yellow throat. The bamboo orchid (unlike many cultivated hybrid orchids) does bear fruit in Hawai'i; prominently ribbed capsules are green when fresh and brown when they dry and split open, releasing thousands of tiny wind-borne seeds. This species has an extremely high reproductive potential, for in addition to numerous seeds, each plant is capable of forming small plantlets on the stem below flowers, a form of asexual reproduction.

The bamboo orchid was introduced to Hawai'i as a cultivated plant some-time earlier this century, and by 1945 it had escaped and become natural-ized. It is now widespread on at least four of the main Hawaiian Islands and is particularly abundant in Puna District on Hawai'i Island. In fact, it is primarily because of this nonnative orchid that the Hawaii Visitor's Bureau and other tourist organizations designated Hawai'i Island the "Orchid Isle." In Hawaii Volcanoes, this orchid may be readily seen from Crater Rim Drive near Steaming Bluffs and is quite common along Chain of Craters Road. Bamboo orchid flowers also lend a splash of color to the arid grasslands of the lowlands, a zone now dominated by alien plants. Although the bamboo orchid is not native to the Park, it is a relatively innocuous alien species for which no control is warranted.

Two other alien orchids that a visitor is likely to see in the Park are the Malaysian ground orchid (*Spathoglottis plicata*) and the Chinese ground orchid (*Phaius tankarvilleae*). Both species are terrestrial rather than epiphytic. The Malaysian ground orchid is seen in the eastern half of the lowlands and may be recognized by its purple flowers and broad, prominently plaited leaves. The Chinese ground orchid occurs primarily in the wet forests and moist woodlands near Kīlauea Caldera. This orchid has tightly clustered, fleshy, bright green leaves and upright inflorescences of large flowers that are white outside and dull brownish purple within.

ʻŌhelo (*Vaccinium reticulatum*)

Heath family (Ericaceae)

Endemic to the Hawaiian Islands

Distribution in the Park: Lowlands to above tree line on Mauna Loa

140

'Ōhelo is one of the best-known native shrubs of the Park, probably because of its edible berries and association with the Hawaiian goddess Pele. A favorite of many people, this native shrub is widely distributed in many ecological zones and may be found in the lowlands, mid-elevation 'ōhi'a woodlands, Ka'ū Desert, subalpine scrub, and even above the tree line at 8,500 ft elevation on Mauna Loa. Although a natural component of many vegetation types, this 'ōhelo is most conspicuous in the open mid-elevation woodlands of the western part of Kīlauea Caldera rim.

Usually less than 4 ft tall, 'ōhelo is divided near its base into few to many stiff, brittle branches. Large shrubs often appear rounded in the Kīlauea area. Typically, 'ōhelo leaves are small, dull green, and toothed, although all three of these characters are variable. The waxy, bell-shaped flowers of 'ōhelo are small but delicately beautiful; they droop from branch tips and are red to yellow-green. The most conspicuous part of the plant is the berries, which are round and glossy red to yellow, with the remains of the flower persistent at the tip of the fruit. While some fruit may be seen on 'ōhelo bushes throughout the year, the summer is the period of heaviest berry production. 'Ōhelo berries are eagerly sought for jams, jellies, and pies. Berry collecting is allowed in the Park, but the amount any individual may collect is limited to one quart per person per month, and collected berries must be for personal or home use only. Collecting within Hawaii Volcanoes National Park for commercial jam production or later sale is illegal. Overcollection of this important natural resource would alter the composition of the native shrub communities in the Park and would also deprive two endemic insects (moths in the fruitworm family, Carposinidae) of their only known host plant. The larval stage of these two native moths is entirely dependent upon 'ōhelo berries, without which they cannot complete their life cycle. The 'ōhelo is also a potentially important component of the diet of the Endangered nēnē or Hawaiian goose.

Currently, two species of 'ōhelo are recognized within the Park: the common 'ōhelo of open woodlands (*V. reticulatum*) and the 'ōhelo kau lā'au or tree 'ōhelo (*V. calycinum*) of closed wet forests. Previously, several other forms of 'ōhelo were considered to be distinct species; one of these, formerly known as *Vaccinium peleanum*, is an 'ōhelo of the subalpine shrublands and tree line community, distinguished by its bluish green, untoothed leaves and blue-violet berries. Another 'ōhelo of the Kīlauea Caldera mid-elevation woodlands was previously called *Vaccinium pahalae*; this form is notable for its diminutive size, leaves with strongly toothed and curled margins, and bright red berries. The most recent taxonomic treatment of the Hawaiian *Vaccinium* considers these forms to be local variants or hybrids; *V. peleanum* and *V. pahalae* are now grouped under the more common 'ōhelo, *V. reticulatum*.

Koʻokoʻolau or Kōkoʻolau (*Bidens hawaiensis*) **and
Spanish Needle** (*Bidens pilosa*)

Sunflower family (Asteraceae)

Endemic to Hawaiʻi Island (koʻokoʻolau); **Alien** (Spanish needle)

Distribution in the Park: Dry mid-elevation woodlands

The sunflower family is one of the largest families of flowering plants in the world and is well represented in the original Hawaiian flora with nearly 100 native species. While many of the Hawaiian members of this family are placed in genera unique to Hawai'i (for example, the silverswords), others like the ko'oko'olau or *Bidens* are more closely related to continental plants. Members of the same genus as Hawaiian ko'oko'olau grow in North and South America as well as Africa, Asia, and Europe.

Nearly 20 endemic species of ko'oko'olau are recognized in the Hawaiian Islands; all are thought to have evolved from only one original colonizing species. Many of the ko'oko'olau species (or subspecies) are restricted to only one or two of the Hawaiian Islands, and several are rare enough to be listed as candidates for Endangered Species status. Hawaiians used both flowers and leaves of many of the ko'oko'olau for medicinal tea.

Only one species of ko'oko'olau (illustrated) is native to Hawaii Volcanoes, and this is very rare in the Park although not considered endangered islandwide. A spindly shrub more than 3 ft tall, this ko'oko'olau (*Bidens hawaiensis*, formerly known as *B. skottsbergii*) has prominently toothed, undivided leaves and large heads of sunflower-like flowers with conspicuous yellow rays. When not in flower, this species is difficult to spot among other native shrubs of its 'ōhi'a woodland habitat. Flowers are usually seen during the fall, particularly in the month of October. 'Āinahou Ranch and Hilina Pali Road are two localities in the Park where the native ko'oko'olau may be seen.

Much more common in the Park is Spanish needle, a nonnative plant often called (and sold for tea as) ko'oko'olau. Also known as beggar's tick, this South American plant has been in Hawai'i more than 100 years and is abundant along roadsides and trails. It is also common in the Park lowlands, where it readily colonizes disturbed areas. This alien plant has compound leaves with three to five toothed leaflets and small yellow heads of flowers, which may have several yellow or white rays or lack them entirely. The tiny seed-like fruits of the Spanish needle are noticeable because they easily become attached to the shoes and clothing of hikers. Close examination of the flat brown fruits reveals the mechanism of attachment to be three sharp-pointed awns or bristles with many barbs angled downward. The fruits of the endemic Hawaiian ko'oko'olau are very similar in appearance, but they typically have two much shorter, often barbless awns, a characteristic that has been interpreted as a loss over time of a trait no longer useful for dispersal in islands lacking native terrestrial mammals.

Molasses Grass (*Melinis minutiflora*),
  Bush Beardgrass (*Schizachryium condensatum*), **and**
  Broomsedge (*Andropogon virginicus*)

Grass family (Poaceae)

Alien; from North America and Africa

Distribution in the Park: Abundant in lowlands and
  open mid-elevation woodlands below 4,000 ft elevation

Three introduced grasses have become the most abundant ground cover in dry to moist open habitats below 4,000 ft elevation in the Park. Molasses grass, native to Africa, was brought to Hawai'i for use as a forage grass in 1913 and has since spread throughout the Islands. Broomsedge, native to eastern North America, was introduced to the islands of Hawai'i and O'ahu in the 1920s but did not become abundant in the Park until the 1960s. An even more recent introduction from tropical America, bush beardgrass (formerly called *Andropogon glomeratus*) has been in Hawaii Volcanoes National Park for approximately 30 years and has rapidly become a major component of lowland grass communities.

Molasses grass (left in illustration) is a robust, mat-forming species with light green, extremely hairy leaf blades. The common name of the grass refers to the sweet odor given off by the foliage. Flower clusters (inflorescences) are feathery and purple when fresh and are most abundant during November and December. Bush beardgrass (center in illustration) and broomsedge (right in illustration) are both tall bunchgrasses that are dry and orange colored during much of the summer. When fresh, broomsedge leaves are pale green, often tinged with purple, and bear soft white hairs at their bases, while bush beardgrass typically has dark green leaves and reddish stems. When flowering, broomsedge and bush beardgrass may be easily distinguished from each other: broomsedge has a tall, narrow inflorescence with clusters of tiny flowers interspersed with long white hairs, while the inflorescence of bush beardgrass is a dense tuft of flower-bearing stalks and leaf-like bracts.

In just a few decades, these three alien grasses (along with others) have greatly altered the appearance of native plant communites over much of the Park. Invading grasses have displaced native grasses and herbs such as the indigenous pili, formerly more common in the Park lowlands, and 'emoloa, an endemic bunchgrass of open woodlands. Other plants, for example the endemic 'ihi mākole, have undergone a range reduction since the arrival and intensification of alien grasses in the Park. 'Ihi mākole, proposed for Federal listing as an Endangered Species, is a low-growing succulent herb related to the ornamental rose moss. 'Ihi mākole frequently occurred in mid-elevation 'ōhi'a woodlands as late as the 1960s; today it appears to be restricted in the Park to a geothermal area or "hot spot," where soils are too warm to support stands of alien bunchgrasses. The impact of alien grasses on native tree and shrub reproduction is not completely understood, but a thick ground cover of grass is likely to decrease or prevent the germination and seedling establishment of many woody plants. Alien grasses may also compete with native plants for water or scarce nutrients such as nitrogen.

Even more insidious than competition with native species is the effect that a heavy ground cover of alien grasses has on the natural fire regime of Hawaii Volcanoes. Since broomsedge, bush beardgrass, and molasses grass have invaded the Park, both the frequency and size of wildfires have greatly increased. The average size of fires occurring after 1968 was 800 times larger than that recorded for fires before that date. Alien grasses have come to dominate the ground cover of plant communities that previously lacked a continuous cover of light fuels to carry fire.

Few native Hawaiian plants respond positively to fire; two exceptions are koa, which is capable of prodigious production of root suckers following fire or other disturbance, and māmane, which resprouts from the base of trunks and has fire-stimulated seed germination. The more common 'ōhi'a trees are typically reduced in number after a fire, and repeated fires in the same area may result in the disappearance of this species. In contrast, introduced broomsedge, bush beardgrass, and molasses grass are well adapted to survive fire and typically resprout from their bases. Frequently, alien grass cover will increase in an area following a fire. Because intense and frequent fires are not considered natural in Hawaii Volcanoes and their effects are usually deleterious, the Park has a policy of total fire suppression. In many U.S. Mainland parks, where fire of natural origin is necessary for the maintenance of many plant communities and fire-adapted species, fires that are naturally caused are tolerated or even encouraged. Fires caused by humans are put out in all parks.

Uluhe or False Staghorn Fern (*Dicranopteris linearis*)

Vine Fern family (Gleicheniaceae)

Indigenous to the Hawaiian Islands; also native to many other
Pacific islands, tropical Asia, China, Japan, tropical America, and
islands of the Caribbean

Distribution in the Park: Moist eastern lowlands, rain forests to
4,000 ft elevation, and open woodlands near Kīlauea Caldera

A large mat-forming fern, uluhe is so widespread, abundant, and fast
growing that it was formerly thought by many to be an introduced weed.
Today the fern is recognized as an indigenous species and is acknowledged
as an important component of many low- to mid-elevation forest and cliff
communities. On the windward sides of the older, more weathered islands
and in the Kohala Mountains of Hawai'i Island, uluhe is often the dominant
cover on steep valley walls and the faces of steep pali (cliffs). Here

uluhe stabilizes the soil and helps prevent erosion and soil slumping. When landslides do occur, uluhe rapidly recolonizes the bare ground and grows quickly, reestablishing vegetative cover in the disturbed area. A similar restoration of ground cover may be seen on steep road cuts artificially cleared of wet forest vegetation. This recuperative power of uluhe is repeatedly displayed along Pali Highway of windward Oʻahu. On Oʻahu, uluhe has recently undergone extensive dieback thought to be caused by an alien insect (the two-spot leaf hopper). Uluhe decline has not been observed at Hawaii Volcanoes.

On Hawaiʻi Island, uluhe is particularly abundant in the very wet Puna District. Here, before the advent of many fast-growing invasive alien plants, uluhe was capable of reclaiming abandoned sugar cane fields and beginning the natural process of secondary succession in these disturbed lands. In Hawaii Volcanoes National Park, uluhe grows in several vegetation types between 1,500 and 4,000 ft elevation but is most abundant in mid-elevation ʻōhiʻa woodlands from Kīlauea Caldera to Kīlauea's lower East Rift. Large stands of uluhe are prominent along the upper part of Chain of Craters Road.

Uluhe is typically a very large fern. In open vegetation, the fern forms an intertwining mat, which spreads by creeping underground stems or rhizomes. Wire-like stipes (leaf stalks) arise from these rhizomes, carrying the tightly rolled frond, and are glossy purple when they emerge. In more closed forests, the shade-intolerant uluhe grows in smaller patches and often climbs to 20 ft or more, supported by the trunks of trees. Uluhe fronds are large and periodically fork in a partially indeterminate growth form. A single frond is composed of a smooth branching axis forked many times, with bright green leaflets lined up along the two axes at each fork. The young fronds at the ultimate frond tips emerge from the terminal bud, rolled up tightly in a fiddlehead. Usually, young fronds are covered with soft reddish hairs; sometimes the undersides of mature fronds have this reddish pubescence. The presence of copious amounts of hair on the fronds is considered by some botanists to be an important diagnostic characteristic, and such plants have been recognized as a distinct uluhe species called *D. emarginata*.

In suitable habitat, uluhe has a high rate of biomass production and produces a large amount of leaf litter. While dead brown fronds remain attached for a long time, they eventually drop to the forest floor and build up a large mass of decomposing litter beneath mats of uluhe. Under dry conditions this litter mat ignites readily and can create a very intense fire. The laddered fuels of the live uluhe fern carry fire into the tree canopy, and the results can be devastating to native rain forests. However, under normal rainy conditions in the Park's lowland and mid-elevation wet forests, fire will not carry far from its point of ignition. This lack of flammability is particularly fortunate because natural ignition sources are present in the many lava flows that periodically emanate from Kīlauea's East Rift. Typically, wet forests of native vegetation will burn only in a narrow strip along the flank of an active lava flow, where preheating from the intensely hot lava dries out the otherwise moist green plants.

'Ama'u (*Sadleria* spp.)

Blechnum family (Blechnaceae)

Endemic to the Hawaiian Islands

Distribution in the Park: Lowlands to subalpine elevations

After the tree ferns, the largest and most conspicuous ferns of the Kīlauea Caldera region are the 'ama'u or 'ama'uma'u. These robust ferns range in height from 2 to 15 ft. Like tree ferns, they have an upright fibrous trunk with brownish orange scales at the trunk apex and along frond stipes. 'Ama'u differ from tree ferns in their narrow oblong fronds, which are only twice divided. The spore-bearing structures (sporangia) of the 'ama'u are unlike those of tree ferns; in 'ama'u, the sporangia are found in linear bars, two on each small lobe of the frond. In tree ferns, the sporangia are grouped in round clusters protected by two valve-like flaps of tissue.

The 'ama'u most often seen is *Sadleria cyatheoides* (illustrated), which occurs in many different habitats including early successional vegetation on lava flows, dry mid-elevation shrublands, open woodlands, rain forests, and subalpine vegetation. Despite its multizonal occurrence, 'ama'u is most likely to be seen by the visitor in the mid-elevation zone. Usually found growing in sunny open areas, it is often over 6 ft high and has large, arching fronds prominently white-colored underneath. Young emerging fronds are typically bright red.

Two other species of 'ama'u occur in the Park but have much more restricted distributions. One of these (*S. pallida*) is seen only in wet forests with dense shade and is typically only 2 to 3 ft tall. While the overall shape of the fern is similar to *S. cyatheoides*, fronds are smaller, more brittle, and have transparent veins. The least common of the Park's 'ama'u is *S. souleyetiana*. This fern can attain a height of 15 ft or more and grows mixed with tree ferns in 'Ōla'a Forest. Young examples of this species resemble the more common *S. cyatheoides* but have larger, more divided fronds with small basal segments overlapping the leaf axis (rachis).

Like tree ferns, the 'ama'u trunks have starchy pith, which is attractive to pigs. Their food value makes 'ama'u vulnerable in areas with high pig populations. In the past, 'ama'u and tree ferns were collected, steamed, and fed to domestic pigs. Although their fibrous trunks are much less massive than those of tree ferns, 'ama'u in forests outside the Park have also been exploited for use in commercial potting mixtures and orchid-growing media.

J. YOSHIOKA

Nēnē or Hawaiian Goose (*Branta sandvicensis*)

Waterfowl family (Anatidae)

Endemic to the Hawaiian Islands. **Federally listed Endangered Species.** Hawai'i State Bird

Distribution in the Park: Sea level to 8,000 ft elevation on Mauna Loa, in open to shrubby areas; most common in 'Āinahou and Kīpuka Kahali'i areas and in Ka'ū Desert, around Kīlauea Caldera

At least nine species of "geese" (some may actually be ducks) evolved in the Islands, probably from ancestors much like the Canada goose currently found on the U.S. Mainland. At least seven of these species were flightless and grazed on the grasses of the ancient Hawaiian landscape on several islands. The bones of the largest were discovered in 1993 on Hualālai Volcano on Hawai'i Island and were four to five times the size of those of today's nēnē. Extinction of flightless geese probably resulted from a combination of habitat destruction in Hawai'i's lowlands and the use of the birds for food by Polynesian people.

Our surviving goose is also a grass eater, but berries (such as 'ōhelo, pūkiawe, and kūkaenēnē) and various weedy plants (such as hairy cat's ear or gosmore) are also consumed. The nēnē has short wings, long legs, and reduced webbing on its toes, indications of the fact that it often walks and seldom swims. A low "nay-nay" call serves as communication between birds and is the source of the Hawaiian name. Nēnē also honk in flight and elsewhere, like other geese. Their three to five white eggs are large for a small goose and are laid in a down-lined nest, often concealed under a bush. Ganders stand guard near the nests and attack intruders in their territories during the nesting season (October-March).

An estimated 25,000 birds were present in Hawai'i at the time of Captain James Cook's arrival in 1778. By the mid 1940s, only 50 birds remained on Hawai'i Island, reduced drastically by introduced predators such as mongooses, dogs, and cats; by disturbance caused by foraging animals such as feral cattle, goats, sheep, and pigs; by hunters in an expanding human population; by introduced plants, which compete with the nēnē's native food and cover plants; and by loss of habitat to agriculture and development at lower elevations.

In 1949 the Territory of Hawaii began a captive breeding and reintroduction program, and in the 1970s Hawaii Volcanoes National Park also began producing birds from a captive flock. Today, nēnē are found only in a small portion of their former distributional range. On Hawai'i Island, they are largely restricted to habitat between 2,500 and 8,000 ft elevation. There are about 400 birds on the Island, with approximately 150 in Hawaii Volcanoes National Park. A population of about 125 birds exists in Haleakalā National Park on Maui, and a small group of birds formerly kept by a rancher is rapidly establishing itself on Kaua'i, an island which has -- so far as we know -- escaped colonization by the small Indian mongoose, an important predator on many ground-nesting birds in Hawaii.

Unless introductions of birds produced in captivity are continued, wild nēnē populations decline, probably because they are confined to less than optimal habitat in the uplands. Nutrition for young birds may not be adequate, and predators such as cats and mongooses reduce breeding success. Maladaptive behavior and the genetics of today's birds may also be problems, partly because of artificial selection in captive breeding programs.

Still, nēnē belong in Hawaii Volcanoes and are a dramatic sight on the wing near Kīlauea Caldera or higher on the slopes of Mauna Loa. During the winter breeding season and when they molt (replace feathers) in the spring, they are sometimes hard to find, but they may be observed in Ka'ū Desert or on their way to and from feeding grounds on the pastures of Kapāpala Ranch or Volcano Golf Course. They may be easily seen at Kīpuka Nēnē and, in post-breeding periods (June-September), grazing on Volcano Golf Course, where they are regularly injured or even killed by golf balls. Automobiles on Highway 11 and Crater Rim Drive also kill or injure a few birds each year.

Birds marked with aluminum and colored leg bands usually originated in captive breeding programs. Park managers and researchers keep track of mated pairs, survival, breeding, and movements of many of the banded birds throughout the year. However, our hope is that one day we will understand enough about nēnē and their needs so that all birds can originate in the wild. More intensive management of the remaining nēnē habitat (*e.g.*, mowing, fertilizing, watering, and burning grasslands) will probably be necessary to accomplish this.

White-tailed Tropicbird or Koa'e Kea (*Phaethon lepturus*)

Tropicbird family (Phaethontidae)

Indigenous; pantropical except easternmost Pacific

Distribution in the Park: Kīlauea Caldera most commonly, but occasionally Ka'ū Desert, Mauna Ulu, and coastal pali (cliffs)

154

White-tailed tropicbirds are found in tropical and subtropical waters all over the world, but in Hawaiʻi they are restricted to the main Islands. A closely related species, the larger koaʻe ʻula or red-tailed tropicbird *(P. rubricauda)*, breeds throughout the Hawaiian Islands (including the Northwestern or Leeward Hawaiian Islands) but is more coastal in distribution, whereas koaʻe kea nest in inland areas.

Koaʻe kea, or "crater birds" as they are called locally (because they especially favor these areas), are medium-sized (30 in. including tail), almost pure white seabirds with black eye stripes and black bars on upper wings and outer primary feathers. They have strong yellow bills and white central tail "streamers" as long as the body; sexes look alike. Usually a few birds can be seen soaring over Kīlauea Caldera or, during nesting season, perched in nesting nooks along the steep walls. Records exist of birds nesting even during eruptions, although sometimes adults and young perish from fumes and heat.

Koaʻe kea lay a single large, tan to purplish egg in a rocky recess. The egg is incubated for about 40 days, and the chick finally leaves home after 10 to 12 weeks. Adults spend the last 8 to 10 weeks fishing, returning to feed the young only every 17 hours or so; once fledging occurs, the young are no longer fed by adults. Young birds leave the nesting area by late October. They return to breeding sites two to three years later, when dark bills and barred backs are replaced by the adult bill color and plumage.

Although tropicbirds nest about 10 mi from the sea in the Park, they fish for squid, crustaceans, and small fishes, usually out of sight of land. These solitary birds feed by plunge-diving with folded wings like boobies or pelicans, to which they are closely related. A layer of air sacs cushions the impact when they hit the water.

Tropicbirds have webbed feet and small legs set so far back on their bodies that locomotion on land is accomplished by lurching forward on their stomachs after pushing with their feet. In the air, strong steady beats of the short wings and soaring glides sustain tropicbirds for long periods at sea. Courtship acrobatics are spectacular, including tandem flights, alternate flapping and gliding by groups of birds, and touchdowns at prospective nest sites on cliff faces inaccessible to humans. Vocalizations include raucous calls and shrill, discordant screams that reminded sailors of bosun's whistles; "bosun bird" is a common name in other parts of the world for this bird.

Western Yellowjacket (*Vespula pensylvanica*)

**Ant, Wasp, and Bee order (Hymenoptera);
  Paper Nest Wasp and Yellowjacket family (Vespidae)**

Alien; probably from the western United States

Distribution in the Park: Mid to upper elevations

156

This familiar yellow and black wasp has been present on Kaua'i since 1919 but did not become a problem on Hawai'i Island and Maui until 1978. Most likely, a new strain was introduced about that time, probably with Christmas tree shipments from the western U.S., where yellowjackets are native and considered pests. Whatever the reason for the increase in numbers and areas occupied in Hawai'i, the alarm was sounded because people were being stung by yellowjackets. While this is certainly of importance, especially to those allergic to stings, yellowjackets are also of concern because they prey on native invertebrates including spiders, butterflies, beetles, and bees, especially in larval forms. Yellowjackets even cut up dead members of their own species or road-killed animals to obtain animal protein for hungry larvae at the nest.

The life cycle of the western yellowjacket in Hawai'i contributes to its rapid population expansion. Normally, fertilized queen yellowjackets emerge individually in the spring from underground hibernation to begin small (24-cell) colonies and feed developing workers for two to three months. Rapid egg laying begins when these workers can provide enough food for the queen. Such annual colonies can reach large sizes in Hawai'i because of the mild climate, but the insects (except for queens) usually die out over the winter. When colonies do survive the winter, workers are available and queens can efficiently produce eggs immediately in the spring. Numbers of foraging workers then greatly increase over the summer.

Yellowjacket colonies in Hawai'i are larger than on the U.S. Mainland, with annual nests often measuring over 3 x 3 ft and producing about 40,000 wasps (double the production of nests on the U.S. Mainland). One large colony in Kīpuka Puaulu in the Park contained over 500,000 small (worker) cells and 40,000 large (queen) cells, probably producing at least a million wasps. Most nests have been found between 1,000 and 4,000 ft elevation on the Island, and 30 or more nests are probably active in the Park each year. Yellowjacket numbers are considerably influenced by weather, and activity may peak in different areas at different times of the summer and fall.

Yellowjackets require large numbers of prey insects to sustain larvae in nest colonies. Prey intake at a large nest in the Park was 22,000 items in just one day. Spiders and butterflies and moths were the predominant prey at five sites sampled in Hawaii Volcanoes, but true bugs (Heteroptera), crickets and grasshoppers (Orthoptera), and flies (Diptera) were also important items in some areas. In a study conducted on Maui, endemic predaceous caterpillars (*Eupethecia*) were found to be an important food; in Hawaii Volcanoes, the declines of endemic picture wing flies may be at least partly the result of predation on larval forms by yellow-jackets. Most soft-bodied, slow-moving invertebrates are probably at risk, although yellowjackets do seem to forage more often in forest clearings and edges than in deep forests. Common 'amakihi and probably some other birds have likely been affected by loss of their invertebrate foods.

Yellowjackets can be controlled by mechanical and chemical destruction of their nests and through use of toxicants. In the Park, an attractant (heptyl-butyrate) has been used in some areas to encourage yellowjackets to eat chicken laced with a toxicant (encapsulated diazanon). The bait is carried back to the nest by workers and quickly spread through the colony. Monitoring studies show that wasp numbers can be reduced locally by this method and that few native insects are at risk. The bait dispenser is constructed to prevent entry by birds. Chemical control of yellowjackets is carefully used in limited areas important for ecological values, intensive human use, or both. Such measures probably will be necessary from now on if certain unique and rare native invertebrates are to be preserved for future generations.

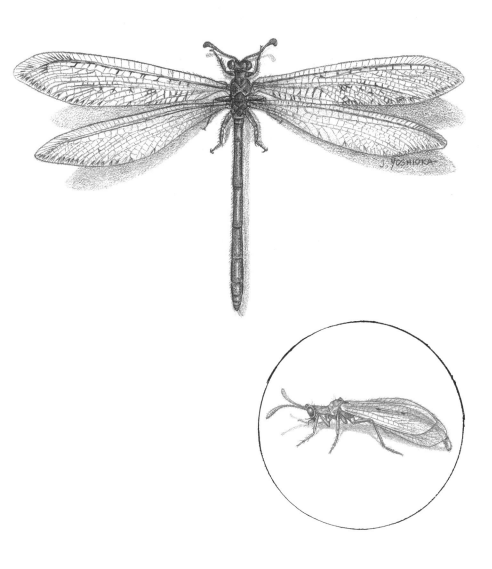

Antlion (*Eidoleon* **sp.**)

Nerve-winged Insects order (Neuroptera), Antlion family (Myrmeleontidae)

Endemic (several species) to the Hawaiian Islands

Distribution in the Park: Mid-elevation woodlands
 in dry areas with appropriate substrate

The insect order Neuroptera is a fairly diverse group in Hawai'i, with four recognized families (three lacewing and one antlion) and 61 known species. Most species (52) are endemic, and many have not yet been described. The larvae of neuropterans are predators on small arthropods, but adults may be either predators or feeders on sweet substances such as honeydew. Some species are able to feign death when disturbed, and some have evolved to become flightless forms. Green lacewings (Chrysopidae family) are common, but brown lacewings (Hemerobiidae family) are usually rare. Brown lacewing larvae are called "aphid wolves" or "aphid lions" elsewhere, but without native aphids in Hawai'i, endemic lacewings evolved with other feeding strategies. Prey such as booklice (psocids), plant lice (psyllids), and various hoppers and scale insects (Homoptera) may be eaten by lacewings.

Antlions, the larvae of which are called "doodlebugs," are a separate family in the order Neuroptera. Three endemic species are currently known from the State, all occurring on more than one Island. Adults look something like hairy damselflies (Odonata), with long slender wings and bodies, but antennae are turned outward and thickened (clubbed) at the tips. The species known from Hawaii Volcanoes (illustrated) was first identified in 1976 by the late C.J. Davis; it was not previously known from the Island. (It is illustrated from the top, with the wings spread to show the venation, and to illustrate the clubbed antennae; in life [inset], the wings are usually held together like those of damselflies at rest.) The antlion formerly ranged from sea level to 6,000 ft elevation in the Park but is now considerably more restricted in distribution. Likely spots to find it are the Footprints Trail area, Namakani Paio Campground, open areas along Mauna Loa Strip Road, and Kīpuka Nēnē. Adult insects are most evident at dusk and on cloudy days as they fly weakly for short distances.

Antlion larvae are about 0.3 in. long with six weak legs, a soft body, small head, and two sickle-shaped jaws. Many antlion larvae elsewhere in the world dig substantial pits in soft substrates and feed on ants that tumble in. Hawai'i has no native ants, so, like lacewings, these tiny predators undoubtedly also evolved with other prey. The Park antlion does not form a deep pit but does bury itself until only jaws, head, and thorax are above the surface. Antlions are able to quickly grab invertebrates that wander too near, inject a toxin through their jaws, and suck the fluids from the prey. Possibly as a result of an intermittent food supply that slows their development as larvae, antlions may live up to two years.

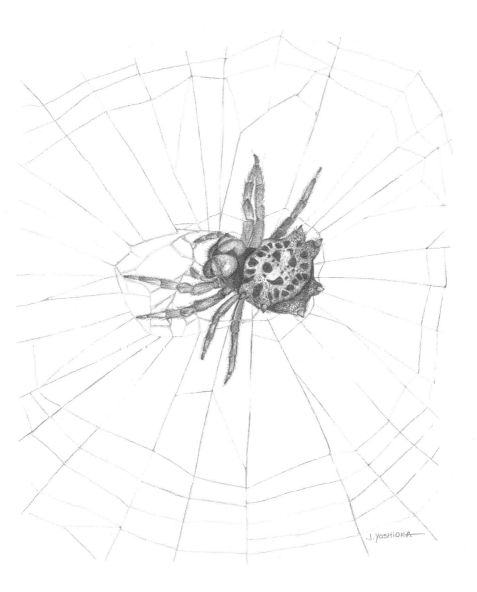

Spinybacked Spiders (*Gasteracantha mammosa* and *G. crancriformis*)

Spider, Tick, Mite, Pseudoscorpion, and Scorpion class (Arachnida); Orb-weaver family (Araneidae)

Alien

Distribution in the Park: Parkwide except extremely dry areas to 4,000 ft or so; especially numerous in cave entrances, moist areas, and around human habitations

Spinybacked spiders are widely known in Hawai'i as "crab spiders," but true crab spiders (family Thomisidae) do not make webs; instead, they lie in wait on flowers for insect prey. In contrast, spinybacked spiders build numerous orb webs. They are often encountered around human habitations and other buildings and in orchards, gardens, and native forests of the lowlands and mid-elevation zone. These spiders may bite when trapped between clothing and skin, causing welts on people who are sensitive.

One species of spinyback (*G. crancriformis*) has been established in Hawai'i since the 1950s and is not nearly as troublesome as the Asian spinybacked spider, *G. mammosa*, established in 1985. Both species were apparently introduced inadvertently. The "older" spinybacked spider has a white back with six black spots and six 0.1 in. red spiny abdominal projections. The Asian spinybacked spider (illustrated) has shorter spines and two distinct yellow spots on its back, giving it a creamy appearance as opposed to the other spinyback's distinctive red, white, and black pattern. Both indeed look like small crabs and are about 0.5 in. wide.

The creamy-colored Asian spinybacked spider is prolific, with females laying masses of flattened egg cases, each containing about 200 eggs. Numbers seem to increase during the fall and winter and rapidly decline in spring and summer. First noted in Hilo in 1985, these spinybacks spread to Kona by 1986 and reached invasive levels on Kaua'i and Maui in the late 1980s.

Effects of alien web-building spiders on native insects are unknown. However, spinybacked spiders prefer cool, wet weather and are found in some of Hawai'i's remaining native forest. Native invertebrates in these areas are potentially vulnerable to the numerous sticky webs built by this species. A predatory wasp attacks eggs of the Asian spinybacked spider, but another predatory wasp attacks the predator of the spinybacked spider. Both wasps have been in Hawai'i since the early 1900s and were not purposely introduced.

Control methods recommended for spinybacked spiders around human habitations include swatting and direct spraying with insecticide. Spraying can damage plants and people too, if not carefully done. Destruction of egg cases is also recommended. Removal of webs simply results in rapid replacement. Biological control is now deliberately being investigated because spinybacked spiders are a nuisance to humans. If successful, control of these alien spiders may also be of some benefit to our native invertebrates.

J. YOSHIOKA

Psyllids or Jumping Plant Lice

Hopper, Whitefly, Aphis, and Scale Insect order (Homoptera),
  Jumping Plant Lice family (Psyllidae)

Endemic and **alien**

Distribution in the Park: Sea level to 8,000 ft

Insects in the order Homoptera feed on sap in plant tissue. About 23 families are recognized in this diverse group in Hawai'i, but only about six of these have endemic species. Some of the pioneering work on the planthopper family (Cixiidae) in this order has been done in Park caves by workers from Germany collaborating with B.P. Bishop Museum personnel. These scientists have found that each population of the cave cixiid *Oliarus polyphemus* seems to have its own "song," inaudible to humans. Songs are transmitted through vibration of substrates by these tiny creatures, rather than through the air.

Although cave planthoppers are not seen by the average visitor to the Park, evidence of one prominent group of homopterans can be seen by all. Over 30 species of endemic psyllids are known in Hawai'i, and several species are present in the Park. These small (0.06-0.12 in.) insects are readily visible as leaf galls, rounded or conical bumps on leaves or stems of woody plants. Adult psyllids imbed eggs in plant host tissue, from which nymphs hatch. A single nymph develops within each gall, feeding on sap from the swollen plant tissue until ready to emerge. Each nymph emerges through a tiny hole in the gall and molts to adult size outside the plant, beginning the life cycle again.

Most 'ōhi'a trees in the Park bear some galls on their leaves (illustrated). As many as 10 species of psyllids may feed on this tree in Hawai'i, and several of these live in Hawaii Volcanoes. Primary gall formers on 'ōhi'a leaves in the Park are three species of psyllids in the genus *Trioza*; 'ōhi'a is the only known host plant for these species. Elevations between 3,000 and 4,000 ft are most favorable for 'ōhi'a psyllids and other 'ōhi'a insects in the Park. Trees at these elevations may be especially vigorous and tall, but other unstudied variables may also influence psyllid abundance and diversity. Natural enemies of psyllids include spiders, mites, ladybird beetles, and parasitic wasps.

Although large numbers of galls certainly interfere with normal growth and functioning of 'ōhi'a leaves and may result in stunting of leaves or branches, trees are not killed by infestations of these native insects. Other native psyllids form galls on host plants such as alani and pāpala kēpau in the Park.

SPECIAL MID-ELEVATION WOODLANDS
SYSTEMS

J.YOSHIOKA

KAʻŪ DESERT

Ka'ū Desert is characterized by sparse vegetation adapted to dry conditions including a porous and shifting ash substrate. Desert conditions are especially severe in the summer, partly as a result of a rain shadow blocking the area from moisture carried by prevailing northeast tradewinds. However, the desert character of the area results largely from the youth and texture of the substrate. In addition to dry conditions, Ka'ū Desert is subjected to large volumes of sulfur dioxide, possibly some mercury emitted by Halema'uma'u Crater fumaroles and vents in the area, other volcanic gases, and to natural acid rain. The life forms that exist in the Desert have adapted to harsh conditions indeed.

A study conducted in Ka'ū Desert in 1979 suggests that plants have different strategies for dealing with sporadically high levels of toxic gases over the long term. Two native plants of the Desert, 'ōhi'a (*Metrosideros polymorpha*) and 'a'ali'i (*Dodonaea viscosa*), provide examples. Mature 'ōhi'a trees are stimulated to close gas exchange openings (stomata) in the leaves upon contact with sulfur dioxide, thus excluding the pollutant; this species shows no visual symptoms of sulfur dioxide stress. In contrast, 'a'ali'i shows no stomatal response, but instead loses leaves or develops chlorosis (yellowing), followed by rapid resprouting. A third response in some species might be to detoxify sulfur dioxide in the leaf. The cosmopolitan lichen *Usnea australis*, notoriously sensitive to acid rain elsewhere, apparently has adapted to toxicants in the Desert, since it shows unperturbed photosynthetic processes even after extended exposure to sulfuric acid, an important component of rainfall near active volcanoes. Alien grasses such as broomsedge (*Andropogon virginicus*) and molasses grass (*Melinis minutiflora*) generally increase in density with distance from gaseous emissions toward the sea. Because of the sparse vegetation in the area, especially downwind of Halema'uma'u, fires are less likely than in other mid-elevation woodland areas.

Ka'ū Desert is used by the nēnē or Hawaiian goose (*Branta sandvicensis*) for breeding and molting. The presence of fruiting bushes such as pūkiawe, 'ōhelo, pohā or cape gooseberry, and blackberry (*Styphelia tameiameiae, Vaccinium reticulatum, Physalis peruviana, Rubus argutus*), together with sparse alien grasses, provides some nutrients for adult nēnē, but hatchlings must walk to lush grasslands on neighboring ranches if they are to survive. The Desert is also a less suitable place for small Indian mongooses (*Herpestes auropunctatus*) than most areas, and mongooses may, over time, affect where nēnē survive to nest.

Rare plants found in the Desert, such as the Hawaiian catchfly (*Silene hawaiiensis*), a member of the pink family (Caryophyllaceae) recently proposed for Federal listing as an Endangered Species, are at risk when Desert backcountry roads are carelessly and illegally driven with four-wheel drive vehicles.

PUHIMAU HOT SPOT

The Puhimau Thermal Area or Hot Spot, located near Kōkoʻolau Crater, was formed in the winter of 1937-38 when magma intruded close to the ground surface but did not erupt. The ʻōhiʻa (*Metrosideros polymorpha*) forest existing there at the time was killed but not burned, and some of the fumaroles around charred tree trunks now support a distinctive plant community. The Hot Spot is located at about 3,900 ft elevation on the East Rift zone of Kīlauea in the transition zone between the mid-elevation woodlands and the rain forest. The temperature of silty, well-drained loam soils 3 to 6 ft deep is 102 to 199°F at the surface up to 40 in. from active vents. Heat is the primary influence on life in the area; sustained sulfur dioxide and hydrogen sulfide gases have not been emitted from vents in the Thermal Area in recent years.

Two distinct zones are evident at the Puhimau Hot Spot. A sparsely vegetated central zone is dominated by the moss *Campylopus praemorsus*, upon which the lichen *Cladonia* grows epiphytically. Another lichen (*Stereocaulon*), the alien broomsedge (*Andropogon virginicus*), and a native sedge (*Carex wahuensis*) are common on elevated sites where the moss grows; broomsedge is the most dense of the three. Only the candidate Endangered Species ʻihi mākole (*Portulaca sclerocarpa*), a succulent herb with white flowers; *Portulaca pilosa*, a nonnative herb with purple flowers; the indigenous shrub ʻuhaloa (*Waltheria indica*); and the lichen *Diploschistes* grow on the heated substrate. Toward the edges of the central zone, low-stature ʻōhiʻa snags (less than 6 ft high) support blue-green algae where steam condenses, and a number of bryophytes, mosses, and lichens can be found. Epiphytic ʻōhiʻa, club moss (family Lycopodiaceae), and other plants also grow on the ʻōhiʻa snags.

In the peripheral zone, broomsedge and bush beardgrass (*Schizachyrium condensatum*) are most abundant. Bush beardgrass dominates in the surrounding community but is less heat tolerant than broomsedge; broomsedge is thus more abundant than bush beardgrass in the peripheral zone. Root systems of the heat-tolerant broomsedge are normally confined to the top 2 in. of soil, however. ʻIhi mākole is also found in the transition zone, and the heat-tolerant moss *Campylopus* thrives between broomsedge clumps. Various lichens, especially *Cladonia*, are quite common in some areas and can tolerate high temperatures when dry. However, most lichens are sensitive to heat when wet and are readily killed by steam blasts or continual high temperatures. Only *Campylopus* can directly tolerate the high soil temperatures in the Puhimau Thermal Area. In this sensitive and unique area, the moss makes it possible for other native and alien plants to survive by providing substrates above the heated soil on which they can grow. Because of the presence of rare and Endangered plants, the vulnerability of the substrate and ground cover to disturbance, and the presence of ongoing geological and botanical monitoring, the Puhimau Thermal area should not be entered by visitors.

RAIN FOREST

RAIN FOREST

Rain forests are characterized by high rainfall (exceeding 75-100 in. annually) and no distinct dry period throughout the year. Because of Kīlauea Volcano's location on the east flank of Mauna Loa, which receives the benefit of the moisture-laden northeast tradewinds most of the year, much of the eastern section of the Park between the elevations of 1,000 and 4,000 ft receives sufficient rainfall to support this type of vegetation. Because more than 90 percent of the surface of Kīlauea has been covered by lava in the last 1,000 years, only the older substrates have had the several centuries required for soil development and the growth of a mature forest.

Despite Kīlauea's status as one of the world's most active volcanoes, rain forests are prominent on the northern and eastern side of the Caldera and Kīlauea Iki; they stretch along Kīlauea's East Rift to the Park's eastern boundary downslope of the currently active vent, Puʻu ʻŌʻō. Until the 1960s, the Park contained a large expanse of rain forest along the East Rift, but eruptions from Mauna Ulu (1969-74) and Puʻu ʻŌʻō (1983-present) have covered thousands of acres and have fragmented the rain forest into many disjunct stands. In addition to the rain forests of Kīlauea, the Park includes ʻOlaʻa Forest, a 9,000-acre, noncontiguous parcel on ancient Mauna Loa substrates covered by deep ash soils.

Unlike tropical rain forests of South America and Asia, where hundreds of tree species may be found in the canopy of a relatively small area, Hawaiian rain forests are dominated by only one or two tree species. ʻŌhiʻa (*Metrosideros polymorpha*) is the canopy dominant in almost all Park rain forests. In only one remote stand within ʻOlaʻa is koa (*Acacia koa*) a dominant or codominant element in the rain forest canopy, where it emerges far above the slower-growing ʻōhiʻa. Hawaiian rain forests are typically multilayered, with several tree, tree fern, and shrub layers between the canopy and the ground. Greater diversity is displayed in the second tree layer of Park rain forests, where up to 10 species form an open to closed canopy ranging in height from about 20 to 40 ft. ʻŌlapa (*Cheirodendron trigynum*) is perhaps the most abundant tree species in the rain forest understory, where it is often seen growing epiphytically on much larger ʻōhiʻa trees. Kāwaʻu or Hawaiian holly (*Ilex anomala*) and kōlea lau nui (*Myrsine lessertiana*) are typical understory components of most Park rain forests but may sometimes grow taller, reaching the uppermost canopy of the forest. Other rain forest understory trees that are typically small when mature include pilo (*Coprosma* spp.), alani (*Melicope* spp.), olomea (*Perrottetia sandwicensis*), māmaki (*Pipturus albidus*), and, more rarely, ōpuhe (*Urera glabra*).

As elevation and substrate age change, Park rain forests vary somewhat in their understory species composition, with some species more common at higher elevations and others at low-elevation sites. In lower-elevation forests of Kīlauea's East Rift, kōpiko ʻula (*Psychotria hawaiiensis*) is a common understory element along with species of alani (*Melicope clusiifolia* and *M. radiata*), and at some sites hame (*Antidesma platyphyllum*).

Below the secondary canopy of mixed native tree species, Park rain forests usually have a distinct layer dominated by tree ferns (hāpuʻu). Hāpuʻu pulu (*Cibotium glaucum*) is the most common species in the Park, but hāpuʻu ʻiʻi (*C. chamissoi* or *C. menziesii*) and meu (*C. hawaiiense*) are also frequently seen. A tree fern layer seems to be characteristic of Hawaiʻi Island rain forests; tree ferns are much less abundant in wet forests of the older Hawaiian Islands. While individual tree ferns may be taller than 30 ft, the tree fern layer is typically 20 ft tall at the top of the large, arching fronds.

Most of the biological diversity of Hawaiian rain forests is contained in the understory, especially the ground-cover layer. In this lowermost layer of the forest grow a profusion of shade-loving native plants that require cool, humid conditions to thrive. Chief among these are the ferns; more than 50 species are found within the Park's ʻOlaʻa Forest. An observer could compile a list of dozens of native ferns within a few yards of Wright Road (Highway 148). Some of the most abundant terrestrial ferns of the rain forest are the stout-trunked ʻamaʻu (*Sadleria pallida*), the edible hōʻiʻo (*Diplazium sandwichianum*), the lacy-fronded ʻākōlea (*Athyrium microphyllum*), and the stiff-textured, gray-green hōʻiʻo kula (*Pneumatopteris sandwicensis*, or *Thelypteris sandwicensis*). More rarely seen is the tall rain forest ʻamaʻu (*Sadleria souleytiana*), which may sometimes rival the tree fern in size. All these and an assortment of other native fern species are denizens of closed-canopy rain forests and are rarely seen in sunny openings or drier woodland vegetation.

Sharing the forest floor with the ferns are a few species of native herbs, shrubs, and saplings of canopy tree species. The most abundant herbaceous flowering plants of the rain forest floor are ʻalaʻala wai nui (*Peperomia* spp.), weak-stemmed trailing members of the black pepper family. At least six endemic species of ʻalaʻala wai nui are found in Park rain forests; some have showy, shiny leaves decorated with red markings on their undersides. Shrub species most commonly encountered are the endemic hydrangea pūʻahanui (*Broussaisia arguta*), ʻōhelo kau laʻau or tree ʻōhelo (*Vaccinium calycinum*), and the brittle-stemmed ʻilihia (*Cyrtandra platyphylla*), an African violet relative with large, fleshy, heart-shaped leaves covered with soft golden hairs. Other less-frequently seen shrubs include kāmakahala (*Labordia hedyosmifolia*, a member of the strychnine family), and succulent members of the lobelia subfamily in the endemic Hawaiian genera *Clermontia, Cyanea,* and *Trematolobelia.*

Unlike many other tropical forests, Hawaiian rain forests do not support large numbers of climbing vines or lianas. Nonetheless, several native vines are notable components of many Park forests. ʻIeʻie (*Freycinetia arborea*), a fibrous-stemmed, prickly-leaved climber in the screwpine family, festoons the ʻōhiʻa trees of remote East Rift forests and is occasionally seen in the Kīlauea area. Hoi kuahiwi (*Smilax melastomifolia*), a relative of the greenbriars (*Smilax* spp.) of temperate

American forests, is common in forests in Kīlauea Caldera. This Hawaiian endemic has prominently veined, heart-shaped leaves and smooth or bumpy twining stems.   More rarely encountered are delicate vines in the mint family; *Stenogyne calaminthoides*, a small vine with oblong, scallop-margined leaves, is the most frequently seen Hawaiian mint in the Park. These "mintless mints" lack strongly scented oils and are highly palatable to feral ungulates; thus they have been eliminated or much reduced in pig-impacted forests.

A distinguishing feature of rain forests is the abundance of epiphytes on tree trunks and branches. The presence of mats of mosses and liverworts and clusters of epiphytic ferns and tree seedlings is a strong indicator of high rainfall and consistent humidity.   In areas with very high rainfall, mosses may drape tree branches like soft green curtains. A more typical scene in forests of Kīlauea Caldera has mosses, liverworts, and small filmy ferns covering the trunks of large-diameter 'ōhi'a trees 3 to 6 ft above the forest floor. Many species of native shrubs and trees also get their start in life as epiphytes on tree trunks or on branches high in the canopy.   Sun-loving species like 'ōlapa are particularly noticeable as epiphytes high in 'ōhi'a trees in forests of 'Ōla'a and the East Rift.   In these forests epiphytes and trees may be so intertwined that it is difficult to identify the original host tree.   In areas disturbed by feral pigs (*Sus scrofa*), many species may survive only as epiphytes.

The rain forests of Hawaii Volcanoes National Park are important reser-voirs of biological diversity and are habitat for many species of endemic birds, insects, and spiders.   However, not all Park rain forests are pro-tected from the depredations of feral pigs, and few forest sites are actively managed to control alien plant and insect invasions.   Feral pigs, destructive agents of forest decline, have been removed from less than one-third of the Park's rain forests.   Eradication of feral pigs from all areas in the Park dominated by native species would be desirable, but this would be prohibitively time consuming and expensive.   In most areas pig-proof fencing is the first step; this may cost $35,000 per mile through dense rain forest.   Such fences may be seen near Nahuku (Thurston Lava Tube), where pigs were removed in 1984. Cattle guards across roads prevent feral pigs from reinvading fenced areas along roads.

Alien plants present an even more difficult management problem. Park rain forests have been invaded by dozens of nonnative plants.   Six alien plant species are particularly invasive and disruptive in the forests of 'Ōla'a and Kīlauea: banana poka (*Passiflora mollissima*), yellow Himalayan raspberry (*Rubus ellipticus*), kāhili ginger (*Hedychium gardnerianum*), strawberry guava (*Psidium cattleianum*), cane tibouchina (*Tibouchina herbacea*), and palm grass (*Setaria palmifolia*).   Even remoteness is no protection; birds may carry weed seeds for miles and deposit them in forests far from roads or trails. Currently, park managers control the most disruptive alien plants in approximately 600 acres of Park rain forests, but the challenge for the future is the expansion of alien plant control to areas free of feral pigs in salvageable Park forests.   Only then will the irreplaceable tropical rain forests of Hawaii Volcanoes be truly preserved for future generations.

Loulu (*Pritchardia beccariana*)

Palm family (Arecaceae)

Endemic to Hawai‘i Island

Distribution in the Park: ‘Ōla‘a Forest

Of all the many different kinds of palms seen in the Hawaiian Islands, only one group of fan palms is actually native here. Loulu palms belong to a genus that is restricted to tropical islands of the Pacific Ocean. Nineteen different species occur in the Hawaiian Islands, each endemic to just one island. Of the four loulu species peculiar to Hawai'i Island, one is a conspicuous component of the Park's 'Ola'a Forest, where it is easily seen from Wright Road (Highway 148). The loulu of 'Ola'a is a striking tree, which when mature emerges far above the canopy of 'ōhi'a, tree fern, and other common rain forest trees. The trunk of a tall loulu is light gray or tan, straight, and quite smooth with inconspicuous rings.

Loulu leaves are bright green, large, and fan-shaped, usually more than 3 ft broad. They are rigid, with leaf tips pointing upward rather than drooping. As the leaves die and turn brown, they do not immediately drop off the tree, but are retained for a while at the base of live leaves where they form a sort of "hula skirt" at the top of the trunk. When the wind blows briskly, these dead leaves rattle loudly, enabling an observer to locate loulu palms by sound even in dense rain forest, where the tops of the palms are obscured by a heavy cover of tree ferns.

The flowers of the loulu palm are individually small and inconspicuous but are borne in an inflorescence that may reach 5 ft in length, originating from the growing tip of the tree. Fruits of this species of loulu are relatively small (about 1 in. diameter) and round and are generally seen in clusters. They are green when young and darken to brown or black with age. Loulu fruits are edible and were eaten by Hawaiians in the past. The young fruits and flowers of one species of loulu in the Kohala Mountains were apparently an important food source for an endemic Hawaiian honeycreeper, the bright red, dramatically marked 'ula 'ai hāwane, a bird last seen a century ago and now considered extinct.

Today in 'Ola'a the fruits of the loulu are often eaten by rats. Introduced black and Polynesian rats are common in 'Ola'a rain forests, and the extent of their impact on loulu palm reproduction can only be guessed. In areas from which feral pigs have not been removed, these omnivorous animals are known to eat loulu fruits that fall to the ground at the base of the tree. Most of the loulu fruits found on the ground seem to be infested with insect larvae, but how severely such insect damage is impacting loulu reproduction is unknown. Some fruit-eating insects such as the fruit moth *Carposina* sp. are native. Loulu seedlings are observed in 'Ola'a Forest (especially in pig-free exclosures), but young palm trees are only rarely encountered.

The loulu palm of the 'Ola'a rain forest is also distributed over uncleared forest outside the Park and is therefore not a rare plant; however, threats to reproduction may be important factors to monitor. In the future, some form of management may be necessary to ensure the population stability and continued existence of this magnificent endemic Hawaiian palm.

'Ōlapa (*Cheirodendron trigynum*)

Ginseng family (Araliaceae)

Endemic to the Hawaiian Islands

Distribution in the Park: Restricted to rain forests, primarily
 'Ōla'a Forest and Kīlauea's East Rift, but also rim of Kīlauea Caldera

One of the most beautiful of all Hawaiian trees, 'ōlapa is a common sight in the Park's rain forests. In forests of both 'Ola'a and the East Rift, 'ōlapa is often the most abundant species in the secondary tree layer. By contrast, in the more accessible forests of Kīlauea Caldera, 'ōlapa is a relatively minor component of the understory.

A small to medium-sized tree, 'ōlapa is most easily recognized by its leaves. These are bright yellow-green and are compound, with three to five shiny, toothed leaflets arranged palmately (attached at one place on the tip of the leaf stalk). In a light breeze, 'ōlapa leaves flutter gracefully and sparkle with reflected sunlight; when the wind is strong, the leaves brush together and make a flapping sound.

The tiny green and purple 'ōlapa flowers lack showy petals and are borne in erect open clusters near branch tips. These inconspicuous flowers develop into small, round to three-sided fruits, which are purplish or brown when mature. 'Ōlapa fruits, along with those of other common native forest trees such as kāwa'u and pilo, are frequently eaten by the 'ōma'o or Hawai'i thrush and seasonally may be an important part of their diet.

'Ōlapa seedlings and saplings are seen on the forest floor only in areas protected from feral pigs or in forests with low pig populations. More often in the Park, young 'ōlapa trees are seen as epiphytes, either on logs, tree fern trunks, or branches of larger trees. In 'Ola'a Forest, even large 30-ft 'ōlapa trees grow as epiphytes, with their pale-barked roots encircling 'ōhi'a trees en route to the ground.

'Ōlapa is vulnerable not only to pigs but also to wild cattle, which find the bark of young trees palatable. In cattle-infested areas like the remote forests of Kīlauea's East Rift, these feral ungulates knock down 'ōlapa trees and strip them of their soft bark, which emits a strong carrot-like odor when damaged.

The 'ōlapa found in Hawaii Volcanoes and elsewhere on the Island is the most common and morphologically variable of five endemic Hawaiian *Cheirodendron* species. The Park's 'ōlapa (*C. trigynum*) is also found on all the major Hawaiian Islands except Kaho'olawe, but the other Hawaiian species of 'ōlapa are limited to Kaua'i and O'ahu. On the older Hawaiian Islands such as O'ahu, Moloka'i, and Maui, 'ōlapa is frequently the second-most abundant tree (after 'ōhi'a) in cloud-shrouded forests of mountain ridges and peaks. Perhaps the best place in the Park to see 'ōlapa is 'Ola'a Forest, but the tree can also be found at Nahuku (Thurston Lava Tube) and along the highway near the Park's eastern boundary.

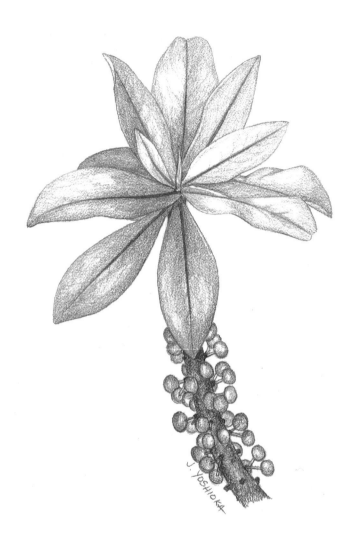

Kōlea Lau Nui (*Myrsine lessertiana*)

Myrsine family (Myrsinaceae)

Endemic to the six largest Hawaiian Islands

Distribution in the Park: Rain forests of Kīlauea and ʻŌlaʻa and moist forests of Kīpuka Puaulu and Kīpuka Kī

Kōlea lau nui (illustrated) is one of the most common understory trees in Park rain forests, where it grows mixed with other native tree species and tree ferns. In forests of Kīlauea Caldera, kōlea lau nui is usually a tree less than 30 ft tall with dark green foliage clustered near branch tips. Leaves vary in size and shape but are often about 5 in. long and 2 in. wide, with the widest part of the leaf blade near the tip. Kōlea leaves are thick with a shiny surface, smooth margins, prominent light-colored midribs, and inconspicuous secondary veins. Young leaves and midribs of kōlea lau nui are often tinged with a bright magenta-pink, allowing identification even when flowers and fruits are absent. Flowers are small and greenish and are found in clusters just below the leaves of smaller branches. Kōlea fruits are small and round and are borne on slender stalks clustered on persistent woody knobs. Fruits are black or purplish when ripe and contain only one seed.

This typically small or medium-sized kōlea tree of the rain forest grows much taller in the moist kīpuka forests of the Park's uplands. In Kīpuka Puaulu and Kīpuka Kī on deep ash soils, kōlea trees may be taller than 60 ft and have trunks 2 to 3 ft in diameter. Very tall kōlea trees reach the uppermost canopy, which they share with the dominant 'ōhi'a, koa, and a'e or soapberry. The bark of large kōlea trees is dark gray and roughly bumpy but unfurrowed. Elsewhere on Hawai'i Island, kōlea lau nui is an important component of upper-elevation vegetation, which is transitional from rain forest to drier, more open subalpine forest.

Kōlea lau nui is the most common species of *Myrsine* in the Park (as well as on Hawai'i Island), but two other related species are also found here. Kōlea lau li'i (*M. sandwicensis*; the Hawaiian name means small-leaved kōlea) is infrequently seen in the Park's lower-elevation rain forests and in a few mid-elevation woodlands. Kōlea lau li'i is typically a shrubby species with spoon-shaped leaves only about 1 in. long. A third species (*M. lanaiensis*), typical of dry forests, is rare in the Park. The dry-forest kōlea differs from kōlea lau nui in having smaller leaves with a conspicuous network of veins. Kōlea trees were used in Hawaiian times as a source of house timbers, and bark and sap were collected for use in dyeing kapa (bark cloth).

Pilo (*Coprosma ochracea* and other *Coprosma*)

Coffee family (Rubiaceae)

Endemic to the Hawaiian Islands

Distribution in the Park: Rain forests of Kīlauea Caldera
and 'Ōla'a Forest (*C. ochracea*)

One species of pilo (*Coprosma ochracea*, <u>illustrated</u>) is an important component of Park rain forests. Usually less than 20 ft tall, it grows among the tree ferns and shares the canopy of the secondary tree layer with 'ōlapa, kāwa'u, kōpiko 'ula, and alani. Pilo trees have thin, smooth bark, which is pale gray with darker splotches. The tree branching pattern is asymmetrical, with some side branches typically much longer than others. Leaves are thick, 1 to 4 in. long, usually widest near the tip, and have prominent secondary veins. The young leaves and branch tips are densely hairy with soft buff-colored pubescence. Pointed leaflike structures called stipules clasp the stem above the attachment of each pair of opposite leaves; the size and shape of these stipules are characters important for the identification of the different species in the genus *Coprosma.*

Like many other native Hawaiian tree species, male and female flowers of pilo are found on different trees. Flowers are tiny, greenish white, and are clustered in leaf axils near branch tips. Male flowers can be recognized by their pendent stamens, which extend beyond the tiny tubular corolla. Female flowers develop into small, ovoid, fleshy fruits that are reddish orange. Pilo fruits are crowned with tiny teeth, which are the remains of the outer parts of the flower. The two large seeds within each fruit are flattened on one side and resemble diminutive coffee beans. Along with 'ōhelo, 'ōlapa, kāwa'u, and other small berries, pilo fruits are eaten by the native 'ōma'o or Hawai'i thrush. Apparently pilo fruits are a favored food in some areas, as 'ōma'o have been observed guarding productive fruit-laden pilo trees and chasing off intruding birds.

More than a dozen species of pilo or *Coprosma* are native to the Hawaiian Islands, and at least five of them are found in Hawaii Volcanoes National Park. One member of the genus very dissimilar in appearance to the others is the trailing viny shrub called kūkaenēnē *(C. emodeoides);* this plant is discussed in the section on the subalpine zone. The other four Park species are small trees or shrubs similar in appearance to the rain forest pilo *(C. ochracea)* described above, distinguished from one another by their occurrence in different habitats. After the common pilo of the rain forest, the pilo most often seen is *C. rhynchocarpa,* an understory tree abundant in the moist forests of Kīpuka Puaulu and Kīpuka Kī. Although much like the rain forest pilo in size and growth form, *C. rhynchocarpa* may be identified by its longer, thinner leaves and its fruits, which have an elongated beak at their tips. The ranges of these two species overlap, and they may possibly hybridize with one another.

Another pilo is usually found in open woodlands below 3,000 ft elevation. This species *(C. menziesii)* is a sprawling shrub with long, arching, hairless branches and small thick leaves. Its fruits are borne on short stalks, but in shape and color they are very similar to the rain forest pilo. This pilo of the mid-elevation forests and woodlands can be seen along the Chain of Craters and Hilina Pali roads, and in open vegetation traversed by trails of Kīlauea's East Rift, such as the Kalapana, Nāulu, and Nāpau trails.

Restricted to upper elevations is *C. montana,* a small, shrubby tree rarely seen below 6,000 ft elevation in the Park. It may be distinguished from other pilo species by its leathery, small, rounded leaves on short, stout, lateral branches. This type of pilo may be seen near the top of Mauna Loa Strip Road, where it grows mixed with other native shrubs.

Kāwaʻu or Hawaiian Holly (*Ilex anomala*)

Holly family (Aquifoliaceae)

Indigenous to the Hawaiian Islands;
  also native to Tahiti and the Marquesas

Distribution in the Park: Rain forests of Kīlauea Caldera,
  East Rift, and ʻŌlaʻa

In many rain forests of Kīlauea Caldera, kāwaʻu is the second-most abundant tree after the dominant ʻōhiʻa. A typical component of the rain forest understory, where it is often a straggling small tree with few branches, kāwaʻu sometimes grows into the upper canopy. In the old soils of ʻOlaʻa Forest, kāwaʻu trees are often taller than 60 ft and have large, multibranched trunks with pale, splotchy, unfurrowed bark.

Leaves of the kāwaʻu vary in shape and size but are often elliptic or round, usually between 2 and 5 in. long. Like other members of the holly family, kāwaʻu leaves are thick, shiny, and dark green, but adult leaves lack the sharp-pointed teeth associated with the genus. The leaves of kāwaʻu seedlings, however, retain this trait and have conspicuously toothed margins. One characteristic of kāwaʻu leaves that distinguishes the species from many other understory trees is the prominent netted venation pattern that is visible on both sides of the leaf and is impressed or sunken into the upper surface. Flowers of the kāwaʻu are white and tubular with up to 10 lobes; they are borne in small clusters among the leaves. Male and female flowers are found on different trees. Female flowers develop into squat, round fruits, which are black outside with purple flesh. These are an important food of the ʻōmaʻo or Hawaiʻi thrush.

Kāwaʻu trees are abundant in forests of eastern Kīlauea Caldera; the rain forest near Nahuku (Thurston Lava Tube) is a good place to look for kāwaʻu trees and to listen for the ʻōmaʻo. In this area, the endemic happyface spider may sometimes be found on the undersides of kāwaʻu leaves.

Strawberry Guava (*Psidium cattleianum*)

Myrtle family (Myrtaceae)

Alien

Distribution in the Park: Lowlands, rain forests, and
moist forests of low and middle elevations

Strawberry guava, locally known as waiawī, is one of the most abundant
and widespread nonnative trees in the Hawaiian Islands. The tree was a
relatively early post-contact introduction to Hawai'i; it was probably

introduced as a fruit tree in 1825 on *HMS Blonde*, a ship that brought many fruit and nut trees, as well as seeds, from England and Brazil. This guava is native to coastal forests of Brazil, where it occurs as scattered individuals mixed with other tree species.

Usually a small or medium-sized tree, strawberry guava has leathery, dark green, glossy leaves 2 to 5 in. long, widest near the tip. Strawberry guava trees are often multitrunked with smooth, varicolored, peeling bark. Flowers of this guava are borne in leaf axils and have small white petals and numerous white stamens in the flower center. The fleshy fruits of strawberry guava are edible and are technically berries, with many round seeds embedded in white, slightly acidic flesh. Globose and about 1 in. long, the fruits of strawberry guava may be either red or yellow skinned. These color variants were formally recognized in the past as either varieties (var.) or forms (f.): *cattleianum* was the red form and *lucidum* the yellow-fruited one. Both color forms are common on Hawai'i Island, and both occur in the Park. Another strawberry guava, previously recognized as a variety (*littorale*), has yellow fruits that are pear shaped rather than spherical; this guava reaches the size of a tall tree and is most often seen in lowland rain forests.

Because it has glossy foliage and colorful bark, the strawberry guava is sometimes planted as an ornamental at lower elevations. Smaller-fruited than the common guava and not commercially cultivated, strawberry guava fruits are nonetheless used to make jams, jellies, and fruit juices. Because of its usefulness as food, many people consider it a desirable plant, but strawberry guava is also recognized as one of the worst plant pests in Hawai'i.

The negative impact of strawberry guava on native wet forests is serious; in many windward areas, the tree forms a dense understory in 'ōhi'a forests, replaces native tree and shrub species, and prevents the reproduction and establishment of many native plants. To make matters worse, the leaf litter of strawberry guava is allelopathic, chemically inhibiting the growth of other plants. The heavy shade from a dense stand of strawberry guava also discourages the establishment of other plants, and the abundant production of guava fruits attracts and encourages the destructive activity of feral pigs. Guava seeds are spread by both pigs and forest birds, and the species can reproduce vegetatively, forming dense stands in the places where it is established.

Strawberry guava is one of the alien plant species targeted for eradication in Special Ecological Areas (such as the forests at Nahuku [Thurston Lava Tube] and Kīpuka Puaulu) because of its community-altering properties. The tree has been removed from more than 600 acres of Hawaii Volcanoes, and areas in which guava is controlled will probably expand in the future. Strawberry guava is now being evaluated as a biological control target. Despite active reduction efforts, strawberry guava trees may still be commonly seen in the Park in forests not yet treated for the pest, for example in parts of the rim of Kīlauea Caldera, 'Ōla'a Forest, and along Kalapana Trail.

J. YOSHIOKA

Hāpuʻu Pulu (*Cibotium glaucum*) and Other Tree Ferns

Tree fern family (Dicksoniaceae)

Endemic to the Hawaiian Islands

Distribution in the Park: Widely distributed in wet and moist
vegetation from near sea level to above 5,000 ft elevation; most
abundant in rain forests between 1,500 and 4,000 ft

To a visitor accustomed to temperate mainland forests and small terrestrial ferns, the hāpuʻu pulu is one of the most unusual plants of Kīlauea's rain forests, where these tree ferns typically reach heights of 20 ft and form a distinct layer beneath the closed ʻōhiʻa canopy and a layer of mixed native trees. When intact, this layer of tree ferns maintains cool, moist conditions on the rain forest floor and greatly decreases the likelihood of nonnative plant invasion. The trunks of tree ferns are important sites for seed germination and establishment of native trees and shrubs. It is not unusual to see rain forest trees, particularly ʻōhiʻa, with multiple basal trunks and a gap, representing the long-deteriorated tree fern trunk or log upon which they began life.

Three distinct species of tree ferns are found in the Park. All have large, triangular, arching fronds, sturdy stipes (leaf stalks), and upright fibrous trunks. As with other ferns, reproduction is by means of tiny spores borne in clusters on the undersides of fronds. In Hawaiian tree ferns, spores are contained within a capsule-like structure made up of two tiny valves, which open when spores are ripe. By far the most common of the tree ferns is the hāpuʻu pulu (illustrated), which can be identified by the orange silky hairs (pulu) clothing stipe bases and fiddleheads at the growing tip of the trunk. Fiddleheads, or developing young fern fronds, are always present at the trunk apex but are most obvious when they unfurl in the spring, usually between March and May. The mature fronds of the hāpuʻu pulu are conspicuously bluish white on their undersides and have a life span of several years. While most abundant in rain forests of ʻOlaʻa, the rim of Kīlauea Caldera, and the East Rift, this species is found occasionally in low-elevation shrublands, mid-elevation woodlands, and the moist kīpuka forests of the lower Mauna Loa Strip.

A second species of tree fern, hāpuʻu ʻiʻi (*Cibotium chamissoi* or *C. menziesii*), may be distinguished from hāpuʻu pulu by its stiff, black or reddish-black hairs along frond stipes. Its fronds are light green rather than white on their undersides. Hāpuʻu ʻiʻi is most common in lower-elevation rain forests but often grows mixed with hāpuʻu pulu to above 4,000 ft elevation.

The most uncommon of the three tree ferns in the Park is the meu (*Cibotium hawaiiense*, called *C. chamissoi* by some), which has a much more slender trunk than the other two Park species and retains its dried dead fronds as a skirt at the top of the trunk. This fern can be seen in ʻOlaʻa Forest, where all three species grow together and are the dominant plants in areas where ʻōhiʻa dieback has opened much of the tree canopy.

The scientific names of several of the tree ferns are currently being revised. When this revision is published the hapuʻu ʻiʻi will be known as *Cibotium menziesii*, an older name, and the meu (now named *Cibotium hawaiiense*) will be called *Cibotium chamissoi*.

Tree ferns are vulnerable to the ravages of feral pigs, which are capable of pushing over even tall-trunked plants and ripping them open to get at the starchy pith inside. In rain forests unprotected from these alien mammals, the hollowed-out shells of tree fern trunks are an all-too-common sight; standing water in downed tree ferns provides breeding sites for nonnative southern house mosquitoes. These insects are the vectors of avian malaria, a disease implicated in the decline of Hawaiʻi's endemic forest birds. In many rain forests, the long-term consequences of dense populations of feral pigs is the complete destruction of the tree fern layer and replacement of the understory with alien plants.

Pigs are not the only agents of tree fern destruction; in the middle and late 1800s, tree ferns of Kīlauea were cut to collect the soft pulu concentrated at the top of the trunk and base of the fronds. Collected pulu was hauled to the coast and shipped to mainland North America for use as pillow and mattress stuffing. The pulu trade went on for several decades, when hundreds of thousands of pounds of pulu were exported each year from the Kīlauea region. Later in the early 20th century, some commercial use was made of tree fern cores for laundry starch. On private lands outside the Park, tree ferns are still harvested for their fibrous trunks, which are shredded and used commercially as a potting medium for plants.

Lobelioids:
  'Ōhā (*Clermontia parviflora*),
  Cyanea pilosa **subsp.** *longipedunculata*, **and**
  Koli'i (*Trematolobelia grandifolia*)

Bellflower family (Campanulaceae), Lobelia subfamily (Lobelioideae)

Endemic to Hawai'i Island

Distribution in the Park: Rain forests of 'Ōla'a,
  the rim of Kīlauea Caldera, and Kīlauea East Rift

The lobelioids are a group of fleshy shrubs and small trees formerly placed in their own family (Lobeliaceae) but now generally recognized as a subfamily of the bellflower family (Campanulaceae). From several original immigrants, this group has speciated remarkably in the Hawaiian Islands with 110 currently recognized species, a number amounting to more than 10 percent of the native flora. All the native Hawaiian species in this group are endemic to the Hawaiian Islands and are usually restricted in distribution to just one island. These plants have evolved such different forms from the original colonizers of Hawai'i that six of the seven genera native to the Islands are also endemic and occur naturally nowhere else in the world.

Members of three of these endemic lobelioid genera occur in Hawaii Volcanoes National Park. The most commonly seen is 'ōhā (*Clermontia parviflora*, lower illustration), a species of widespread occurrence on the windward side of Hawai'i Island. Usually a shrub, 'ōhā may occasionally attain a height of more than 10 ft. Like other members of the genus *Clermontia*, 'ōhā has branches that arch upward in a pattern resembling the arms of candelabra. Although woody, the pale gray branches of this shrub are soft, fleshy, and easily broken; when a branch or any other part of the plant is wounded it exudes a thick, milky white sap. Leaves of the 'ōhā are narrow, 3 to 7 in. long, with finely toothed margins and an elongated, pointed tip. They are dark green and glistening on their upper surface and pale green below. Often young developing leaves at branch tips are dull purple. Inflorescences (flower clusters) are axillary clusters of three or more small tubular flowers. Individual flowers are about 1 in. long with a curved corolla tube and spreading lobes. Flower color is variable but is usually white with purple streaks. 'Ōhā fruits are small, bright orange, oblong berries, most abundant in the fall. The 'ōhā may be seen near Nahuku (Thurston Lava Tube), where it may be terrestrial or an epiphyte on tree ferns, fallen logs, and large tree branches. In 'Ola'a Forest, this shrub is more often seen as an epiphyte, because its brittle, fleshy stems are susceptible to damage from the trampling and rooting of feral pigs.

A second, rarer 'ōhā is 'ōhā kēpau (*C. hawaiiensis*), a tree with large, curved, green and white to purple flowers and large, orange ridged fruit. 'Ōhā kēpau occurs rarely near Nahuku and grows in scattered localities along Kalapana Trail.

Far less common in the Park than 'ōhā is a lobelioid of a second endemic genus, *Cyanea pilosa* subsp. *longipedunculata* (upper left illustration). Like many relatively rare upland plant species, this *Cyanea* has no recorded Hawaiian name specific to it. A shrub with fleshy, unbranched stems rarely over 5 to 6 ft tall, this *Cyanea* bears most of its large leaves at the plant apex in a growth form often described as palmaeform or palmlike. Leaves are fleshy, up to 17 in. long and 6 in. wide, have irregular margins, and are densely covered with soft hairs. Inflorescences appear in the winter or early spring and are long, pendent clusters of many white to pink curved flowers. Like the 'ōhā, the fruits of this *Cyanea* are bright orange, fleshy berries. This species is seen in the Park's 'Ola'a Forest and on adjacent State lands, particularly in areas fenced and protected from feral pigs or on rocky substrates unsuitable for pig digging. Another *Cyanea* that is extremely rare in 'Ōla'a Forest is 'akū (*C. tritomantha*), a tall, single-stemmed plant with long, prickly leaves. This species is a candidate for Federal listing as an Endangered Species.

The third lobelioid genus native to the Park is *Trematolobelia*, represented here by one species, the koli'i (*T. grandifolia*, upper right illustration). Another unbranched shrub, the koli'i has narrow leaves that may be more than 15 in. long but only 1 in. wide. Shiny green on top and paler beneath, koli'i leaves are concentrated at the tops of slender stems. This plant could be confused with a *Clermontia, Cyanea,* or *Lobelia* when not flowering. However, its inflorescence is unique among the lobelioids: it is composed of several branches 1 to 2 ft long, borne like the spokes of a wheel at the top of the stem. Individual flowers are 2 to 3 in. long with a curved, white to pink corolla, stiff green calyx lobes, and a long staminal column extending beyond the corolla. Also unusual are the fruits of the koli'i. Unlike the fleshy berries typical of *Clermontia* and *Cyanea,* koli'i fruits are rounded, many-ribbed capsules, which release their seeds through holes that form as the outer fruit wall decomposes. In the Park, the koli'i is restricted to rain forests of 'Ōla'a, Kīlauea Caldera, and the East Rift near Kāne Nui o Hamo.

Whether rare or common, all the Park's lobelioids are extremely vulnerable to disturbance. Most can exist only in the moist shady understory of closed-canopy rain forest. In the past, lobelioids have been subject to the depredations of feral pigs, but as fencing and pig removal are completed, more of the Park forests will become safe havens for these and other endemic species.

'Ōhelo Kau Lā'au or Tree 'Ōhelo (*Vaccinium calycinum*)

Heath family (Ericaceae)

Endemic to the Hawaiian Islands

Distribution in the Park: Widespread in wet upland forests

Two species of 'ōhelo are native to Hawaii Volcanoes, but the one most often seen in wet forests is 'ōhelo kau lā'au (illustrated). This 'ōhelo is a tall shrub with thin, bright green leaves and purplish brown, smooth bark. One of the few common Hawaiian plants that is partially deciduous in the winter, this 'ōhelo loses many of its leaves after they turn reddish, yellow, or bronze. Its small tubular flowers vary from greenish to red and are relatively inconspicuous.

By contrast, the fruits of 'ōhelo kau la'au are attractive, bright red berries and are seen primarily in the summer. In shape, 'ōhelo berries resemble their well-known relatives, blueberries and cranberries, all members of the genus *Vaccinium*, including more than 100 species distributed worldwide. While edible, the tart berries of 'ōhelo kau lā'au are not as tasty as the fruits of the species of 'ōhelo found in Kīlauea's drier open forests and shrublands (*V. reticulatum*). However, they were used medicinally by Hawaiians in the past and are sometimes added to other types of 'ōhelo berries collected for jams and jellies. While 'ōhelo kau lā'au berries are not extensively used by humans, they may be an important seasonal component of the diet of the endemic 'ōma'o or Hawai'i thrush.

Although basically restricted to wet forests, 'ōhelo kau lā'au is still relatively common in Park rain forests, where it is scattered in the understory. In areas disturbed by feral pigs, such as parts of 'Ola'a Forest, this 'ōhelo usually grows epiphytically on 'ōhi'a trees or logs. A good place to see 'ōhelo kau lā'au is the trail to Nahuku (Thurston Lava Tube), an accessible spot in an 'ōhi'a/hāpu'u ('ōhi'a/ tree fern) forest protected from pigs since 1981.

Kāhili Ginger (*Hedychium gardnerianum*)

Ginger family (Zingiberaceae)

Alien; introduced from the Himalayan region of Asia

Distribution in the Park: Kīlauea Caldera forests, 'Ōla'a Forest, Kīpuka Puaulu

While gingers, or 'awapuhi, along with many other eye-catching tropical flowers, are often prominently depicted in advertisements for Hawai'i by the visitor industry, most are not native to the Hawaiian Islands. Ginger was first introduced by the Polynesians, who brought shampoo ginger (*Zingiber zerumbet*) with them to Hawai'i. Stands of shampoo ginger may still be seen in moist lowland regions near old Hawaiian villages and cultivated fields of Puna District, but the species is common in the Park only near the eastern boundary in upslope forests of Kamoamoa.

White and yellow ginger (*Hedychium coronarium* and *H. flavescens*) were introduced in the late 1800s for their showy, fragrant flowers and have spread along roadsides and streambeds of most of the Hawaiian Islands, primarily at lower elevations. Both these ginger species occur in Hawaii Volcanoes but are not considered problem plants here, because they have not spread far from the original sites of introduction. They are most noticeable near Park Headquarters and Nahuku (Thurston Lava Tube).

The most abundant and conspicuous species of ginger found in Hawaii Volcanoes is kāhili ginger (illustrated), introduced to Hawai'i as an ornamental sometime before 1943. This is a robust herbaceous plant consisting of large, glossy, dark green, leafy shoots, which grow from a mass of fleshy rhizomes resembling the ginger "root" of commerce. Fragrant yellow and red flowers are borne at shoot tips in the summer. Its common name is derived from the resemblance of its attractive inflorescences to the kāhili (Hawaiian symbol of rank, consisting of tufts of feathers mounted on the end of a pole).

Unlike many other ginger species in Hawai'i, kāhili ginger is a prolific producer of fruits and seeds. The fruits are round capsules, which split open in late fall and winter to reveal an orange interior and bright red seeds attractive to birds. Because of its bird-dispersed seeds, kāhili ginger is capable of spreading to remote forests. Once established, the ginger may spread vegetatively by growth of its rhizome mass. In time, this species may completely dominate the ground cover of invaded forests, replacing natural understory plants and preventing the regeneration of native trees.

Kāhili ginger did not invade Hawaii Volcanoes from outside but was intentionally planted in the Park housing area about 50 years ago, in an era before the harmful impacts of introduced plants were widely recognized. Today the densest stands of ginger in the Park are found in the rain forests of Kīlauea between Volcano House and Nahuku, but the plant has also spread to more distant native forests. While it is unlikely that kāhili ginger will ever be completely eliminated from Park forests, much progress has been made in removing it from biologically diverse areas like Kīpuka Puaulu by digging up and hauling away rhizomes, a highly labor-intensive control method.

Banana Poka (*Passiflora mollissima*) and Other Passion Flowers

Passion Flower family (Passifloraceae)

Alien; introduced from South America

Distribution in the Park: Banana poka in 'Ōla'a Forest;
others in lowland wet forests or grasslands

Banana poka (<u>illustrated</u>) is a large woody vine brought to the Island as an ornamental early in the 20th century. The common name of this passion flower vine, a relative of the edible liliko'i (*P. edulis*), is derived from the resemblance of its yellow oblong fruit to a banana. Its pendent, pink flowers, three-parted leaves, and delicate curling tendrils are deceptively beautiful, for banana poka is a killer of native rain forests. In areas infested with banana poka, the fast-growing vine smothers young trees and plants of the forest floor and even grows into the canopy of tall 'ōhi'a and koa trees, where it reduces sunlight necessary for photosynthesis. It also structurally weakens trees, making them more susceptible to damage from wind. When tree branches break from the weight of the vine and infested trees topple, the resulting forest openings encourage more growth of the sun-loving banana poka. The spread of banana poka is facilitated by the presence of feral pigs, which disturb the forest floor through rooting and digging, and open up the forest understory by feeding on tree ferns and other plants. Both pigs and nonnative birds such as the kalij pheasant feed on the elongated yellow fruits and spread banana poka seeds.

Banana poka was not an intentional introduction to the Park but spread to 'Ōla'a Forest from a planting on a nearby farm about 30 years ago. A major storm with high winds in the early 1980s opened up the fern subcanopy and apparently allowed the vine to become well established in 'Ōla'a, where it has now spread over more than half of the 9,300-acre tract. While this vine is a serious pest in Park rain forests, as well as in other natural areas on the slopes of Hualālai and Mauna Kea, there is hope that research and management programs may help control its negative impacts on native forests. In Hawaii Volcanoes National Park, banana poka does not seem to greatly intensify in lightly infested areas from which feral pigs are excluded by fences. Also encouraging has been the discovery and propagation of potential biocontrol agents from South America, an iridescent blue moth (*Cyanotricha necyria*) and a small brown moth (*Pyrausta perelegans*). These two insect species feed on banana poka leaves or flowers during their larval stage. Both have been introduced to Hawai'i, but neither has yet become established in forests infested with banana poka. Biocontrol research on banana poka continues, with the goal of finding additional insects or plant diseases to combat this alien vine.

Three other passion flower species occur in Hawaii Volcanoes, but none of them pose a serious threat to native vegetation. Liliko'i occurs scattered throughout low-elevation rain forests, where it has probably spread from inhabited areas outside the Park. Liliko'i leaves are three-parted and similar in shape to those of banana poka, but the smaller flowers are white and purple. Liliko'i fruits are round and may be either yellow or purple. Sweet granadilla *(P. ligularis)* is rarely encountered in 'Ōla'a. This large liana has heart-shaped, undivided leaves and showy flowers with a crown of purple-and-white striped filaments.

Of all passion flower species in the Park, the one visitors are most likely to encounter is the foetid passion flower or "love-in-a-mist" (*P. foetida*). This vine is common in the lowlands and near the coast, where it climbs on lowland shrubs and grasses. Its small, three-lobed leaves are covered with fine hairs and have a strong, unpleasant odor when crushed. Flowers are white and about 1 in. wide. The thin-walled fruit of this passion flower is red, about 1 in. long, and is enclosed by finely divided green bracts.

Paʻiniu (*Astelia menziesiana*)

Lily family (Liliaceae)

Endemic to the Hawaiian Islands

Distribution in the Park: Rain forests of ʻŌlaʻa,
Kīlauea Caldera, Kīlauea Iki, and East Rift

200

Few lilies are represented in the endemic flora of Hawai'i; the silvery-leaved pa'iniu is one of only two native genera in the family. One of the most beautiful native Hawaiian plants, the pa'iniu is striking even without its fruit or flowers. An herbaceous, relatively succulent plant, the pa'iniu has long, narrow, keeled leaves that glisten with a silvery coat above and are covered with soft silver or white hairs below. These shiny leaves are eagerly sought by makers of haku (woven) or wili (twisted) Hawaiian leis.

The small, unisexual flowers of pa'iniu are not particularly showy; they are borne in stiff, upright inflorescences, the male and female flowers on separate plants. Usually white or greenish, each individual male flower resembles that of a lily in miniature, with six petals and six prominent stamens (male organs). Female flowers are similar, except the central female organ, the pistil, is well developed and the six stamens are not functional. After pollination, the female flowers develop into conspicuous bright orange berries.

In Hawaiian rain forests disturbed by feral pigs, the pa'iniu is seen only as an epiphyte, growing on fallen logs and lateral tree branches. The fleshy pa'iniu leaves are very palatable to pigs, which seek out the plants and devour them, scattering bits of leaves and roots in the process. Pig rooting and trampling also damages pa'iniu and associated terrestrial herbaceous plants, as well as native tree seedlings. In areas protected from the depredations of pigs, pa'iniu may be either epiphytic or terrestrial; in some upper-elevation rain and cloud forests, the silvery herb may even be a dominant component of the ground cover.

While no site in the Park has an abundance of pa'iniu, the species has become rather common in the forests on the rim of Kīlauea Caldera since the removal of feral pigs from the area in the early 1980s. Crater Rim Trail and adjacent trails between Nahuku (Thurston Lava Tube) and Byron Ledge are particularly good places to view this lovely endemic lily.

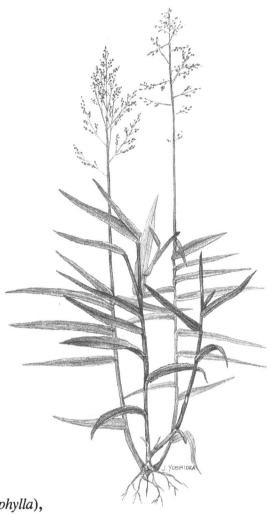

Grasses and Sedges:
'Ohe (*Isachne distichophylla*),
Kikuyu Grass (*Pennisetum clandestinum*),
Hilo Grass (*Paspalum conjugatum*), and
'Uki (*Machaerina angustifolia*)

Grass family (Poaceae) and Sedge family (Cyperaceae)

Endemic ('ohe); **Indigenous** ('uki);
Alien (Kikuyu grass, Hilo grass)

Distribution in the Park: 'Ohe and Hilo grass in rain forests;
'uki in rain forests, mid-elevation woodlands, wet lava flows, and
cinder fields; kikuyu in upland rain forests, moist forests,
and koa woodlands

The only native grass that is common in rain forests of the Park is 'ohe (illustrated), which shares its Hawaiian common name with bamboo, a much larger member of the grass family. The 'ohe of Kīlauea forests grows in loose clumps with stout, upright stems 2 to 3 ft tall. Leaf blades of 'ohe are stiffly horizontal to the stem, about 6 in. long, arranged with alternating blades at 90 degrees from each other. The tiny stalked flowers of 'ohe are arranged in delicate open inflorescences; often these flower clusters are purplish red. 'Ohe is a frequent component of rain forests between 2,000 and 4,000 ft elevation in the Park.

Few alien grasses are capable of invading intact rain forests, but several nonnative species may be found in disturbed openings or along forest edges. Kikuyu grass is the principal species in Park lawns and is often seen along roadsides near the rim of Kīlauea Caldera. In many areas, this alien stoloniferous (creeping) grass has entered the rain forest along corridors of disturbance. A bright green, mat-forming species with smooth alternate leaf blades spreading at right angles from the creeping stem, kikuyu grass has tiny inconspicuous flowers and apparently does not set seed in Hawai'i. Nonetheless, it spreads vegetatively with ease and may form a dense ground cover impenetrable to native plants. Kikuyu may also produce chemicals that prevent other plants from growing near it (allelopathy). An important range and pasture grass in Hawai'i, kikuyu grass was imported from Africa and has been widely planted on island ranches.

Hilo grass, a serious invader of some Hawaiian rain forests, occurs sporadically in forests of Kīlauea. This grass may be readily recognized by its inflorescence, composed of two curved arms bearing round, flattened grains.

Several native sedges are frequently seen in rain forests of Kīlauea; the most abundant and conspicuous species in forests and woodlands near the Caldera is 'uki. This sedge grows in large clumps and is often taller than 4 ft. Long stiff leaves about 0.5 to 1 in. wide arise in two ranks from the flattened base of the plant. These leaves are thick, dark green, and shiny. Tender, fleshy leaf bases are eaten by feral pigs; 'uki plants may be greatly reduced in pig-inhabited forests. 'Uki flowers are borne in elongate dense clusters on an erect stalk rising above the clumps of leaves. Shiny dark brown or black branches of these inflorescences are used in lei making. 'Uki is not limited to wet forests and grows also in open woodlands and on many lava flows and cinder fields of Kīlauea's East Rift.

Wāwaeʻiole (*Lycopodium cernuum* **or** *Palhinhaea cernua*)

Club Moss family (Lycopodiaceae)

Indigenous to the Hawaiian Islands

Distribution in the Park: Mid-elevation woodlands
  and upper-elevation rain forests

Despite its resemblance to a miniature conifer, wāwae'iole is not related to pines but belongs to a group of primitive vascular plants related to ferns. Club mosses were important components of worldwide vegetation several hundred million years ago. Like ferns, they are spore-bearing plants, but they differ in that they bear their bright yellow spores in conelike structures of specialized scales at branch tips. Agreement regarding proper species determinations of the Hawaiian club mosses has not been reached among the various authorities; we include here alternative names for the species known to occur in Hawaii Volcanoes.

A sprawling plant, wāwae'iole is usually seen as patches of upright shoots 2 to 4 ft tall growing from stems running along the ground. Lacking true leaves, the much-branched wāwae'iole is covered with soft, curved, bright yellow-green scales, spirally arranged. The Hawaiian name wāwae'iole literally means "rat's foot," perhaps referring to the down-curved, forked ends of branches. Wāwae'iole is common in the forests of Kīlauea Crater Rim and can always be seen along forested portions of Kīlauea Iki Trail. The plant is also abundant along the highway east of the Park, where it is often collected for use in flower arrangements.

At least four other species of club mosses occur in the Park. Two of these (*L. phyllanthum* and *L. polytrichoides*, also known as *Phlegmariurus phyllanthus* and *P. filiformis*) are relatively uncommon epiphytes seen growing on tree trunks in rain forests of Kīlauea Caldera and East Rift. Another epiphytic species (*L. serratum* or *Huperzia serrata*) is a tiny, erect plant seen very rarely in 'Ōla'a Forest. One terrestrial species (*L. venustulum*) is found sparingly at higher elevations and at drier mid-elevation sites. The taxonomy of club mosses in Hawai'i is currently being revised.

Epiphytic Ferns, Mosses, and Fern Allies

Indigenous and **Endemic**

Distribution in the Park: ʻŌlaʻa Forest, forests of Kīlauea Caldera and Kīlauea's East Rift

While some epiphytic plants, particularly lichens, are found in all but the driest vegetation types, the presence of numerous epiphytic ferns, mosses, liverworts, and tree seedlings is an indication that a forest is truly wet enough to be called a rain forest. Epiphytes are plants growing on other plants but not dependent on them for sustenance, as are parasitic plants like mistletoe.

Ferns, like flowering plants, possess a well-developed vascular system (the water- and food-conducting tissues), but they lack flowers, fruits, and seeds; instead, they reproduce by means of tiny spores. The structures bearing these spores vary among groups of ferns, and their arrangement on the fern frond often serves to characterize that species as a member of a particular fern family. One fern family restricted to rain forests is that of the filmy ferns (Hymenophyllaceae); their fronds are only one or two cells thick and are a glistening, translucent green. Two commonly seen epiphytic filmy ferns in the Park are 'ōhi'a kū (*Mecodium recurvum*) and palai hinahina (*Sphaerocionium lanceolatum*). Although very similar in appearance, with delicate, much-dissected fronds and round, two-valved, capsule-like structures enclosing the spores, the 'ōhi'a kū (upper and center right in illustration) is hairless and larger, often 6 to 8 in. long. In contrast, the palai hinahina is only 1 to 2 in. long and has long, prominent, orange-brown hairs on frond margins. Both of these filmy ferns are typically seen on the bases of 'ōhi'a tree trunks.

Another group of ferns, including primarily small epiphytic plants of the rain forest, is the grammitis family (Grammitaceae). One often-seen epiphyte in this group is wahine noho mauna (*Adenophorus tamariscinus*, lower right in illustration); this occurs with considerable frequency in all the rain forests of the Park and is noticeable on tree trunks, branches, and fallen logs of Kīlauea Caldera forests. Typically 6 in. long, the small fronds of this fern are bipinnate (twice divided) with tiny linear lobes. The spores are borne in round yellow clusters on the undersides of fronds. Two other small ferns in the same family are frequent epiphytes in forests of Kīlauea and 'Ōla'a. The kihi (*Xiphopteris saffordii* or *Lellingeria saffordii*, upper center in illustration) is rarely over 2 in. long and has narrow linear fronds with prominently toothed margins. Approximately 6 in. long, the mākuʻe lau liʻi (*Grammitis hookeri*) is made up of clusters of soft-textured, unlobed, strap-shaped fronds densely covered with stiff orange-brown hairs. When fertile, the underside of each frond bears two rows of round, yellow spore clusters. The closely related kolokolo (*G. tenella*, lower left in illustration) has narrow, stiffly erect, hairless fronds with a similar arrangement of spore clusters.

Several larger epiphytic ferns grow in Park forests, among them several species called 'ēkaha (middle left in illustration) by the Hawaiians. Most abundant is a scaly 'ēkaha (*Elaphoglossum hirtum* or *E. paleaceum*, family Elaphoglossaceae) composed of a dense cluster of long, pendent, straplike fronds covered with soft brown scales. This and other 'ēkaha bear their spores over the entire lower surface of the frond; when ripe the spores are dark brown or black.

Several primitive vascular plants or fern allies are common forest epiphytes in Hawai'i; the most abundant of these is the whisk fern (called moa or pipi by Hawaiians) (*Psilotum complanatum*, family Psilotaceae or whisk ferns). This completely leafless plant (upper left in illustration) is composed of flattened, much-divided green branches, which hang pendent from a single stem rooted on tree trunks or lower tree branches. When fertile, the whisk fern bears globose, yellow, spore-containing structures along the sides of branch tips.

In addition to these and many other species of epiphytic ferns, tree trunks and branches of rain forest trees are often covered with damp mats of mosses and liverworts. Mosses and liverworts belong to a division of plants (Bryophyta) distinct from that of the ferns and flowering plants (Tracheophyta). Mosses are grouped together into the class Musci, and liverworts belong to the class Hepaticae. These plants are small, limited in size by a lack of vascular tissue. Lacking a waxy coating on tiny leaves, mosses and liverworts grow most successfully under damp shady conditions. Mosses and liverworts have not been well studied in Hawaii Volcanoes, but the Park probably contains more than 150 native species of these tiny plants, most found within rain forests.

Kalij Pheasant (*Lophura leucomelana*)

Gallinaceous Bird family (Phasianidae)

Alien; introduced from the Himalayas

Distribution in the Park: In forests from 1,000 to 7,500 ft elevation; habitat ranges from rain forest of 'Ōla'a and Nahuku (Thurston) areas to koa kīpuka on Mauna Loa Strip

In 1962, 67 of these attractive Asian pheasants with vertical, wedge-shaped tails were introduced from Michigan and Texas game farms to Pu'uwa'awa'a Ranch on northwestern Hawai'i Island. The kalij pheasant was one of many gamebird species introduced for hunting at that time. By 1977, they were recorded near Kīlauea Caldera in the Park and were so widespread that they were declared a game species on Hawai'i Island. Thus, in 14 years, moving at an average rate of about 5 mi per year through dry, moist, and wet habitats, these pheasants were able to colonize about one-third of the island area from one release site. In Hawaii Volcanoes, numbers are still increasing alarmingly, with birds becoming much more abundant in the past several years.

The metallic blue-black cocks and brownish hens are most active in early morning or late evening along Park roads, where they display, forage, and pick up small rocks to serve as grit to aid digestion. Small seeds from various fruits are also retained in their gizzards for this purpose. Mated pairs or family groups are commonly seen on Mauna Loa Strip Road, near Nahuku (Thurston Lava Tube), and on Chain of Craters Road. Feeding birds utter quiet, pig-like grunts, but harsh crowing, high-pitched squealing, and "wing fluttering" by the cock are also characteristic noises.

Kalij pheasants lay 10 to 17 eggs between mid-March and mid-June over a 21-day period. Eggs hatch from May to early July. The precocial brood (feathered and ambulatory when hatched) is cared for by the mated pair or either sex alone. This species is primarily monogamous in Hawai'i.

Kalij pheasants are strongly associated with invasive alien plant species such as banana poka, thimbleberry, blackberry, and guava, which the birds are known to spread throughout the areas they inhabit. Other food items include native plant fruits, snails, slugs, sowbugs, various insects, earthworms, and bird eggs. Kalij scratchings are evident in areas they frequent and are sometimes confused with feral pig digging, although the area disturbed by pheasants is far less than that exposed by "rototilling" pigs.

Large populations of introduced birds, including kalij pheasants, are a concern to Park managers, especially when they are present in native plant and animal communities that have not been invaded by alien plants. In addition to spreading alien plants and eating native plants and animals, pheasants and other introduced birds may be reservoirs for pathogens causing diseases such as avian malaria and pox. Native birds are less able to withstand long-term infections than species that have evolved with these diseases.

ʻŌmaʻo or Hawaiʻi Thrush (*Myadestes obscurus*)

Old World Insect Eater family (Muscicapidae), Thrush subfamily (Turdinae)

Endemic to Hawaiʻi Island

Distribution in the Park: Rain forests at mid-elevation
(ʻŌlaʻa Forest, Nahuku [Thurston Lava Tube], Kīlauea Caldera);
moist forests and scrub (Kīpuka Puaulu, Kīpuka Kī);
shrubland and woodland to above tree line (over 9,000 ft)

Like small children, 'ōma'o are often heard before they are seen. They utter various loud calls and songs, including a jerky series of slurred flutelike notes and a loud trill like a police whistle. Calls and songs are repeated often, and frequently several birds in the same area alternate similar vocalizations. 'Ōma'o sing year round, sitting without moving within dense foliage, often in deep, closed-canopy wet forest. In moist, more open areas of Mauna Loa Strip, 'ōma'o are less abundant but more readily seen, especially along the trail to Pu'u 'Ula'ula or Red Hill (10,000 ft elevation).

'Ōma'o are dark gray-brown above and pale gray below, about 7 in. long, and the sexes look alike. Bill and legs are dark, and the tail is short. Immature birds are more spotted and brownish than adults. Adults and young often display wing drooping and body quivering, usually associated with begging behavior of young in other species.

Fleshy fruits such as those of 'ōlapa or 'ōhelo are favored foods, but invertebrates and seeds are also eaten. Although 'ōma'o often sing from high in the forest canopy, they frequently forage in understory vegetation. Some authorities believe that 'ōma'o may have once concentrated in numbers in native forests to take advantage of caterpillar outbreaks, much as introduced common mynas probably once did.

'Ōma'o nests have been found in tree cavities, sheltered spots on tree ferns, rock cracks and crannies in lava tubes, and on ledges. Eggs are grayish white with small, irregular, reddish brown markings. Much more remains to be learned about the breeding behavior of this secretive species.

Other endemic Hawaiian thrushes (each now considered a distinct species) also exist on Kaua'i and Moloka'i and, unlike the 'ōma'o, they are Endangered Species. Even though 'ōma'o are not as abundant at low elevations on Hawai'i Island as they once were and are no longer found on the kona (leeward) side of the Island, numbers in the Park have probably increased since the 1940s. Populations in both rain forest and koa-'ōhi'a parklands may be larger. As long as these habitats exist in a relatively undisturbed state, this unusual and attractive bird may continue to be heard in numbers where the songs of many other species have been silenced.

'Apapane (*Himatione sanguinea*)

**Finch family (Fringillidae),
Hawaiian Honeycreeper and Finch subfamily (Drepanidinae)**

Endemic to the Hawaiian Islands

Distribution in the Park: Generally from 1,500 ft to tree line, but
occasionally lower and higher elevations, in forests and shrublands

This crimson-red bird with fluffy white undertail feathers is the most abundant and widely distributed of native forest species and the most likely to be seen by visitors in the Park. 'Apapane are small (5.25 in.), active birds with black legs and are often seen in the very tops of 'ōhi'a trees, sipping nectar from red blossoms (lehua) or catching small invertebrates. The short, slightly curved, black bill appears light in color at the tip because a brushy, whitish tongue often protrudes slightly. Black tails and wings are often held jauntily as 'apapane forage or as males court females. Immature birds are dull brown instead of crimson, turning red as they mature to adult plumage.

'Apapane breed from January to July. Two to four whitish eggs with scattered brownish markings and splotches near the larger end of the egg are laid in cup-shaped nests, usually in 'ōhi'a trees or on tree ferns, but even in lava tube entrances. Young 'apapane hatch out in about two weeks and are fed by both parents. Nestlings usually leave the nest at 16 to 17 days of age and are able to fly from tree to tree at this stage.

'Apapane feed in flowering koa and māmane as well as 'ōhi'a trees; they also take nectar and insects from introduced plants such as eucalyptus. These birds generally follow the flowering or "bloom" of 'ōhi'a on different trees in different areas and are probably essential for 'ōhi'a pollination. Dozens or even hundreds of birds make flights (several miles) in search of nectar, especially in the nonbreeding season. On long journeys, sometimes over barren lava flows at high elevations, 'apapane may fly high enough (a few hundred feet) to be out of sight to human observers. When they are within earshot, however, 'apapane wings make a characteristic whistling sound, and a short call is sometimes given in flight.

'Apapane are perhaps the best vocalists among the surviving Hawaiian honeycreepers. They have various songs and calls composed of whistles, clucks, buzzes, trills, and squawks. 'Apapane sing at any time of the day during the breeding season; singing occurs less consistently at other times of the year. Birds no doubt recognize each other through individualized song contents and patterns.

This abundant bird is easily seen and heard on Crater Rim Trail, from which one may look down on tree canopies, in which birds are most active. 'Apapane can be found in wet to moist native forests in most areas of the Park, including Nahuku (Thurston Lava Tube), Kīpuka Puaulu and Kīpuka Kī, and in koa woodlands along Mauna Loa Strip Road. This species is among the first to consistently use areas in which forest trees are regenerating after clearcutting. It may also be found in dry, subalpine areas.

Long-distance movements made by 'apapane in search of nectar may make them vulnerable to diseases such as avian malaria and pox, transmitted by southern house mosquitoes active at night and abundant at lower elevations. Both 'apapane and 'i'iwi make daily altitudinal movements in warmer, drier months, moving upslope in the late afternoon from mid elevations (4,000 ft) and back down again in the morning. Recent evidence suggests that about 30 percent of 'apapane have been exposed to malaria, but whether the birds generally die or act as a disease reservoir is unknown. Some observers believe that daily movements are now more apparent because sedentary 'apapane were vulnerable to mosquito-borne malaria parasites at lower elevations. According to this view, birds that presently remain are the descendants of 'apapane that avoided being bitten by nocturnally active lowland mosquitoes through movements upslope before nightfall. Before establishment of the malaria protozoan, especially in game- and songbirds introduced by humans, 'apapane and other nectar feeders may not have made energy-demanding daily movements. Instead, they may have followed the advancing bloom of 'ōhi'a upslope with the seasons.

Domestic Pig (*Sus scrofa*)

Old World Swine family (Suidae)

Alien; introduced by Polynesians early in colonization period
(400 A.D.), then by Europeans (first by Captain James Cook in 1778
on Ni'ihau)

Distribution in the Park: Formerly all rain forests except
inaccessible areas such as pit craters or remote kīpuka, and from
coastal shrublands to tree line on Mauna Loa

When you drive down Chain of Craters Road or ascend Mauna Loa Strip Road, be alert for "cattle guards" on the road with fencing on either side. In the Park, the fences and breaks in the road are really designed to prevent the movement of feral pigs from one Park management unit to another. Fortunately for other animals and plants in the management units, feral pigs have now been eliminated from most fenced areas (about one-third of the suitable pig habitat in the Park) by systematic hunting and other means.

Because Hawaiian plants have evolved without defenses against large animals that "rototill," trample, and consume nearly all vegetation within reach, feral pigs are able to destroy considerable quantities of habitat for native plants and animals. Tree ferns, knocked over by pigs for starchy interiors, or pith, accumulate water in which mosquitoes that transmit avian malaria parasites breed. Many native birds are probably now limited in distribution and numbers, at least in part, by diseases. Pigs also transport invasive alien plants such as strawberry guava and banana poka over comparatively long distances (some individual pigs range over 2,000 acres of wet forest during several months). Native Hawaiian plants and animals and nonnative ungulates (hoofed mammals) just don't mix, even if pigs are present only in small numbers. Pig-resistant fences allow the public to experience natural conditions and native species inside, with more modified conditions and recreational hunting outside. (Ironically, in Hawai'i we fence our wild areas in and exclude feral pigs from them to protect wilderness for the future.) Pig control is costly -- perhaps $35,000 per mile for pig fences, not to mention the actual cost of removing the animals inside, and long-term fence maintenance. About 40 mi of pig fence had been constructed in the Park by 1993, enclosing about 20,000 acres.

Feral pigs are descendants of European domestic breeds in Hawai'i and may be seen in all colors, shapes, and sizes. In the Park and other remote areas, they are usually black, and young often have characteristic "watermelon" striping similar to European wild pigs, the ancestors of the European domestic stock. Asiatic domestic pigs brought by early Polynesians were small, carefully husbanded, and not often found away from settlements. In contrast, the larger European domestic stock brought in the 18th century was allowed to roam free in wild areas. The Polynesian pig no longer exists.

Most adult feral pigs today weigh about 100 pounds, but pigs up to 500 pounds have been taken, and boars over 200 pounds are not uncommon. Pig hunting is now a popular, exciting, but dangerous sport in Hawai'i; 1,500 animals per year are reportedly taken statewide (undoubtedly an underestimate), generally with dogs that track and hold the animal until the hunter can dispatch the tusked and angry quarry, usually with a knife. Pig meat is delicious, especially when cooked in an imu (underground oven) and prepared as kalua pig.

Feral pigs are extremely prolific for a large animal; they produce an average of five young per litter, as often as twice a year. Populations can potentially double in less than a year. In the Park, starch in tree fern trunks, starchy roots, fleshy fruits, koa seedlings, various grasses, and earthworms and slugs are favored foods; numbers of pigs are probably not limited by food abundance (quantity). Animal protein (in the form of earthworms and slugs) is sought after; food quality may limit pig numbers, growth, or condition, especially in some areas of the Park where soils are thin and animal protein is scarce. Some young piglets in grassy nests are also killed by cold and wet conditions, but we don't know how important this is in terms of total mortality. Disease organisms, including those causing tuberculosis, brucellosis, trichinosis, and pseudorabies, most of which can be transmitted to humans, are present in feral pigs and also kill some animals.

Feral pigs are found in highest densities in wet forests, and the best chance of seeing them or their tracks, droppings, wallows, digging, nests, or feeding sites is now probably in the East Rift area around Nāpau Crater and Makaopuhi, where public hunting is permitted. Pig numbers there can be reduced, but the risk of building fences in this volcanically active area precludes total elimination of pigs. A barrier fence to restrict pig movements has been constructed to facilitate management efforts.

Feral pigs are found in many areas outside the Park, such as State Forest Reserves managed for public hunting. On State, Federal, and private lands in Hawai'i that are managed for intact and sustainable native vegetation (about 15% of Hawai'i's total land area), feral pig elimination is the ultimate goal in the most restorable areas. Because management costs are high and labor is limited, often the best parts of the legally protected areas (those least disturbed by pigs and alien plants, and with highest diversity of native species) are managed first to remove feral pigs. Once pig disturbance has been eliminated, reduction of alien plants and reintroduction of missing native flora and fauna can begin.

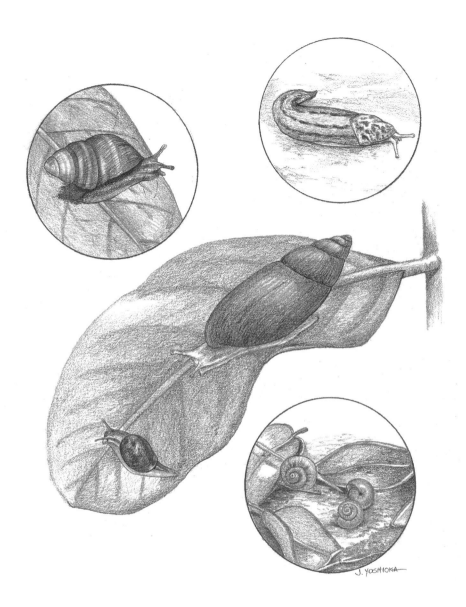

J. YOSHIOKA

Land Snails and Slugs

Stomach-footed Mollusk class (Gastropoda),
  Air-breathing Gastropod order (Pulmonata)

Alien and **native**

Distribution in the Park: Sea level to tree line, especially in wet areas

Mollusks (from a Latin word for "soft") are known as pūpū in Hawaiian, a word now used to refer to appetizers for humans. Slugs and snails are gastropod (stomach-footed) mollusks, and about 1,800 species can be found in the ocean, freshwater streams, and damp areas on land in Hawai'i. All mollusks at some stage in their life cycle have shells, which are secreted by a fold of the body wall called the mantle; adult land snails have shells, but adult land slugs do not.

Most Hawaiian land snails and slugs are air-breathing gastropods, or pulmonates: between the mantle and the body is a cavity used as an air-breathing "lung," with a small hole to let air in and out. Snails and slugs have glands in their bodies that produce mucus or slime, which is excreted just beneath their mouths; the animals slide slowly along the mucous layer beneath their bodies by contracting their muscular "stomach foot." All mollusks have a radula, a tongue of tissue containing chitinous teeth or plates, which functions as the food-gathering organ. Most pulmonates are vegetarians that feed by scraping up particles of plants and detritus with their raspy radulae. Pulmonate gastropods are hermaphroditic, each individual producing both sperm and eggs; some species are entirely self-fertilizing -- a handy feature when numbers of individuals are small -- and some are capable of both self- and cross-fertilization.

Hawaiian tree snails (endemic subfamily Achatinellinae, family Achatinellidae) attracted early attention in Hawai'i because of their abundance, variety, and beauty. Although members of the subfamily have been found on all islands except Kaua'i and Ni'ihau, the genus *Achatinella* ("little agate;" upper left illustration) is found only on O'ahu. The entire genus (41 species, of which 21 are probably extinct) has been placed on the Federal Endangered Species list. Loss of large numbers of species of tree snails has resulted from uncontrolled collection by scientists and hobbyists, intrinsically low reproductive rates, extremely small individual home ranges (sometimes confined to a single plant), narrow host plant tolerance, destruction of habitat, predation by rats, and (probably) diseases. In addition, the arboreal carnivorous snail *Euglandina rosea* (right center illustration), introduced from Florida to control the alien giant African snail (*Achatina fulica*), which grows as long as 5 to 8 in., has been a major cause of the recent drastic reduction of Hawaiian tree snail populations. The carnivorous snail has been reported from the 'Ainahou Ranch area of the Park.

The most commonly encountered tree snails in Hawaii Volcanoes National Park are in the indigenous genus *Succinea* in the family Succineidae (lower left center illustration), small (less than 1 in.) animals with transparent paper-like shells lacking the size and color of the Achatinellinae. The eggs of succineids are laid on leaves in mucous globs that absorb moisture, swell, and form a protective chamber. Adult succineids are prey for forest birds and rats.

Hawaiian "ground snails" (lower right illustration) in several families were formerly more diverse than tree snails, but not much is known about these animals. Some small and inconspicuous species in this group are known to hitchhike on bird feathers from place to place. All endemic

Hawaiian land snails, including species up to 3 in. long (*Carelia*, on Kaua'i), probably evolved from small species that arrived in Hawai'i by "air express."

Alien slugs such as the spotted garden slug (*Limax maximus*, upper right illustration) are sometimes abundant in rain forest areas such as 'Ola'a. No native species of this nocturnally active group are known from Hawai'i. Like alien snails in gardens, slugs in native forests can damage some plants such as rare endemic ground orchids and greenswords. In Haleakalā National Park, the slug *Milax gagates* probably attracted feral pigs to fragile greensword bogs; rooting by pigs in these areas became so destructive that the bogs had to be fenced to exclude them. Some leathery lowland slugs (*Veronicella* spp.) are able to withstand desiccation better than many species commonly found in upland wet areas and can forage farther afield in daylight hours. Alien land mollusks (both slugs and snails) are more abundant than natives at elevations below 1,000 ft and in drier areas.

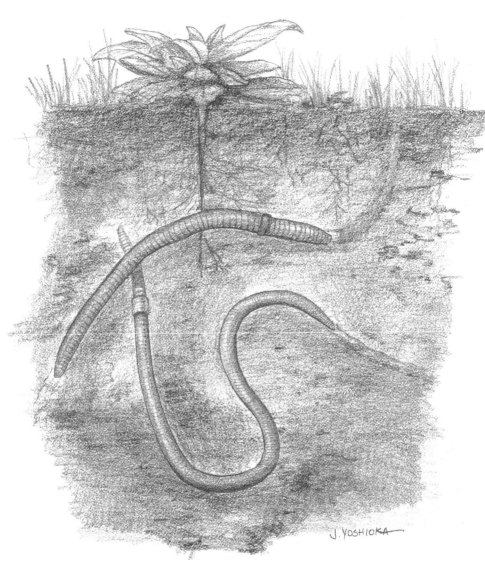

Earthworms

Segmented Worm phylum (Annelida); Earthworm, Fresh or Brackish Worm, and Leech class (Oligochaeta); several families

Alien and **Polynesian introduction**

Distribution in the Park: Probably parkwide where sufficient soil occurs

Earthworms probably first arrived in Hawai'i in soil on food plants carried in Polynesian canoes. While other stowaways, such as geckos, skinks, and Polynesian rats, are often noted in early writings about Hawai'i, earthworms are seldom mentioned even though their effects on Hawai'i's natural areas are important. Additional species of earthworms came with European trade, possibly in ballast used to stabilize early sailing ships. Now at least 20 species of earthworms in three families, some of them found in tropical areas around the world and others found in more temperate areas, occur in Hawai'i. The families Megascolecidae, Glossoscolecidae, and Lumbricidae are important in Hawai'i, with most species in Megascolecidae.

Earthworms can be recognized by their rounded, segmented bodies with a complete or partial swollen glandular band called a clitellum in the anterior part of the body. The clitellum secretes mucus that produces a slime tube useful in protecting the worm during dry spells and in allowing eggs and sperm to be transferred outside of the body. Each individual earthworm possesses both male and female reproductive systems, but reproductive material is usually exchanged from worm to worm. Once the exchange is complete, the animals back out of their slime tubes, leaving fertilized eggs within cocoons. Nourished by the proteinaceous mucus, one or many worms develop in a few weeks. Eggs can also develop into embryos within cocoons parthenogenetically (without being fertilized), a handy feature when numbers of worms are low.

Earthworms generally move through the soil by ingesting soil particles and voiding digested feces or "casts." Casts are a rich source of nutrients for plants. The burrowing of earthworms increases the aeration of the soil and improves its moisture-holding capacity. In wet periods, earthworms move to the surface, but in dry periods they may become inactive, coiled up within their mucous cocoons. Some species specialize in organic surface layers of soil, while others live deeper in more mineralized substrates. Small bristles, or chaetae, borne singly on each segment move in and out to grip the soil as earthworms burrow.

In the Park, different species of earthworms predominate under native 'ōhi'a trees and under alien firetrees. Studies show that earthworm biomass is two to eight times higher under firetrees than in nearby shrubland on the same substrate or in rain forests. Since firetrees capture nitrogen from the air and produce enriched litter, earthworms, in processing the litter, increase the rate of nitrogen uptake and cycling in the ecosystem. Because Hawai'i's soils, to which native plants are well adapted, are often low in nitrogen, the enrichment resulting from firetrees and the further enrichment and soil structure changes caused by earthworms can favor alien plants (including firetree itself) and alter the rate and course of ecosystem development. Earthworms are also favorite foods of feral pigs, providing an important source of animal protein that these alien ungulates (hoofed mammals) need for optimum growth and reproduction.

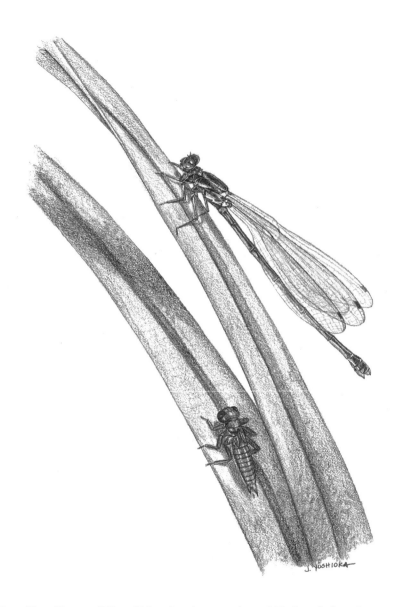

Hawaiian Damselflies (*Megalagrion* spp.) and Related Species

Dragonfly and Damselfly order (Odonata),
 Narrow-winged Damselfly family (Coenagrionidae) (*Megalagrion*);
 Darner family (Aeshidae); Skimmer family (Libellulidae)

Endemic

Distribution in the Park: Wet forests, anchialine pools (damselflies), but also drier areas (dragonflies)

224

Forty species of dragonflies and damselflies, 34 of which are endemic, are found in Hawai'i. Two families, the darners (Aeshidae) and the common skimmers (Libellulidae), are dragonflies, recognizable at rest when membraneous, many-veined wings are held horizontally or outstretched. Hawai'i has one endemic species in each dragonfly family, and one of these, the giant aeshid *Anax strenuus* with a wingspan of up to 6 in., is found in the Park. This species, known as pinao to Hawaiians, is the largest native Hawaiian insect and the largest insect in the United States.

Both dragonflies and damselflies have large compound eyes in moveable heads, biting mouthparts, long legs for holding insects captured on the wing, and four long wings that can move independently of each other. All of these are adaptations for capturing insects in flight. Mating also occurs in the air, with insects characteristically locked together for a time and flying in tandem. Eggs are usually laid in or near water, but as mentioned below, there are exceptions in Hawai'i. Immature insects, called naiads, that develop from the eggs of damselflies and dragonflies are effective predators on aquatic lifeforms, including mosquito larvae.

Damselflies, recognized by their habit of holding their wings together (or in a vertical plane) when at rest, are sometimes prey for their larger relatives. The largest damselfly species in Hawai'i, the bright red *Megalagrion blackburni*, is less than 2.5 in. long.

Narrow-winged damselflies in the genus *Megalagrion* have radiated into 29 species in Hawai'i, with naiads developing in a wide variety of habitats. Four of the nine species found on Hawai'i Island are considered candidates for Federal listing as Endangered Species. One endemic species, *M. peles* (illustrated), lays eggs in the leaf axils of the native lily pa'iniu in the Park. The naiad of this species waits in the axils of pa'iniu for prey to come close enough to capture and eat. (The naiad is illustrated exposed on the lily leaf, in contrast to its normal hidden position in the leaf axil.)

Naiads of aquatic damselflies are eaten by mosquito fish and possibly long-legged ants; naiads of terrestrial forms are threatened by feral pigs, which destroy their habitat. Although pig activity may create some breeding habitat for *M. calliphya*, which breeds in wet leaf litter and soil, native plants such as pa'iniu, 'ie'ie, lobelioids, and other rare plants that are important for rare native invertebrates (including other *Megalagrion*), for birds, and for natural forest structure and function are destroyed. Recent studies show that the abundance and diversity of picture wing flies, soil microarthropods, and earthworms are significantly higher in Park forests where feral pigs have been removed than in those where they still remain. The effects of feral pigs on *Megalagrion* and moth diversity and abundance in the Park are currently under study.

J. YOSHIOKA

Picture Wing Flies

True Fly order (Diptera), Pomace Fly family (Drosophilidae)

Endemic

Distribution in the Park: Wet and moist forests and shrublands

The Hawaiian Archipelago probably hosts close to one-third of the species of pomace flies in the world. Derived from one (or possibly two) ancestral species, some 800 species evolved by island-hopping speciation, perhaps starting on the now-submerged Emperor Seamounts, to the northwest of the Hawaiian Archipelago, 70 million years ago when they occupied the same location as the present Hawaiian Islands. Drosophila species now occupy a range of habitats on all the Hawaiian Islands and feed on items including rotting fruit and leaves, tree sap, and fungi. True fruit flies (family Tephritidae) typically lay eggs on fruit still attached to the plant. This group contains introduced agricultural pests (Mediterranean, Oriental, and melon fruit flies) as well as many unique endemic forms that are seed predators and gall formers. Obviously, proposed chemical control of pestiferous fruit flies in natural areas would threaten many closely related native insects including endemic drosophila species.

Some Hawaiian drosophila have evolved spectacular courtship displays; about 100 Hawaiian species are "giants," with nearly 1-in. wingspans. These giant picture wing flies have ornate wing and body patterns, enabling members of the same species to recognize each other before wasting too much time. Large body sizes (accompanied by loud buzzing noises) may also make them less vulnerable to bird predation than smaller insects, but larger size is probably primarily related to advantages in mating behavior.

Picture wing flies have received considerable study in Hawai'i, and much of the research has occurred in Park rain forests. Male flies set up breeding territories, called leks, away from their feeding areas, and females are attracted to these sites. Males engage in head-butting and wing-wrestling contests among themselves, but they dance elegantly when females appear. Stroking, touching, tasting, and even perfuming (with sexual attractants or pheromones) can accompany the dancing, wing-fluttering, and/or buzzing by males. However, females really control mating through their reactions. Staged encounters between closely related species at laboratory "singles bars" have shown that courtship usually proceeds more readily when flies are "lonely," a situation likely to occur in derived rather than ancestral species in the island-hopping evolutionary marathon. Derived (lonely) populations start with a few colonizers, and mating rituals in these small populations usually lose complexity. Males from derived populations are rarely able to satisfy fussy females from the more plentiful ancestral populations, but females from derived populations usually accept ancestral males. (Perhaps males are just not as fussy wherever they are!)

The international importance of Hawai'i's picture wing flies in the study of evolution and island ecology cannot be overemphasized. Because these marvelous insects are found in tiny patches of habitat (foods and mating sites required are quite specific), they can easily be reduced to small numbers or eliminated by forest clearing, degradation, or introduced predators and parasites to which they are not adapted. Two species once found in the Park in wet forests (*D. heteroneura* and *D. sylvestris*) are no longer present. Today, numbers of many other species of picture wings in Hawai'i appear to be declining rapidly. A major cause may be the introduced western yellowjacket known to prey upon them. Effects of parasitoids (parasites of insects) have been little studied, but new species continually arrive with new host insects and also may reduce native insects to the point that populations become extinct. And the effects of human collectors on Hawai'i's invertebrates can no longer be ignored as quality habitat and populations shrink. In the case of our native invertebrates, what we don't know can hurt them -- and we humans are the poorer for it.

Predaceous or Grappler Caterpillars (*Eupithecia* spp.)

Butterfly and Moth order (Lepidoptera), Measuring Worm or Inchworm family (Geometridae)

Endemic

Distribution in the Park: Wet forests and shrublands

The inchworm family is a large one, with thousands of species on each continent. Caterpillars in this group move by holding on with three pairs of jointed front legs, hunching up the center of the body, and bringing two pairs of prolegs (unjointed posterior abdominal appendages) forward. The prolegs (which are not true legs) then anchor the caterpillar, and the body is extended forward to another anchor point. Inchworms have to move like this because they have lost the intermediate false body legs that allow most caterpillars to move slowly along without such acrobatics.

Inchworm caterpillars are slender, and their green, gray, or brown coloration mimics twigs and leaves, thereby reducing predation by birds and other animals. The brown grappler caterpillar (*Eupithecia stauro-phragma*) and the green grappler caterpillar (*E. orichloris*) are two species that can be found in the Park. The former uses sticks, and the latter leaf edges, for ambush perches. Geometrid moths (the adult stage of inchworms) also display brown or green camouflage coloration and blend with their surroundings with wings extended sideways, parallel to the surface on which they rest.

All but one of Hawai'i's 19 known species of *Eupithecia* (some are still being identified) capture active animal prey, which makes them different from all other geometrids -- and indeed from the 100,000 or so caterpillar species in the world. (The odd species [*E. monticolens*] in Hawai'i eats protein-rich pollen, a possible stage in the evolution from eating plant carbohydrates to animal protein.) Affectionately known as "pred leps" (for predaceous lepidopterans), Hawai'i's little (about 1 in. long) "ambush predators" use their camouflage not merely to avoid being eaten, but to lie inconspicuously in wait for flies, spiders, crickets, wasps, or anything palatable that moves. Anchored by the rear pairs of prolegs and sometimes backed into notches they carve out in leaves, these small animals strike when sensory bristles or setae on their rear ends are touched. About 0.1 second is required to catch an unsuspecting insect (often larger than the caterpillar) with the six elongated, talon-tipped front legs. Prey is devoured alive in a savage but natural spectacle unnoticed by most of us.

Adult geometrid moths lay about 100 eggs, which hatch in two weeks or so. The caterpillars split their skins in molting four times, and in each stage they emerge hungry. After the fourth molt they construct a cocoon and three weeks later appear as moths. Adults are very short-lived.

Look for these fierce miniature "dragons" on understory vegetation especially in wet forest areas in the Park. Predaceous caterpillars are often found on fern fronds and, because they are not herbivorous, are not closely dependent on any specific food plants. The pollen-eating forms can be found in the blossoms (lehua) of the 'ōhi'a. Remember, all members of this group are tiny and well camouflaged, so look carefully at twigs and leaves. After you have walked through the forest, you may even find one of these small predators on your arm, sizing you up!

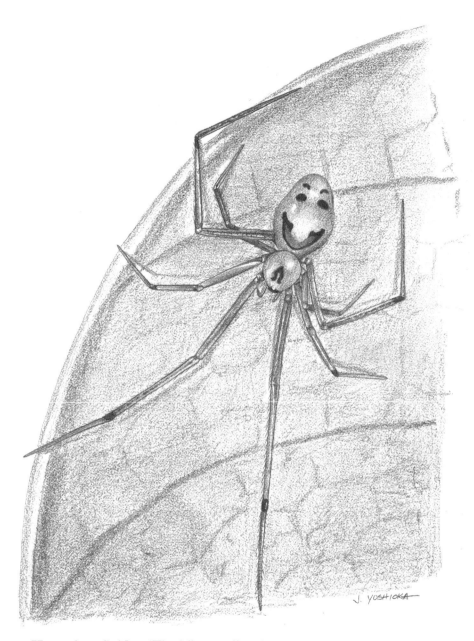

Happyface Spider (*Theridion grallator*)

Spider, Tick, Mite, Pseudoscorpion, and Scorpion class (Arachnida);
  Comb-footed Spider family (Theridiidae)

Endemic

Distribution in the Park: Wet forests at middle elevations

With translucent, yellowish bodies and red and black markings, these living smiley-buttons seem to say "Have a good day" to us humans. Many patterns other than comic faces appear on the abdomens of these small (less than 0.25 in.) spiders and may serve to camouflage them in sun and shadow to protect against predation by such forest birds as the common 'amakihi and Japanese white-eye.

Happyfaces live on the undersides of leaves of plants (such as kōpiko 'ula, kāwa'u, and pū'ahanui) in the forest. Females of this species care for their young for several weeks after eggs hatch, an unusual behavior pattern in spiders. Small flies and other insects that land on the top side of the leaf or that seek shelter under the leaf in the rain are stalked, lassoed with a sticky lariat, and fed to young happyfaces by these modern mothers, which earn their living and care for their young at the same time.

Happyface spiders were first scientifically described in 1900. No further study was done until 1972, when specimens with the "happyface" pattern were first found and the species began to be studied more closely. Since 1972, much new information on range, ecology, variable pattern morphology, and behavior has been obtained. Hawaiian happyface spiders now have become widely known among biologists and nonbiologists alike.

Recent studies suggest that this species is in the process of speciation. Not only do different populations look different, behavior is also variable to the point that male and female spiders from different areas may not breed when brought together by human matchmakers in the laboratory. Habitat differences among sites seem to result in morphological differences that reduce compatibility in the populations. Human disturbance of spider habitat through clearing of forests may also provide barriers that this not-so-mobile species can't cross, thus eliminating the genetic interchange needed to prevent divergence in form and function. Happyfaces, faced with habitat fragmentation, which separates populations, and rapid life cycles, may form new species within the time of a human lifespan.

SPECIAL RAIN FOREST SYSTEM:
PIT CRATERS

Pit craters are steep-sided depressions that form by collapse of the ground. Often surrounded by flat rims that allow close approach, they afford exciting views of inaccessible terrain in sparsely vegetated areas. Many pit craters along Chain of Craters Road and near Mauna Loa and Kīlauea Rift zones provide the visitor with readily observable examples of volcanic phenomena.

Equally dramatic, but of biological interest as well, are various pit craters located in rain forest vegetation throughout the Park. Pit craters near Nahuku (Thurston Lava Tube) are the most easily visited, but many other examples are present in remote rain forest along the East Rift, in 'Ola'a Forest, and elsewhere. Most pit craters are not noted on maps, and probably some await discovery. Because of their steep sides, pit craters have been less disturbed by feral pigs, hikers, and hunters than surrounding areas; vegetation on the floors and sides of the craters may thus provide a good idea of what wet forests were once like. However, dense vegetation, including the native uluhe fern, may prevent easy viewing of the crater floor, so be careful!

Plants sensitive to pig disturbance and those that grow best in shaded, moist habitats are usually more prevalent in pit craters, perhaps partly because of a more favorable microclimate as well as reduced disturbance. Species that once grew more abundantly on the ground before decades of feral pig disturbance are often found in these protected places in surprisingly high numbers, and some plants are unusually large. Sensitive species such as small ferns, liverworts, mosses, fragile mints and orchids, lobelioids, the brittle-stemmed 'ilihia (*Cyrtandra platyphylla*), and the native lily pa'iniu (*Astelia menziesiana*) are among the plants that are seen in pit craters relatively undisturbed by pigs.

Over the years, even large and dominant tree ferns (*Cibotium* spp.) may be affected by feral pigs, as shown in a study conducted in two pit craters and surrounding forest near Nahuku. Tree ferns were found to grow more densely in the craters than in surrounding areas. Tree ferns are a favorite food of introduced pigs, which are known to knock down even sizeable specimens for their starchy cores. As numbers of these dominant plants decline, the forest understory is opened to more sunlight, precluding the survival of shade-tolerant native species. Light-loving alien plants may then invade, changing the very composition of the forest so that it differs considerably from that still evident in some protected pit craters.

UPLAND FORESTS AND WOODLANDS

UPLAND FORESTS AND WOODLANDS

The upper-elevation lands of Hawaii Volcanoes National Park consist of a strip stretching upslope from south of Kīpuka Puaulu near 4,000 ft elevation to the summit of Mauna Loa at 13,677 ft. This strip on the eastern slope of Mauna Loa encompasses three major ecological zones (upland forests and woodlands, subalpine, and alpine/aeolian) and many different vegetation types. The upland forests and woodlands of Mauna Loa Strip include Kīpuka Puaulu and extend to the top of Mauna Loa Strip Road (6,700 ft elevation) where woodlands grade into subalpine vegetation. Mauna Loa Strip was added to the Park in 1927, primarily as a connecting corridor between Kīlauea Caldera and the summit of Mauna Loa. At the time of its establishment (as Hawaii National Park with Haleakalā National Park), Hawaii Volcanoes was viewed primarily as a geological park, and the importance of its biological resources was not fully recognized. Bordered by ranches on the east and west, today the forest and woodland vegetation of Mauna Loa Strip sharply contrasts with the open pastures just outside the Park boundary.

The climate of Mauna Loa Strip is drier than that of the rain forests just a short distance downslope and to the east. The upland zone has a seasonal climate, with a dry period typically occurring for several months during the summer; the months of July, August, and September often have little rain. Mean annual rainfall ranges from approximately 60 in. at 4,000 ft elevation to less than 40 in. near the upper elevational limit of the zone. Mean annual temperatures in the zone fall between 50 and 60°F. Frost typically occurs during the winter only at the upper reaches of this zone. Frost and even snow are infrequent occurrences as low as Park headquarters.

The interface of Mauna Loa and Kīlauea volcanoes is just south of Kīpuka Puaulu. All the flows of Mauna Loa Strip originate from Mauna Loa. Substrates of the upland forest and woodland zone range from ancient deep ash soils to lava flows with little soil development. The oldest flows of the region are over 4,000 years old; these include the bedrock beneath the deep ash soils of Kīpuka Puaulu and Kīpuka Kī and substrates of several other kīpuka along Mauna Loa Strip Road. Most of the lavas of the upland zone are dated between 750 and 4,000 years. The most recent lava flows here are late prehistoric 'a'ā of the massive Ke'āmoku flow; the Strip Road crosses the youngest lobe of this flow at about 5,600 ft. Soil development is greatest in the lower part of Mauna Loa Strip, where Kīpuka Puaulu and Kīpuka Kī have layers of ash soil greater than 20 ft deep. Most soils above 5,000 ft elevation are shallow, discontinuous ash deposits over weathered pāhoehoe lava.

Vegetation of the upland forests and woodlands varies considerably with substrate age and soil depth. The most diverse and well-developed forests of the zone are found in Kīpuka Puaulu and Kīpuka Kī. These islands of old soil support the only protected koa/a'e/'ōhi'a (*Acacia koa/Sapindus saponaria/Metrosideros polymorpha*) forests in the State. The understory of Kīpuka Puaulu contains more than 20 species of native trees and shrubs, including several candidate Endangered Species and other species that are rare or absent elsewhere in the Park. Open patches now invaded by alien grasses and blackberry (*Rubus argutus*) may be the result of grazing by cattle (*Bos taurus*) earlier this century, or they may have been natural openings created by fires in the distant past. Surrounding these old kīpuka forests are more recent substrates supporting less diverse open forests of either 'ōhi'a or koa.

Upslope of Kīpuka Kī, koa is the sole dominant canopy tree of most upland forests. Where substrates are older, koa trees are tall and have an understory of 'a'ali'i (*Dodonaea viscosa*) in a tree form. However, the most prevalent vegetation of the Park's upland zone is a woodland composed of a mosaic of groves of koa trees, shrublands, and grasslands; this type of vegetation has often been called "mountain parkland" or "koa parkland." Dominant shrubs are 'a'ali'i and pūkiawe (*Styphelia tameiameiae*), but 'ōhelo (*Vaccinium reticulatum*) and kūkaenēnē (*Coprosma ernodeoides*) are also common. Dense stands of native shrubs predominate on rocky sites; grasslands are interspersed among koa groves and shrublands. Above 5,000 ft elevation, the native bunchgrass *Deschampsia nubigena* is the dominant plant of grass communities. Other commonly seen grasses are the endemic mountain pili (*Panicum tenuifolium*), and alien species such as velvet grass (*Holcus lanatus*) and sweet vernalgrass (*Anthoxanthum odoratum*). Although they provide little ground cover, the nonnative herbs gosmore (*Hypochoeris radicata*), a yellow-flowered dandelion relative, and sheep sorrel (*Rumex acetosella*) are nearly ubiquitous in upland grasslands. Grasslands below 5,000 ft elevation are often composed of alien grasses; dallis grass (*Paspalum dilatatum*), Vasey grass (*P. urvillei*), and kikuyu (*Pennisetum clandestinum*) are particularly abundant in open sites, and meadow ricegrass (*Ehrharta stipoides*) usually covers the ground beneath koa groves.

Lava flows from Mauna Loa cross the upper reaches of this zone and separate older substrates covered by koa woodland into two large kīpuka that extend upslope into the subalpine zone. Ranging from several hundred to several thousand years in age, some lava flows appear nearly barren, while others support scattered 'ōhi'a trees and native shrubs, ferns, and sedges. Few alien plants thrive under the harsh conditions on these upland flows.

The upland zone (and the lower portion of the subalpine zone) of Mauna Loa Strip contains the greatest densities of native birds of any of the Park's major ecological zones. While 'apapane (*Himatione sanguinea*) and common 'amakihi (*Hemignathus virens*) are widespread in several Park zones, they are particularly abundant in the Park's uplands. The 'i'iwi (*Vestiaria coccinea*) seems to have undergone a range reduction in both the upland forests and the rain forests in the Park in the last several decades but remains relatively common above 5,000 ft elevation in the Strip. 'Elepaio (*Chasiempis sandwichensis*) are heard frequently in Mauna Loa woodlands and may still be seen along the trail in Kīpuka Puaulu.

Although it is commonly referred to as "Bird Park," Kīpuka Puaulu is not a particularly good site to view native birds. While 'apapane are seasonally common in the canopies of the very tall 'ōhi'a trees scattered throughout the Kīpuka, most of the birds seen and heard there today are introduced species, such as the house finch (*Carpodacus mexicanus*), red-billed leiothrix (*Leiothrix lutea*), hwamei or melodious laughing thrush (*Garrulax canorus*), northern cardinal (*Cardinalis cardinalis*), nutmeg mannikin (*Lonchura punctulata*), and the ubiquitous Japanese white-eye (*Zosterops japonicus*). Groups of kalij pheasant (*Lophura leucomelana*) are frequently seen foraging in the underbrush along Kīpuka Puaulu Trail; kalij pheasants are also the most abundant gamebird of the koa woodlands along Mauna Loa Strip Road, where they seem to congregate, particularly in the early morning. The koa forests and woodlands of the upland zone were the former habitat of the Endangered 'ākepa (*Loxops coccineus*), 'akiapōlā'au (*Hemignathus munroi*), and Hawai'i creeper (*Oreomystis mana*); the Endangered nēnē (*Branta sandvicensis*) and 'io or Hawaiian hawk (*Buteo solitarius*) may still be seen in this section of the Park.

The upland forests and woodlands are notable for the many endemic insect species that may still be found there. The Kamehameha butterfly (*Vanessa tameamea*) and Blackburn butterfly (*Udara blackburni*), although also numerous in other zones, are perhaps the most prominent insects of the upland woodlands, which contain an abundance of their host plants (māmaki [*Pipturus albidus*] and koa). Both these butterflies are also found at lower elevations in areas where their native host plants still occur. Less-noticeable species of native moths occur in the native vegetation of the uplands; their larvae, along with the larvae of endemic long-horned beetles (family Cerambycidae), are critical elements in the diets of many native birds, particularly during the breeding season. Kīpuka Puaulu and Kīpuka Kī are home to many native insects, including two species of pomace flies found almost nowhere else: *Drosophila engyochracea* and *D. mimica* are Hawai'i Island endemics restricted to areas supporting their host plant a'e or soapberry (*Sapindus saponaria*). While abundant in these two Park kīpuka forests, a'e is extremely rare elsewhere on the Island. The rotting fruits and bark of the a'e are essential to the successful reproduction of these native flies.

The Park's upland forests and woodlands are a living demonstration of the ability of native ecosystems to recover after disturbance. Most of Mauna Loa Strip was grazed by cattle for decades before its incorporation into Hawaii Volcanoes National Park. Kīpuka Puaulu was fenced to exclude cattle before 1930, but grazing continued to be permitted elsewhere in the Strip until 1940. Cattle were removed when it was recognized that they were preventing koa regeneration and damaging the forests of the Park. Grazing resumed during World War II, but cattle were finally eliminated in 1948, and today boundary fences keep cattle from adjacent ranches out of the Park. Feral goats (*Capra hircus*) have also impacted vegetation of Mauna Loa Strip. The effects of goats on reproduction of koa and māmane (*Sophora chrysophylla*) have been studied, but their impacts on rare plants and biodiversity have not been well documented in the Park. Goats were excluded from the Strip below 6,800 ft by a fence constructed in the

1970s, and by the early 1980s the enclosed area was goat-free. Recovery of native vegetation since has been remarkable, and there is evidence that the associated native insect fauna is also increasing. For example, *Drosophila hawaiiensis*, a picture wing fly that breeds on koa, probably has become more numerous since the 1970s.

Feral pigs (*Sus scrofa*) were the last ungulates (hoofed mammals) to be removed from Mauna Loa Strip. Although they were present in low densities, their repeated digging in Park grasslands favored alien grasses over the native bunchgrasses. In the mid-1980s, boundary fences were made pig-proof, cross fences were built above Kīpuka Kī and near 5,000 ft elevation, and pigs were eradicated by hunting and trapping.

Fire caused by humans has also been a perturbation in upland woodlands; in 1975 a wildfire burned more than 2,000 acres between Kīpuka Kī and 5,000 ft elevation (including pastureland on the adjacent ranch). Although shrub species composition was altered and some alien grasses probably increased because of the fire, koa regenerated well, and today the lower part of Mauna Loa Strip supports thick stands of young, vigorously growing koa.

The upland forests and woodlands are accessible to the visitor along Mauna Loa Strip Road, which bisects Kīpuka Kī, encounters most of the zone's vegetation types, and ends near the upland forests and woodlands/ subalpine interface.

Koa (*Acacia koa*)

Pea family (Fabaceae)

Endemic to the Hawaiian Islands

Distribution in the Park: Moist kīpuka forests and moist to dry woodlands
of Mauna Loa Strip; also planted in the Kīlauea Caldera region

Koa is one of the best-known native tree species. In old Hawai'i, koa logs were highly valued for use as canoe hulls. Today, the beautiful wood is made into fine furniture, paneling, bowls, and many other handcrafted articles. The high value of koa wood products and the scarcity of koa forests for commercial logging lead many people to think that koa is rare or Endangered. In fact, koa occurs on six of the Hawaiian Islands and is still relatively common in undeveloped upland habitats of Hawai'i Island, but unlogged koa/'ōhi'a wet forests supporting the tall, straight-trunked koa trees preferred by loggers are extremely rare. Almost all of the lowland koa forest of Hawai'i and Maui was logged in the 19th century, and most high-elevation koa forests and woodlands on Hawai'i Island have been converted to cattle ranches.

The Mauna Loa section of the Park is one of the few places where koa woodlands and forests are protected from cattle grazing, logging, and the depredations of feral ungulates. In Kīpuka Puaulu and Kīpuka Kī, deep ash soil allows koa to reach heights of nearly 100 ft. At higher elevations, substrates are shallower soils over lava, and koa trees are shorter and more branched. Only one stand of very tall straight-trunked rain forest koa occurs in the Park, in a remote kīpuka within 'Ola'a Forest, far from roads or trails.

Young koa trees have whitish gray, smooth bark, but as the tree ages the bark darkens to orange-brown, roughens, and becomes longitudinally furrowed. Two types of leaves may be seen on koa. Seedlings, young saplings, and some branches on mature trees bear compound leaves with many tiny, soft-textured leaflets arranged opposite one another on about eight pinnae (leaf divisions). The "leaves" of mature trees and older saplings are curved, sickle-shaped, thick-textured phyllodes, which are not true leaves but modified flattened petioles or leaf stalks. Koa saplings about a year old often display leaf forms intermediate between the juvenile compound true leaf and the mature phyllodes; these have leaflets at their tips and partially flattened petioles at their bases. Other members of the genus *Acacia* (which contains more than 1,200 species worldwide) also have this leaf dimorphism, which probably evolved as an adaptation for drought conditions. Studies of Hawaiian koa leaves and phyllodes have indicated that the mature "leaf" form is better at controlling water loss than is the juvenile form. The greater surface area of the juvenile leaf form may be an advantage under the shaded conditions of the forest floor, where many koa seedlings start life. The Hawaiian species of koa seems to be related to other *Acacia* species from Australia and islands of the Indian Ocean, which also bear phyllodes as their adult foliage.

Flowers of koa are clustered in round, cream-colored or pale yellowish heads less than 0.5 in. wide, arranged in branched inflorescences arising from leaf axils. These appear in the winter and spring, with flowering commencing at lower elevations and reaching the higher regions by late spring. Fruits are flattened pods, from 3 to 12 in. long when mature. When dry, the pods split open lengthwise to release shiny, dark brown, flattened seeds. Pods are most conspicuous on koa trees in the late summer and fall (August-October).

Koa is a fast-growing species and like many other legumes can fix or capture atmospheric nitrogen. Seedlings, suckers, and foliage are palatable to grazing and browsing animals, such as cattle and goats. Much of Mauna Loa Strip was used for cattle grazing, even after its addition to the Park in 1927. By the 1940s the koa parkland was open, with scattered old trees and little reproduction of young plants. Alien pasture grasses became established in the heavily grazed areas, and trampling by cattle resulted in opening up the forest understory and damaging the shallow root systems of koa. Cattle were permanently removed from the Park in 1948, and goats were excluded by the early 1980s, allowing koa to successfully regenerate. A large and intense fire was ignited accidentally in the lower portion of the Strip in 1975; this fire burned more than 2,000 acres of the koa woodlands and pasture. However, koa is one of the few native tree species that responds positively to fire. Fire stimulated koa to produce suckers or shoots from shallow roots. Seed germination may also have been enhanced. Today, areas formerly burned are covered by koa groves with dense stands of young trees, often with a large old individual or dead stump in the center.

The ability of koa to recover from feral ungulate browsing and fire is encouraging to Park managers, whose aim is the preservation of native species in naturally functioning systems. Koa is a keystone species for a large part of the Park's Mauna Loa Strip. It is extremely important as a host plant and food source for native invertebrates, including many species of endemic moths, the koa bug, endemic yellow-faced bees, and wood-boring beetles. Insects and their larvae, in turn, are a critical item in the diet of native forest birds, particularly during the period of breeding and raising young. The success of koa as a forest dominant thus provides for the continued existence of a complex web of native organisms.

J. YOSHIOKA

A'e, Mānele, or Soapberry (*Sapindus saponaria*)

Soapberry family (Sapindaceae)

Indigenous to Hawai'i Island; also native to South America, Mexico, Africa, and other Pacific islands

Distribution in the Park: Kīpuka Puaulu, Kīpuka Kī, and nearby slopes of Mauna Loa

The a'e or soapberry is one of the tallest trees in the moist forests of Kīpuka Puaulu and Kīpuka Kī, where it is a codominant with koa and 'ōhi'a. In these ancient ash substrates, a'e trees may achieve heights greater than 80 ft and trunk diameters of more than 4 ft. While the spreading canopy of the a'e is often far above the forest floor, the tree may be recognized by its light-colored, scaly bark, which peels off the trunk in large irregular plates.

Unlike most native Hawaiian trees, the a'e is strongly deciduous in the winter, when the floor of the kīpuka forests and adjacent trails and roads are littered with its fallen yellow leaves. By late winter or early spring, new, bright green leaves emerge throughout the canopy. When mature, leaves are dark green and compound with long, curved, sharp-tipped leaflets. Tiny flowers are borne in large inflorescences, often high in the canopy. These develop into clusters of round, fleshy fruits, which are conspicuous only when the leaves fall in the winter. Just under 1 in. in diameter, a'e fruits are shiny green when young and dark brown when mature. In other lands where this tree occurs, a soap-like substance is obtained from the pulp of the fruit, but the early Hawaiians had more suitable plants (*e.g.*, shampoo ginger) for this purpose in the lowland areas they inhabited.

In the partial shade of the kīpuka forests, the a'e produces many seedlings and saplings. Leaves of young plants are also compound but have a winged central rachis (leaflet stem) not found on mature trees. Saplings grow slowly and are unable to establish themselves in areas with a heavy ground cover of alien grasses (for example, between Kīpuka Puaulu and Kīpuka Kī).

The forests of Kīpuka Puaulu and Kīpuka Kī are perhaps the most botanically diverse in the Park. Early in the century, Kīpuka Puaulu contained 40 native species of trees and shrubs. While many of these have been lost through years of cattle grazing and the depredations of feral goats and pigs, this kīpuka remains the habitat of several candidate Endangered plant species and many others rare in the younger forests of the edge of Kīlauea Caldera. The combination of koa, a'e, and 'ōhi'a as canopy dominants is an extremely rare vegetation type in Hawai'i and occurs outside the Park only on the slopes of Hualālai, the volcano of the kona (leeward) side of Hawai'i Island.

Māmane (*Sophora chrysophylla*)

Pea family (Fabaceae)

Endemic to the Hawaiian Islands

Distribution in the Park: Subalpine shrublands, koa woodlands of Mauna Loa, upland kīpuka forests, rain forests, and mid-elevation woodlands

    After koa and the almost ubiquitous ʻōhiʻa, māmane is perhaps the most important native tree in many Hawaiian plant communities. On older substrates of Mauna Kea and in the saddle between Mauna Kea and Mauna Loa, māmane is the dominant tree of upper-elevation forests. Māmane is not dominant in any forests within the Park, even though it is a component of many vegetation types between 1,000 and 8,000 ft elevation.

Although it may grow taller than 50 ft in rich moist-forest habitats, māmane is usually a small tree with a rounded, spreading canopy. Its bark is strongly furrowed in old trees but merely knobby in young individuals. Leaves are compound with many round-tipped elliptical leaflets opposing each other on a central rachis (leaflet stem). Often young leaves and stem tips are clothed with soft golden hairs. When in flower, māmane trees are dramatically beautiful, bearing an abundance of bright yellow, curved flowers. These flowers produce sweet nectar, which is an important food source for native honeycreepers such as 'i'iwi and 'apapane. Māmane nectar may be especially important during times when 'ōhi'a lehua blossoms are scarce. The fruits that develop from pollinated flowers are long, narrow, winged pods with constrictions between the seeds. These persist on māmane trees after they mature and turn brown. Māmane seeds are bright yellow-orange and have a very hard seed coat. This probably serves to ensure that germination will not occur until heavy rains wash the seeds over rock or cinders and abrade or scarify them.

The wood of māmane is very hard and was favored by Hawaiians for adz handles and farming implements such as digging sticks. Māmane wood was also used to make the runners of sleds (papa hōlua), which were run down specially constructed stone and earthen tracks in a popular sport of the ali'i (Hawaiian nobility). After the development of cattle ranching in the Hawaiian Islands, the durable wood of the māmane was used for fence posts. Even today, māmane wood is sought after as fuel for smoking meat.

Māmane, like 'a'ali'i and koa, is one of the few native Hawaiian plants that often survives fires and readily resprouts from the base. Increased numbers of māmane seedlings may also appear following fires. At several sites along the Chain of Craters and Hilina Pali roads, there are 'ōhi'a woodlands that have burned in fires caused either by lava flows, lightning strikes, or human carelessness. Where māmane was present before the fires, young vigorously-growing trees are now seen, a striking contrast to the dead, bleached skeletons of 'ōhi'a that succumbed to the flames.

While resistant to fires, māmane trees are vulnerable to the impacts of browsing by feral goats and sheep. Before the goat removal efforts of the 1970s and 1980s, these animals were abundant in montane forests of Mauna Loa Strip and mid-elevation woodlands near Hilina Pali and 'Ainahou Ranch. When feral animal populations were high, māmane reproduction was prevented; even mature māmane were killed by girdling when goats repeatedly fed on the inner bark. Today, feral sheep and goats are excluded by fences from the Park below 6,800 ft elevation, and boundary fences partially restrict the movement of ungulates into the Park at higher elevations. The abundant seedlings and young trees seen along the Strip Road are evidence that the māmane is recovering from the depredations of feral ungulates and will continue to play an important role in Park forests and woodlands.

Pāpala Kēpau (*Pisonia brunoniana*)

Four-o'clock family (Nyctaginaceae)

Indigenous to the Hawaiian Islands; also native to Australia,
New Zealand, and several South Pacific islands

Distribution in the Park: Kīpuka Kī, Kīpuka Puaulu, and ʻŌlaʻa Forest

Pāpala kēpau (formerly known as *Pisonia inermis*) is one of the most common understory trees of Kīpuka Kī and Kīpuka Puaulu of Mauna Loa Strip, but it is rarely seen elsewhere in the Park. Usually a small tree up to 20 ft tall, pāpala kēpau is often multitrunked from the base. Its bark is smooth, thin, and pale gray. The wood of pāpala kēpau is soft and brittle; the tree belongs to a primarily tropical family containing mostly herbs and shrubs, such as the common four-o'clock and bougainvillea, ornamentals introduced to Hawai'i.

Leaves of the pāpala kēpau are large, about 8 in. long, opposite on the stem, and have a shiny, smooth surface. Elliptical in shape, they are obscurely veined and often have pink-tinged petioles (leaf stalks). Individual flowers are small, white, and funnel shaped, with prominent ribs on the tiny, flared corolla tubes. They are borne in large, open clusters in the axils of leaves near branch tips. Pāpala kēpau flowers are most abundant in the spring and are followed by sticky fruits in the summer and fall. These dry, five-ribbed capsules about 1 in. long develop from the flowers. Ripe capsules are remarkable for their outer coating of incredibly sticky, mucilaginous glue.

Pāpala kēpau glue was used in old Hawai'i to enable bird catchers to capture native birds for their brightly colored feathers. Pāpala kēpau glue or "bird lime" was collected and spread upon potential bird perches on tree branches. When a bird landed on the sticky branch, it would be trapped, and its showy red or yellow feathers could be plucked for later use in feather capes or leis. It is uncertain whether birds were always killed during this plucking process. Some, like the now-extinct Hawai'i mamo, had only patches of bright yellow feathers, primarily on its rump, and conceivably could survive such selective feather plucking. Other birds, such as the 'i'iwi, have their entire bodies covered with intense scarlet feathers and could not have suffered the complete loss of their plumage and lived. Bird catchers may also have cooked and eaten birds after removing their feathers.

The pāpala kēpau tree sometimes catches birds even without human manipulation of its fruits. Small birds, particularly alien Japanese white-eyes or mejiro, occasionally blunder into a cluster of viscous, adhesive-covered pāpala kēpau fruits still on the tree and are unable to extricate themselves. Numerous insects are also trapped in the glue, and these may attract birds. Sticky fruits adhere to the feathers of larger birds and can be widely dispersed by birds that visit the tree and fly away.

Māmaki (*Pipturus albidus*)

Nettle family (Urticaceae)

Endemic to the Hawaiian Islands

Distribution in the Park: Moist forests and rain forests between 2,000 and 4,500 ft elevation, moist sheltered parts of open woodlands

Found on all the main Hawaiian Islands, māmaki (including plants formerly known as *Pipturus hawaiiensis*) is a shrub or small tree in the nettle family. All the Hawaiian members of this family, with one exception, are remarkable in lacking the stinging hairs that characterize this family on the U.S. Mainland and in other parts of the world. Although it is seen occasionally in open woodlands along the Chain of Craters and Hilina Pali roads and is distributed throughout most of the Park's rain forests, māmaki is most abundant in the moist forests of Kīpuka Puaulu and Kīpuka Kī. In these forests, māmaki forms dense thickets in the understory beneath 'ōhi'a, koa, and a'e or soapberry trees.

While usually a much-branched shrub, older māmaki may be single-trunked and more than 20 ft tall. The bark of māmaki is thin and bumpy, often of an orange hue. Leaves are usually ovate and are extremely variable in size, ranging from 2 to 16 in. long. In sunny exposed areas, plants often bear small leaves, but māmaki in shady forest understories usually have leaves at least 8 in. long and 6 in. wide. Māmaki leaves are typically thick and dull green, with a rough texture above and a covering of short white or gray hairs beneath. Leaf margins are prominently toothed and leaf veins are conspicuous, particularly on the undersides. Sometimes leaf veins, midribs, and petioles are purplish red, but this coloration is quite variable.

The tiny, unisexual flowers of the māmaki are borne in small clusters on the stem at leaf bases, with both male and female flowers on the same plant. Tiny seedlike māmaki fruits develop embedded in fleshy white masses closely adhering to stem branches. These fleshy aggregations of fruits are attractive to birds but are tasteless and of little value as human food. They were used medicinally by Hawaiians to treat children's mouth infections and to dress wounds.

Other parts of the māmaki plant were also useful in old Hawai'i. Leaves were collected and dried for use as a medicinal tea (as they are today). The most important use of māmaki was as a source of fiber to make kapa (tapa) or bark cloth. Although māmaki was not cultivated like the wauke or paper mulberry introduced by Polynesians, it was apparently highly sought-after as a fiber source, particularly on the island of Hawai'i. The inner bark was stripped from māmaki stems and branches and was pounded to cause the fibers to felt together. The resulting dull-colored kapa cloth was strong, but it could not be washed.

Two other endemic members of the nettle family occur in the Park; both resemble the māmaki, with rough, prominently-veined leaves. Olonā is a sprawling shrub restricted to rain forests, and ōpuhe is a small tree found sparingly in both wet and moist forests of the Park. Both of these species were also used by Hawaiians for their fiber. Olonā fibers could be made into strong rope, and ōpuhe bark was used to make fish nets.

Māmaki, and to a lesser extent olonā and ōpuhe, are the host plants of the colorful native Kamehameha butterfly. The larvae of this and other butterflies and moths feed upon māmaki leaves, leaving irregular holes. Evidence of their feeding can always be seen along the trail at Kīpuka Puaulu, but the green caterpillars are more difficult to spot. On sunny days, the bright orange, black-and-white-spotted Kamehameha butterflies (illustrated) can often be seen fluttering around māmaki thickets.

J. YOSHIOKA

Blackberry (*Rubus argutus*) **and 'Ākala or
  Hawaiian Raspberry** (*R. hawaiensis*)

Rose family (Rosaceae)

Alien (Blackberry); **Endemic** to the Hawaiian Islands ('Ākala)

Distribution in the Park: Mauna Loa Strip, Kīpuka Kī,
  Kīpuka Puaulu, woodlands and open areas near Kīlauea Caldera
  and upper Chain of Craters (Blackberry); Kīpuka Puaulu, Mauna Loa Strip,
  and 'Ōla'a Forest ('Ākala)

252

After the native 'ōhelo berry, the blackberry (formerly known as *Rubus penetrans*) is perhaps the most sought-after fruit in Hawaii Volcanoes National Park. While useful for its tasty fruit, this alien shrub may displace native plants in open forests and shrublands at middle elevations. Introduced to Hawai'i around 1900 from the eastern United States, blackberry quickly escaped cultivation and has spread widely on at least four of the Hawaiian Islands. In the Park, blackberry is most abundant in the koa woodlands and kīpuka forests of Mauna Loa Strip, but the plant may also be seen in disturbed or open areas along the rim of Kīlauea Caldera and upper Chain of Craters. Scattered small individuals may also be found in rain forests of Kīlauea and 'Ōla'a. As early as the 1930s, this plant was recognized as a potential pest in the Park.

A sprawling, viny shrub, the blackberry has green or reddish stems covered with stout, curved spines. Leaves are palmately compound with three to five toothed leaflets. During the winter, many of the leaves of blackberry turn bronze or red and are dropped; bright green new leaves appear in the spring. Flowers are more than 1 in. broad with five white petals and a central cluster of stamens and pistils (reproductive structures in flowers). Flowering is heaviest in the spring and early summer, but a few flowers may be seen at other times of the year. Heaviest fruit production is in the summer, when clusters of oblong, aggregate fruits (not true berries) are borne at branch tips. These aggregate fruits are composed of many fused carpels or sections of the female part of the flower, each with two flattened, rough seeds. Fruits change from green to red to black as they develop and ripen. Birds, both alien and native, relish the fruits and are effective at spreading blackberry.

In the Park, the worst infestations of this plant are in Kīpuka Kī and Kīpuka Puaulu, where large impenetrable thickets occur and inhibit native species reproduction. Higher on Mauna Loa Strip, blackberry is abundant primarily near the road and has not been greatly successful at displacing the dominant pūkiawe and 'a'ali'i of the largely native shrublands. Blackberry probably moved into the two kīpuka forests and adjacent woodlands when they were being grazed by cattle, an activity that ended in the 1930s and 1940s. While blackberry is often thought of as an early successional species replaced soon after disturbance ends, it continues to occupy large areas in the two kīpuka forests even 50 years after removal of grazing animals. Mechanical control of large blackberry patches is impossible, so the Park is testing herbicides for use against the pest. Removal of blackberry stimulates native understory species, and tree shade reduces the chance of blackberry reinvasion.

A native raspberry species (*R. hawaiensis*) is also found in Kīpuka Puaulu and at scattered localities of Mauna Loa Strip. This Hawaiian raspberry or 'ākala is an upright shrub with stems sometimes prickly and sometimes smooth. Leaves are three-parted and softly hairy. Flowers have dark pink petals and a central cluster of many yellow stamens. Fruits are large, red to purple when ripe, and tart rather than sweet to the taste. Although uncommon in the Park, 'ākala may be seen at the beginning of Mauna Loa Trail and along the loop trail of Kīpuka Puaulu.

Maile (*Alyxia oliviformis*)

Dogbane family (Apocynaceae)

Endemic to the Hawaiian Islands

Distribution in the Park: Kīpuka Puaulu, Kīpuka Kī, rain forests of
ʻŌlaʻa and Kīlauea's East Rift, mid-elevation woodlands

A woody vine or liana in the same family as the cultivated ornamental plumeria, maile is perhaps best known as a favored lei-making material. The crushed foliage and bark of maile are extremely fragrant, with a long-lasting perfume like freshly cut grass. This quality has been appreciated by Hawaiians since ancient times, and maile is still popular as a lei for special occasions such as weddings, anniversaries, and graduations. Maile leis are made from the young green shoots of the vine, after the bark and attached leaves are stripped from the central woody core of the branch. Since collecting (particularly if repeated frequently) may be destructive to the vine and surrounding plants, and because little maile occurs as distinct patches in the more accessible parts of the Park, no harvesting is allowed within Hawaii Volcanoes.

Maile is a climbing vine, woody at the base and green at the tips. In shady closed-canopy forests, the vine twines on trees and tree ferns and may grow to heights greater than 20 ft. In open, more sunny areas, maile has a more shrubby habit and may form viny thickets. Maile leaves are arranged opposite one another or in whorls of three. They are usually thick, shiny dark green above, and a duller pale green beneath. The leaves of maile are amazingly variable in size and shape, ranging from tiny and round to long and narrow, with most common forms elliptic or ovate. Because of the great variability in leaf morphology and the predominance of some leaf forms in distinct geographical localities, 13 different forms of maile were named in the past, but none are currently given formal taxonomic status.

Two slightly different leaf forms of maile may be seen in Hawaii Volcanoes. Maile of the rain forest has a large leaf to 3 in. long, with a distinct rounded ovate shape and a long pointed tip. This form has been called by Hawaiians "maile lau nui." Maile of the drier forests and more open woodlands at low and high elevations has a small, thick leaf with an elliptical shape (maile lau li'i).

The tubular flowers of maile are easily overlooked, as they are tiny (only 0.25 in. long) and dull yellow. Fruits are fleshy with a hard covering over one seed; these are borne either singly or in jointed chains with narrow constrictions. Fruits are hard and green when immature but ripen to a shiny black. Individual vines or patches of maile are scattered along the loop trail in Kīpuka Puaulu. Other localities where maile may be encountered are Kīpuka Kī, 'Ola'a Forest, rain forests between Makaopuhi and Nāpau craters, and along Kalapana Trail.

Bracken Fern (*Pteridium aquilinum* **var.** *decompositum*)

Hypolepidaceae

Indigenous at the species level

Distribution in the Park: Dry grasslands, shrublands, and woodlands
  between 2,000 and 8,000 ft elevation

Bracken fern is a familiar sight to Park visitors from the U.S. Mainland. The species is widespread in North America and occurs from temperate regions to the tropics. Some botanists consider the bracken fern of Hawai'i to be a distinct species, *P. decompositum*. In Hawaii Volcanoes National Park, bracken grows primarily in moist to dry, sunny or partly shaded habitats. It is a common plant in nonnative grasslands above Hilina Pali and occurs scattered throughout the mid-elevation 'ōhi'a woodlands. The fern is abundant in grassy openings in both Kīpuka Puaulu and Kīpuka Kī and is an important component of ground cover in the grasslands and shrublands of Mauna Loa Strip. Bracken fern's distribution extends into the subalpine zone, but at these higher elevations the plant is low in stature and scattered in occurrence.

A large terrestrial fern, bracken has fronds that may exceed a yard in length and are typically divided three times (tripinnate). Fronds are triangular, firm textured, and have undersides covered with soft, light brown hairs when young. When fertile, the spore-bearing structures are found in a line along the margins of the ultimate leaf divisions, and the edge of the leaf curls protectively over them. The frond stalks, or stipes, and frond axes are hairless, shiny, and yellow or straw-colored; the actual stem or rhizome of the fern is long and narrow and runs just under the soil surface. These fern rhizomes were a favorite food of feral pigs before these mammals were removed from Mauna Loa Strip in the early 1980s. Before their removal, pigs would greatly disrupt grassland vegetation by digging and uprooting plants in their search for fern rhizomes, grass roots, and earthworms.

Bracken fern is one of the few native Hawaiian plants that shows a distinct seasonality. Fronds turn brown and die back to the ground every winter, although the underground stem or rhizome remains alive. In the early spring, bright green fiddleheads emerge from the ground and slowly unfurl into young fern fronds. By late summer or early fall, fronds are mature, and a few have already begun to turn brown.

Bracken fern is a hardy native plant, capable of withstanding fire, pig digging, and cattle grazing. It is one of the few native plants that appears to compete well with alien grasses in the seasonal 'ōhi'a woodlands above Hilina Pali. Despite the use of its habitat by cattle, feral pigs, and feral goats, bracken is one of the most abundant ferns in the Park, exceeded in number and area covered only by uluhe and tree ferns.

Bracken fern is also known by the nonspecific Hawaiian name kilau, used for several different fern species.

Palapalai (*Microlepia strigosa*)

Dennstaedtiaceae

Indigenous to the Hawaiian Islands; also native to India, Malaysia, Taiwan, Japan, and South Pacific islands

Distribution in the Park: Rain forests above 1,500 ft elevation and upper-elevation moist forests

While not as abundant as tree ferns, uluhe, or bracken fern, palapalai is perhaps the most sought-after fern in the Park. The softly hairy, lacy fronds of this medium-sized terrestrial fern are often used to make leis to encircle the heads, wrists, and ankles of hula dancers. Every spring, just before the Merry Monarch Dance Festival in Hilo, a number of hula hālau (dance group) members visit the Park to collect palapalai fronds to fashion into decorations for dancers of the hula kahiko (Hawaiian hula in the ancient style). The Merry Monarch competition is held in honor of King Kalākaua, known for his patronage of Hawaiian dance and culture during the late 19th century. While the hula competition is an important annual event on the Island and collection of palapalai (after obtaining a permit) is an accepted cultural practice in the Park, the focus of fern-picking on the accessible patches of palapalai near roads in Kīpuka Kī can be locally disruptive to the native ground cover of this rare koa/aʻe/ʻōhiʻa forest.

Large, nonnative plants capable of overtopping native ground cover are probably a more serious threat than picking to the continued expansion of the palapalai. Two alien species, Jerusalem cherry, introduced as an ornamental shrub, and blackberry (discussed earlier), introduced for its edible fruit, are particularly abundant in the understory of Kīpuka Kī. Jerusalem cherry has been in the Park more than 50 years and was probably spread by fruit-eating birds from nearby ornamental plantings.

Despite competition from weeds and use by people, palapalai is in no danger of disappearing from the Park; it is a widespread species tolerant of a broad range of moisture and shade conditions. Palapalai is found in rain forests of Kīlauea Caldera and ʻOlaʻa Forest, but in such shady, very wet areas, the fern grows only as scattered individuals. It is in the moist, biologically diverse forests of Kīpuka Puaulu and Kīpuka Kī that this fern is most abundant, growing in large, dense stands beneath the relatively open canopy of tall native trees.

Typically from 1 to 3 ft tall, palapalai plants are composed of arching, light green fronds covered with soft white hairs. Palapalai fronds are usually divided three times (tripinnate), and the ultimate leaf divisions are less than 0.1 in. wide. The lobes of the smallest leaf divisions bear the spores of the fern in small, round clusters partially covered by a round membrane. The frond stalk or stipe is smooth and yellow or straw-colored; the actual stem of the fern is an underground rhizome. This creeping underground stem allows the fern to spread vegetatively, and undisturbed patches can grow laterally to cover large areas in suitable habitat. This rhizomatous growth habit makes palapalai resilient after disturbance and allows the fern to easily hold its own against most invading alien plants. This beautiful indigenous fern is not easily displaced and with minimal protection will continue to grace the forest floors of Park kīpuka.

Deschampsia nubigena **and Velvet Grass** (*Holcus lanatus*)

Grass family (Poaceae)

Endemic to the Hawaiian Islands (*Deschampsia*);
  Alien (Velvet Grass)

Distribution in the Park: Grasslands, shrublands, and some forests
  between 3,000 and 8,000 ft elevation

Most of the common grasses seen in the Park are accidentally introduced species not native to Hawai'i. An exception to this general rule is the endemic bunchgrass *Deschampsia nubigena* (formerly known as *D. australis*); this native is the most common grass seen above 5,000 ft elevation in the Park. *Deschampsia* is also found occasionally in the 'ōhi'a forests of Kīlauea Caldera and along Chain of Craters Road to about 3,000 ft.

A large grass, often 2 to 4 ft tall, *D. nubigena* grows in distinct clumps or bunches made up of narrow, stiffly erect leaves, each about a foot long. Leaves are typically folded over or rolled and thus appear round in cross section. Each grass clump usually contains a great deal of dead gray-colored material, leaf litter from previous years. The tiny flowers of *Deschampsia* are borne in large, erect inflorescences, which are held far above the grass clump on a stout stalk. These pyramid-shaped inflorescences are composed of many flowers attached to the main stalk by delicate drooping filaments. *Deschampsia* inflorescences emerge in the spring but are persistent and may be seen for much of the year.

Deschampsia may be seen occasionally in open woodlands and shrublands on the dry side of Kīlauea Caldera, but it is common only at higher elevations on Mauna Loa Strip. The grass was probably a more important component of vegetation of lower Mauna Loa Strip and forest openings of Kīpuka Puaulu before cattle grazing disturbed the ground cover. Unfortunately, these areas continue to be dominated by alien grasses, even 50 years after the cessation of cattle grazing. Above 5,000 ft elevation, *Deschampsia* is the dominant ground cover in the grassland and shrubland communities that form a patchy mosaic with koa groves in the upland woodlands of Mauna Loa. Other grasses are also common in these communities, particularly the endemic mountain pili, a spreading bunchgrass with softly hairy leaf blades.

Several nonnative grasses are components of the upland grasslands; these primarily pasture species have escaped from nearby ranches. Velvet grass is one of these introduced range grasses and is perhaps the most serious nonnative competitor of *Deschampsia*. A plant with velvety, bluish leaves and compact, pink to beige inflorescences, velvet grass had a competitive edge over *Deschampsia* when feral pigs were common in Mauna Loa Strip. Pigs uprooted *Deschampsia* bunches and exposed patches of bare soil while digging for roots and invertebrates. Velvet grass was able to invade disturbed areas much faster than *Deschampsia* and was therefore increasing its cover to the detriment of the native grass. With the removal of feral pigs from enclosed areas below 6,800 ft elevation, the native grasslands of Mauna Loa Strip are slowly recovering from past disturbance, and *Deschampsia* remains the most abundant grass of many of the upland and subalpine communities.

J. YOSHIOKA

Meadow Ricegrass (*Ehrharta stipoides*)

Grass family (Poaceae)

Alien; native to Australia, New Zealand, and the Philippines

Distribution in the Park: Moist forests and woodlands of Mauna Loa
  Strip and upland rain forests

This perennial grass (formerly known as *Microlaena stipoides*) was previously believed by some authors to be a native Hawaiian plant. It is now recognized as an alien species, introduced in the early 1900s probably for its forage value. Meadow ricegrass is particularly abundant in upland pastures of Hawai'i Island, where 'ōhi'a and koa forests have been converted to grazing land. The grass thrives under partly shaded conditions and may form dense stands, which inhibit the establishment of other plants.

Usually 1 to 2 ft tall, meadow ricegrass is a weakly erect grass that spreads by means of lateral stems at or below ground level. Its light yellow-green, narrow leaves are smooth and hairless, usually 1 to 3 in. long. Meadow ricegrass is most easily recognized by its inflorescences, which are about 4 in. long and arch or nod with the weight of its flowers. Each individual flower bears a long stiff awn or bristle about 0.5 in. long. When inflorescences are completely mature and dry, the awns help disperse the tiny grains of meadow ricegrass by becoming attached to animals (or people) moving through stands of the grass.

Meadow ricegrass is particularly abundant in areas of the Park formerly used to graze cattle. Kīpuka Puaulu, Kīpuka Kī, and Mauna Loa Strip were part of a ranch before their addition to the National Park in 1927; even after this date, grazing continued in much of the Strip until after World War II (with a short hiatus from 1940 to 1942). Grazing opened up forest understories and removed palatable native plants, allowing the establishment of persistent alien grasses adapted to grazing. In the lower section of the Strip where grazing was intensive, alien grasses such as meadow ricegrass and dallis grass persist as dominant elements of ground cover about 50 years after the cessation of grazing. Where grazing ended earlier and understory tree species remained, for example in the central portion of Kīpuka Puaulu, native vegetation has recovered and meadow ricegrass and other alien grasses have been reduced by shading to minor components of the ground cover. Meadow ricegrass still remains an important ground cover in many koa groves throughout Mauna Loa Strip. Koa foliage does not generally produce enough shade to deprive alien grasses of the light they need to grow. Meadow ricegrass and other alien species will likely be a permanent addition to the flora of the upland forests and woodlands.

Pueo or Hawaiian Owl (*Asio flammeus sandwichensis*) **and Common Barn Owl** (*Tyto alba*)

Typical Owl family (Strigidae); Barn Owl family (Tytonidae)

Endemic (pueo) at subspecies level, **indigenous** at species level; **Alien** (barn owl), introduced from California in 1958-1966

Distribution in the Park: Pueo most often seen in grassland, shrubland, and parkland habitat, ʻAinahou Ranch area to Mauna Loa, but reported from sea level to Mauna Loa Strip Road; barn owl in similar areas, but more often in middle to low elevations

These two owls and the Hawaiian hawk or 'io can be seen throughout the Park in low numbers but are most often encountered in this zone. The pueo or Hawaiian owl (right illustration) is an endemic subspecies of the short-eared owl found in the northern hemisphere and on many islands in the Pacific Ocean. It is heavily streaked with brown, has yellow eyes, and is active by day as well as at night. Pueo feed mostly on rats and mice but also take small birds. They nest and roost on the ground, usually in open areas such as grasslands. Sexes look alike, but females are larger (up to 17 in. long) than males (about 13 in.). In flight, the pueo is big headed (in contrast to the 'io) with a short neck, and it flies awkwardly, often near the ground. It often hovers before pouncing on prey. The pueo can sometimes be seen soaring high over open vegetation, which can lead one to confuse it with the 'io. However, pueo rarely soar in spiraling circles, a flight pattern favored by 'io.

The common barn own (left illustration) is larger than the pueo (to 24 in. long), light tan, with a white, heart-shaped facial disk. Barn owls, which are mainly nocturnal, are found in a variety of habitats from sea level to tree line or above; they roost and nest in lava tubes, buildings, and various other cavities. They fly buoyantly and silently and appear very pale in reflected light at night (the pueo is streaked below). Barn owls are well adapted to a rodent diet but also kill colonial seabirds in Hawai'i.

Both owls lay white eggs and may breed throughout the year. Native species of songbirds "mob" both owls, suggesting long association with pueo, or more likely, with other species of native owls now extinct in Hawai'i. Alternatively, mobbing behavior may carry over from ancestral "owl-wise" mainland groups of songbirds that colonized Hawai'i.

Both species of owls regurgitate pellets of undigested fur, feathers, and skeletal materials from their prey. Collection of these pellets under owl roosts helps scientists to determine owl diets in different areas and at different times of the year. Much remains to be learned about these inconspicuous animals, including why dead owls of both species are periodically found in large numbers on all the Islands. Diseases, pesticides, starvation, and the consumption of marine toads have been blamed for the mortality, which has been investigated sporadically for many years. At this time, however, the causes are not known.

J. YOSHIOKA

Common (Ring-necked and Green) Pheasant (*Phasianus colchis*) and California Quail (*Callipepla californica*)

Gallinaceous Bird family (Phasianidae)

Alien; Common pheasants introduced from eastern Asia after 1865; California quail introduced from California before 1855

Distribution in the Park: Common pheasant mostly on Mauna Loa Strip, although formerly along Crater Rim Drive and Chain of Craters Road; California quail along Mauna Loa Strip and on Crater Rim Drive between Kīlauea Military Camp and Jaggar Museum

Common pheasants (formerly known as ring-necked and green pheasants; left in illustration) are large, chicken-like birds. Two color phases of common pheasant are found in the Park. The ring-necked male is a bronze-bodied bird with green head and red wattles and a white neck band, whereas the male green pheasant is glossy blue-green below, brownish above, and lacks the white neck band. Females of both phases are smaller, paler, and have shorter but pointed tails. (Francolins, also found in the Park, are smaller members of the same family but do not have pointed tails.) The green form of common pheasants tends to prefer somewhat wetter and higher-elevation habitat than the ring-necked form, but neither are forest pheasants like the kalij pheasant, found in Park moist and wet forests.

Pheasants tend to skulk through the underbrush and may be seen crossing roads. They are reluctant to fly, but when they do there is an explosion of wings and often considerable squawking. The crowing of cock pheasants in the spring (February-April) is easily recognized by the loud, forced "kok-errrk" followed by the sound of wings fluttering. Females nest on the ground and lay 10 to 12 buff-colored eggs.

The California quail (upper right in illustration) is a small (9-10 in.) grayish brown bird with a single plume on the head. Males have black faces bordered by white, and scale markings on the stomach, while females are duller without facial marks. Usually, quail are found in flocks or coveys, and sometimes the young birds walk in a line behind parents. Birds in a covey communicate by clicking noises, and males utter a loud, clear, plaintive three-note whistle with emphasis on the middle note. When quail take flight, the sound of churring wings can be startling. Nests are built on the ground in dense vegetation, and 10 to 12 brown-spotted eggs are laid.

Introduced birds are potential reservoirs for disease organisms that can harm native birds. Scientists believe that the decline of native bird species in some areas (over 60% of native Hawaiian bird species are now extinct) was caused at least in part by diseases transmitted from large numbers of alien birds brought to Hawai'i for sport and pleasure. The effects of introduced bird diseases on native bird populations today are receiving considerable study. Pheasants and quail also eat various seeds and fruit and probably spread both native and alien plants. The alien blackberry and the native pilo are examples of plants favored by these gamebirds, which may have enhanced dispersal of seeds. Pheasants and quail also feed on insects, especially seasonally.

Many species of alien birds, including Japanese white-eyes, kalij pheasants, turkeys, and hwamei or melodious laughing thrushes, have recently been increasing in the Park, while many species of native birds ('i'iwi, 'o'u, Hawai'i creeper, 'ākepa, 'akiapōlā'au) are declining or have disappeared. Although cause and effect is difficult to establish, it is evident that alien birds can negatively affect both plants (native and alien) and native birds in a number of ways.

Hwamei or Melodious Laughing Thrush (*Garrulax canorus*) and Northern Cardinal (*Cardinalis cardinalis*)

Old World Insect Eater family (Muscicapidae), Babbler subfamily (Timaliinae); Cardinal and Relatives family (Emberizidae)

Alien; hwamei introduced from Southeast Asia in 1900; northern cardinal introduced from eastern U.S. in 1929

Distribution in the Park: Sea level to 9,000 ft, but most common at some low-elevation sites and Kīpuka Puaulu and Mauna Loa Strip

If the hwamei (illustrated), a rusty brown bird with yellow bill, could be observed easily, a good name would be spectacled thrush, since it has a large white eye-ring with white feather patch to the rear of it. But the loud, melodious song composed of repeated phrases is more obvious to observers than physical appearance, for this medium-sized (9 in.) bird skulks in the heavy undergrowth of forests. A dry rattle and antiphonal singing or "dueting" (alternate singing with another bird) are also characteristic of the species.

The hwamei prefers brushy understories in native or alien forests and is one of the few species associated with dense uluhe fern. These babblers (not true thrushes) eat fruit and insects. They lay three to five blue-green eggs often within 15 ft of the ground or sometimes on it. Not much is known about nesting behavior in Hawai'i, but nests have been found from May through July; eggs are incubated 13 to 14 days.

Hwamei have increased in the Park in recent years. They were rarely reported between 1940 and 1975, but now they can usually be heard around the Crater Rim area of Kīlauea Caldera, in Kīpuka Puaulu, and along Mauna Loa Strip Road. Laughing thrushes occupy a wide range of vegetation types, from deep, wet forest to dry scrubland. Like Japanese white-eyes, these introduced birds have been increasing while introduced red-billed leiothrix have been apparently decreasing. Laughing thrushes, like leiothrix, feed near the ground but are considerably larger.

Another loud-voiced, medium-sized (9 in.) bird of the forest understory is the northern cardinal, which, with its thick, powerful bill, eats more seeds and fewer fruits than the hwamei. Unlike laughing thrushes, both male and female cardinals often call from exposed perches, and their clear, penetrating songs include a leisurely descending trill and distinctive "chip" notes heard for long distances. Males are red with a black patch around the reddish orange bill; females are tan to brown with red tinting and similar bills, and immature birds look like blackish-billed females. Both sexes have jaunty crests. Cardinals may be found deep in native forests throughout Hawai'i from sea level to tree line.

J. YOSHIOKA

Red-billed Leiothrix or Japanese Hill Robin (*Leiothrix lutea*)

**Old World Insect Eater family (Muscicapidae),
  Babbler subfamily (Timaliinae)**

Alien; introduced from eastern Asia

Distribution in the Park: Largely above 4,000 ft in mesic to wet areas

This small (5.5 in.) green and yellow bird with an orange-red bill was introduced to Hawai'i as a cage bird as early as 1911. Probably some of these escaped, and additional introductions from the U.S. Mainland and the Orient between 1918 and 1929 were also made. Leiothrix, as the species is commonly called, have yellow throats and breasts; yellow and orange feathers are conspicuous at the edge of the wing, and the forked tail is also distinctive. The species is difficult to observe in Hawaiian forests, however, as it is usually actively foraging on the ground, in thick understory, or singing in dense foliage. Leiothrix are "vocally conspicuous," as the subfamily name "babbler" might indicate. The loud, melodious warble is similar to that of the hwamei or melodious laughing thrush, except without paired phrases. A soft whistle and low-pitched scolding chatter aimed at intruders are also commonly heard.

Red-billed leiothrix seem to prefer wetter areas of native or alien vegetation with dense understory. They eat considerable amounts of fruit such as thimbleberry and strawberry guava and probably help distribute seeds of the species they consume. Invertebrates found on or near the ground are also taken. Nests containing two to four pale blue eggs with irregular reddish blotches have been found in tree ferns, weeds, and various tree species, usually within several feet of the ground.

Breeding season on Hawai'i Island seems to be from March through June. In the nonbreeding season, birds may form large flocks and wander far from breeding territories. Flocks have been observed on Mauna Kea at elevations of over 13,500 feet. Recent information suggests that the distribution of water sources (including fruit concentrations and gamebird watering sites) may limit upper-elevation populations, whereas lowland populations are limited by high temperatures.

Although common and well established on most of the main Hawaiian Islands by the 1960s, this species has since declined in many areas on several islands. In Hawaii Volcanoes, leiothrix were apparently increasing rapidly in 1936, especially in open forests. They were much more common in most areas in the 1940s than in the early 1970s and later, however. As leiothrix declined in the Park during this period, numbers of Japanese white-eyes increased, although the cause has not been established. Changes in understory vegetation caused by invasions of feral pigs and alien plants probably affected survival of the ground-foraging leiothrix far more than the more adaptable white-eye.

Avian malaria, a debilitating disease caused by an organism transmitted by the southern house mosquito, was detected in Park leiothrix in 1947, the first alien species in which the disease-causing protozoan was demonstrated. The variables that determine which species are more abundant in a given area at a given time are difficult to sort out. Possible influences include disease resistance, climatic trends, changes in favored food availability, competition among species, and predation. Much remains to be learned about the population trends of invasive and native species and their causes.

'Elepaio (*Chasiempis sandwichensis*)

Australo-Papua Insect Eater family (Pachycephalidae),
  Monarch, Australian Flycatcher, and Fantail subfamily (Monarchinae)

Endemic to the Hawaiian Islands

Distribution in the Park: Native koa forests and kīpuka along Mauna
  Loa Strip Road from Kīpuka Puaulu to about 6,500 ft; also in wet
  'ōhi'a forest of 'Ōla'a and in forests of Kīlauea Caldera rim

This attractive and active small (5.5 in.) flycatcher was formerly found in forests at Kīpuka Nēnē (3,000 ft elevation) along Hilina Pali Road and at even lower elevations (1,800 ft) in Kalapana. In recent decades, however, numbers have declined at low to middle elevations. Within its geographical range (subspecies are also found on Kaua'i and O'ahu), 'elepaio have successfully adapted to largely alien forests in many areas, perhaps more so than any other native songbird. 'Elepaio are not listed as Endangered, although the O'ahu subspecies is uncommon.

Hawai'i 'elepaio have rufous breasts and streaks on the underparts; black throats marked with white spots (males) or white throats (females); white wing bars, rump patch, and tail-feather tips; and prominent eyebrows. Immatures are dull brown with buffy wing bars. Wet-forest adults are darker below and on the head and throat than dry-forest birds (such as those found on the western slopes of Mauna Kea). Stiff, hairlike feathers (rictal bristles) at the corners of the bill are characteristic of these and other flycatchers.

'Elepaio usually flit from place to place in search of insects on the wing, in foliage, or on branches. They characteristically sit (but not for long!) with cocked tail and are curious enough to investigate humans in their habitat. The song is a loudly whistled "elePAIO" or "twoWHEET," often repeated, and calls include an upslurred, whistled "wheet" and a raspy chatter.

'Elepaio breed from January to June (probably April to June mostly) and weave small, compact, cup-shaped nests of grasses, lichens, spider webs, and roots. Two to three white eggs with reddish spots are laid, incubation takes about 18 days, and nestlings fledge after two weeks or so. Both sexes care for eggs and young. Pairs and family groups of this species seem quite sedentary within their habitat, remaining in the same area year round.

In Hawaiian legend, 'elepaio are considered guardian spirits for canoe makers. In days of old when natives felled koa trees in the forest for canoes, 'elepaio were considered judges of tree quality. If a bird pecked on the fallen log, the wood was considered of poor quality. If the bird simply sang instead, the log was considered sound. An alternative version of this tale has the bird making the judgment before the tree is cut -- certainly a more conservation-oriented and labor-saving strategy! An insect eater like the 'elepaio might indeed find insect-infested timber of interest, whether upright or felled.

'I'iwi (*Vestiaria coccinea*)

Finch family (Fringillidae),
  Hawaiian Honeycreeper and Finch subfamily (Drepanidinae)

Endemic to the Hawaiian Islands

Distribution in the Park: Moist and rain forests from 4,000 to 7,000 ft
  elevation; occasionally seen or heard at lower and higher elevations

This spectacular, orange-red bird with black wings and tail, peach-colored bill, and yellow eye-ring is the favorite of many. Like hummingbirds, beetles, and bumblebees, it is one of those creatures that appears as though it should be incapable of flying, with squat (over 5.5 in.) body, short wings and tail, and a long curved bill that mirrors the shape of tubular flowers in the lobelioid group. White patches decorate the inner portions (secondaries) of 'i'iwi wings, which, like those of the 'apapane, are noisy in flight. Even the voice of this species is an oddity, variously described as squeaky, harsh, rusty, forced, discordant, and strained. 'I'iwi also utter loud, clear whistles and mimic other birds.

'I'iwi were once one of the most common forest birds in Hawai'i; their feathers were much used in Hawaiian featherwork by the people of old. The species was still abundant in the early 1900s and was fairly common in Park 'ōhi'a rain forest and koa/'ōhi'a parkland in the 1940s; it was uncommon below 4,200 ft elevation in the Park by 1970, although it was still found in 'Ola'a Forest, especially in summer months. Where koa forest is regenerating (after removal of ungulates, or hoofed mammals) above 5,500 ft elevation on Mauna Loa, 'i'iwi are found in small but consistent numbers.

'I'iwi breed from February to September. Cup-shaped nests are usually built in tall 'ōhi'a trees, and one to three whitish eggs with chocolate-brown spots are incubated for two weeks. Nestlings fledge in three weeks, and second nestings sometimes occur. Young birds have brownish green bills and yellowish green plumage marked with black; bills gradually change to the adult color of peach, and plumage to vermilion.

Like 'apapane, 'i'iwi eat insects, but they depend more on nectar for sustenance. Individual 'i'iwi dominate 'apapane at feeding sites, but more numerous 'apapane may overwhelm them at a tree in heavy bloom. 'I'iwi are less dependent on 'ōhi'a lehua nectar than 'apapane, often concentrating on other trees and flowering understory plants as well, but they will vigorously defend large feeding territories around 'ōhi'a. 'I'iwi make long journeys in nonbreeding seasons to areas of heavy 'ōhi'a flowering. Towering flights up to 300 ft high may help them locate areas of heavy bloom, since flowering canopies are visible for some distance when viewed from above. Probably because many lobelioids once used by honeycreepers have been decimated or extirpated by feral ungulates or extinction of pollinators, nectar of the introduced banana poka, a forest pest in the passion flower family, is now a favorite food of 'i'iwi.

J.YOSHIOKA

Common 'Amakihi (*Hemignathus virens*)

Finch family (Fringillidae),
 Hawaiian Honeycreeper and Finch subfamily (Drepanidinae)

Endemic to the Hawaiian Islands

Distribution in the Park: Below 1,000 ft elevation in a few places,
 but most birds in moist and rain forest from 2,000 ft to above tree line

Common 'amakihi (formerly known as *Loxops virens*) are smaller (4.5 in.) than 'apapane and are yellowish green. Legs are black, and the lores (area between eyes and bill) are dark except on immatures and females. This most common of the native little green birds can be confused with the most common of the introduced little green birds, the Japanese white-eye. The white-eye, however, is smaller, and has a pronounced white eye-ring. The Hawai'i race of the common 'amakihi can also be confused with the much rarer Hawai'i creeper, which lacks black lores, moves more deliberately, and has not been seen with certainty in the Park since about 1960. Male 'amakihi are somewhat larger and brighter yellow than females and have longer bills.

The short, gray, curved bill of the common 'amakihi suggests that this species feeds more on invertebrates and less on nectar than the 'i'iwi or the 'apapane, and indeed it is often seen searching for invertebrates on small branches and in the tops of trees. 'Amakihi do not make the long-distance flights characteristic of 'i'iwi and 'apapane in search of heavy flowering or bloom areas, also suggesting less dependence on nectar.

Common 'amakihi utter a characteristic complaining "peent" call note and sing a flat trilling song year round. Although they breed from fall to summer, most activity seems to be in late spring to early summer. Two to four eggs with variable purplish brown blotching are laid in a delicate nest, often near the tip of a small branch and sometimes low and poorly concealed. Eggs are incubated for about two weeks, and the young fledge after 17 days or so. Perhaps 'amakihi are successful in areas with high numbers of tree-climbing black rats partly because their nests are at the tips of branches that will not support large rodents. Such nesting habits are characteristic of some species of finches in the Galapagos Archipelago that have evolved in endemic rat habitat.

Common 'amakihi nest at high elevations on Mauna Kea, where adaptation to low temperatures is a necessity, and in sweltering lowlands in the Park with heavy concentrations of alien plants, introduced birds, ants, mosquitoes, and rats. This suggests a wide tolerance to adverse biological and physical conditions, and some resistance to diseases that limit the distribution of other native bird species. Although 'amakihi reach highest densities in upland moist forests and woodlands, they are found in rain forest and even in scrubland around the margins of Ka'ū Desert. In rain forest habitat, 'amakihi are attracted to nectar of the introduced banana poka, another measure of their adaptability to altered forest conditions and a hopeful sign for their continued survival.

Kamehameha Butterfly (*Vanessa tameamea*) and Blackburn Butterfly (*Udara blackburni*)

Butterfly and Moth order (Lepidoptera);
  Brush-footed Butterfly family (Nymphalidae);
  Blue, Copper, and Hairstreak Butterfly family (Lycaenidae)

Endemic to the Hawaiian Islands

Distribution in the Park: Mainly upland woodlands, but windblown and wanders from sea level to high on Mauna Loa (Kamehameha); low to mid-elevation in suitable habitat (Blackburn)

Only two of the 15 species of butterflies found in Hawai'i are natives. The Kamehameha butterfly is the larger (3 in. wingspan) and more colorful of the two and comes from a family of great wanderers. Although it looks and behaves like the alien red admiral and painted lady of the U.S. Mainland and is in the same family as the introduced monarch butterfly, it probably evolved from colonizers that originated in Southeast Asia or the Mariana or Bonin islands.

The Kamehameha butterfly (lower illustration) was the first lepidopteran to be described from Hawai'i, despite the fact that hundreds of species of Hawaiian moths have evolved here. It was named in the early 1800s for Kamehameha I, who united the Hawaiian Islands as a kingdom between 1790 and 1810. The color of the underwings is variable brown or gray and is cryptic enough to camouflage the animal well as it sits with wings folded on a tree. The upper wing surface is a beautiful red-orange with black and white markings. Females can be distinguished from males by several white spots near the tips of upper surfaces of forewings; males have orange spots in the same locations.

Kamehameha butterflies are nectar and sap feeders and may be seen around koa, naio, and other native forest trees as well as near introduced shrubs. Females lay eggs on leaves of native nettles such as māmaki, and caterpillars develop on this host plant. The caterpillars are usually bright green but sometimes brown or purple and have a yellowish line along each side of the body. The head of the Kamehameha butterfly caterpillar looks something like māmaki flowers, and harmless dark spines arise sparsely from the body. The caterpillars pupate about a month after hatching, and the spiny pupal case or chrysalis looks like a dead leaf. Adult butterflies emerge after about two weeks.

The Blackburn butterfly (upper illustration) is small (1 in. wingspan) and more difficult to find. The best place to look is where koa trees grow, since they are the primary host plant for the caterpillars. 'A'ali'i is also often used. The caterpillars of the Blackburn butterfly look like small greenish grubs and are easy to miss as they sit on the ends of small twigs. Young larvae blend in with the yellow ball-like flower heads of koa. Larvae spin lifelines of silk as they move; pupation is on a silk mat and lasts for 8 to 10 days. The wings of both sexes of adult butterflies are iridescent green beneath. The upper sides of the wings of males are iridescent purplish blue where females have paler blue patches, with the rest of the wing dark; green scales cover the thorax. Both sexes have striped black and white antennae.

Open stands of koa and native shrubs along Mauna Loa Strip Road are good places to look for the Blackburn butterfly. 'A'ali'i shrubland near Keala-komo Overlook on Chain of Craters Road is another site where these small butterflies are often seen.

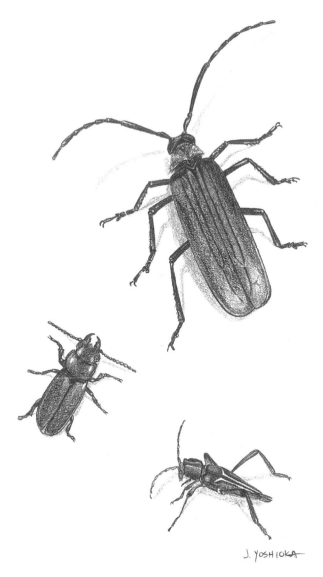

J. YOSHIOKA

Long-horned Woodborers:
(*Plagithmysus* **spp.,** *Megopis reflexa,* **and**
Parandra puncticeps)

Long-horned Beetle family (Cerambycidae)

Endemic

Distribution in the Park: Moist and wet forests,
sea level to tree line

280

The British entomologist J.B.S. Haldane, when asked what could be inferred about God from studying the works of Creation, replied, "An inordinate fondness for beetles." The order Coleoptera (beetles) is the most diverse of insect groups worldwide. In Hawai'i we already know of 1,355 native species in 30 families. Seven of these families have more than 100 species each. One of these diverse families is the long-horned woodborers, with 141 native species. The genus *Plagithmysus* in this family is far more diverse than the other two Hawaiian genera of cerambycids; some 139 species of these elongated, long-legged beetles with long antennae can be found in Hawai'i, whereas only one species of each of the other two genera is known. Of the 46 species of *Plagithmysus* recorded on Hawai'i Island, 16 have been found in the Park, most limited to a single living plant host species. (Four alien cerambycids are established in the Park, generally feeding on more than one species of plant.) Because of their narrow host specificity, many species are very rare. The entire genus has been recommended for Federal listing as Endangered.

Larvae of cerambycid beetles are generally host specific, boring in both living and dying wood of trees, shrubs, or vines. In the Park, koa, 'ohi'a, 'a'ali'i, and alani are among the woody plants attacked. Many beetles are associated with koa trees, including the endemic cerambycid *Megopis reflexa* (upper illustration), the largest beetle in the Park and in Hawai'i (up to 2 in. long). The endemic *Parandra puncticeps* (middle illustration) tunnels in dead wood and is about 1 in. long.

Perhaps the most abundant cerambicid in the Park is a "koa beetle," *Plagithmysus varians*, a spectacular red, white, black, and buff insect about 1.5 in. long. This species is endemic to dry and wet forests on Hawai'i Island, and adults can usually be found on trunks or branches of dying or recently felled trees. Larvae (round-headed borers) girdle the area between koa bark and sound wood as they mature and may spend about a year in the larval stage. The 'ohi'a-dwelling *Plagithmysus bilineatus* (lower illustration) is probably the second-most common native cerambycid in the Park. It is similar to *P. varians* in habits and form but is specific to 'ohi'a trees. Like *P. varians*, *P. bilineatus* is attracted to dying trees. However, it is not the cause of 'ohi'a dieback, which involves the senescence of 'ohi'a cohorts (groups of the same age) initiated by stress of some sort. Rather, *P. bilineatus* generally invades after root problems increase stress on the trees.

The presence of invertebrates in koa and 'ohi'a forests recovering from decades of ungulate (hoofed mammal) damage is an important consideration for future reintroduction of native forest birds. The 'akiapōlā'au seems especially dependent on insect larvae found beneath the bark of old koa trees, and survival of the Hawai'i creeper may be tied to invertebrates found on surfaces of tree trunks and branches. *Plagithmysus* larvae, because of their long development periods and abundance in upland forests, are important food items for native birds. Studies currently being conducted to determine the "entomofauna" of several areas on Mauna Loa Strip and the habits of resident birds will help provide information on the likelihood of reestablishing Endangered forest birds in the Park.

SUBALPINE ZONE

The Park's subalpine zone consists of a band of largely intact native vegetation stretching from the top of Mauna Loa Strip Road (6,700 ft) upslope to approximately 9,000 ft elevation. This high-elevation zone encircles the summit of Mauna Loa and is vast, but Hawaii Volcanoes National Park includes the only subalpine site on the mountain that is legally protected from disturbance. The importance of preserving examples of montane vegetation and native wildlife habitat was not widely appreciated at the time of the Mauna Loa Strip addition to Hawaii Volcanoes National Park in 1927, but as upper-elevation forests and shrublands were converted to pastures or began to deteriorate from feral ungulate impacts, protected areas, such as the Park, became important reservoirs of native plant and animal diversity.

The climate of the subalpine zone is much harsher than that immediately downslope. The average annual temperature here ranges from 40 to 50°F, and frost is common at night. Rainfall averages 30 to 40 in. annually and is decidedly seasonal: summers are dry, and most precipitation falls during the winter. Low-lying clouds and fog are important sources of moisture for plants in this zone.

Substrates on the eastern slope of Mauna Loa are primarily weathered lavas from the Northeast Rift near Pu'u 'Ula'ula (Red Hill). Most flows range in age from 150 to 4,000 years. Two prominent, well-vegetated kīpuka of old pāhoehoe lava (1,500-4,000 years old) extend upslope into this Park zone. Kīpuka Kulalio is crossed by Mauna Loa Trail on the eastern side of Mauna Loa Strip, and Kīpuka Mauna'iu is a less-visited area to the west of the trail. These two kīpuka of older flows and vegetation are bisected by more recent 'a'ā flows (750-1,500 years old). The youngest flow in the Park's subalpine zone is the long, narrow 1880 flow extending from high on Mauna Loa's Northeast Rift to about 4,000 ft elevation outside the Park. Soils of the subalpine zone are shallow ash deposits found mostly on the older pāhoehoe flows.

Vegetation of the older 'a'ā substrates in the subalpine zone is an open 'ōhi'a/māmane (*Metrosideros polymorpha/Sophora chrysophylla*) woodland of scattered trees in a shrubland of mixed native species. On pāhoehoe substrates native shrubs predominate, mixed with fewer 'ōhi'a and māmane trees. In both wood- and shrublands, trees are about 15 ft tall, and large 'ōhi'a are far more common than māmane. Shrubby trees of mountain pilo (*Coprosma montana*) are found here, as are spreading mats of the related kūkaenēnē (*C. ernodeoides*). The widespread native shrubs pūkiawe (*Styphelia tameiameiae*), 'a'ali'i (*Dodonaea viscosa*), and 'ōhelo (*Vaccinium reticulatum*) are dominant elements in Park subalpine vegetation. The bluish leaved 'ōhelo of the subalpine zone is considered to be a high-elevation form of the same species found in mid-elevation and upland woodlands. Ground cover is composed of scattered native sedges (*Gahnia gahniiformis, Carex wahuensis*), grasses (*Deschampsia nubigena,*

Trisetum glomeratum), herbs (*Tetramolopium humile, Luzula hawaiiensis*), ferns such as bracken (*Pteridium aquilinum*) and kalamoho (*Pellaea ternifolia*), and spleenworts (*Asplenium* spp.). A few nonnative plants, such as gosmore (*Hypochoeris radicata*) and velvet grass (*Holcus lanatus*), are common but occupy little area. Plant cover is not continuous in this zone; trees and clumps of shrubs grow in soil pockets and cracks, and there are usually extensive areas of exposed rock and soil.

Most of the native birds of the upland woodland zone also frequent the subalpine zone. Common 'amakihi (*Hemignathus virens*) occur here in large numbers, and 'apapane (*Himatione sanguinea*) and 'i'iwi (*Vestiaria coccinea*) are also seasonally common. These birds and the nonnative house finch (*Carpodacus mexicanus*) and Japanese white-eye (*Zosterops japonicus*) may be seen more easily in the shorter trees of subalpine vegetation than in the thicker forests of the upland zone. Native nectar-feeding birds are conspicuously numerous when 'ōhi'a and māmane trees bear many flowers. At elevations above 6,000 ft on Mauna Loa, a peak in 'ōhi'a flowering often occurs during the winter. 'Ōma'o or Hawai'i thrush (*Myadestes obscurus*), more typical of rain forests, is present in the subalpine zone as a disjunct population surviving on the fruit-producing shrubs so abundant here. Introduced gamebirds may occasionally be seen or heard in open subalpine vegetation; California quail (*Callipepla californica*), chukar (*Alectoris chukar*), and common pheasant (*Phasianus colchicus*) inhabit both the subalpine and upland woodland zones of Mauna Loa Strip.

The subalpine zone of Hawaii Volcanoes has not been overwhelmed by alien insects, although predatory Argentine ants (*Iridomyrmex humilis*) and western yellowjackets (*Vespula pensylvanica*) do occur here. Some of the most visible components of the native insect fauna here are yellow-faced bees in the genus *Hylaeus* (*Nesoprosopis*). While they are also found in lowland, mid-elevation, and upland woodlands, they reach peak abundance in the subalpine zone. These small (0.25-0.5 in.), dark, native bees feed on nectar and pollen of 'ōhi'a lehua and other native plants and are among the most important insect pollinators of all zones in the Islands.

The Park's subalpine zone is remarkable for its native vegetation and animals and its relative paucity of alien invaders. Nonnative plants have not yet become a serious problem here, and fire has not greatly influenced the development of native vegetation. Rocky substrates and the lack of an important herbaceous layer have limited both the occurrence of fires and the impact of cattle (*Bos taurus*) and feral pigs (*Sus scrofa*). Feral goats (*Capra hircus*) have been the most important agents of disturbance to subalpine vegetation. Where these animals have been excluded for a decade, the recovery of native woody vegetation is progressing. The numbers of young, vigorous māmane trees and established seedlings are conspicuously higher below a goat-proof fence near 7,000 ft. Park managers constructed barrier fences along the remote, high-elevation boundaries of Mauna Loa Strip to 9,000 ft elevation in 1992, in an effort to further reduce the numbers of feral goats within the Park and to allow native vegetation to regenerate. Periodic hunting above the fenced enclosure keeps the number of goats at high elevations in the Park at low numbers.

The subalpine zone of Hawaii Volcanoes National Park is reached by driving to the end of Mauna Loa Strip Road. Mauna Loa Trail begins at the end of the road and leads the hiker across the subalpine zone and into the alpine and aeolian zones. This 18-mile trail ends at the summit of Mauna Loa. Overnight trips should only be attempted by hikers prepared for harsh conditions, after obtaining backcountry use permits and registering at Park headquarters.

Naʻenaʻe (*Dubautia ciliolata*)

Sunflower family (Asteraceae)

Endemic to Hawaiʻi Island

Distribution in the Park: Subalpine zone, mid-elevation woodlands, and Kaʻū Desert

Na'ena'e belongs to a group of plants showing remarkable adaptive radiation in the Hawaiian Islands. This group of three genera includes 28 species and many subspecies, all apparently derived from one original immigrant to the Islands. Called the silversword alliance after its most well-known member, the group includes five species of silverswords and greenswords (*Argyroxiphium*) on the islands of Maui and Hawai'i, two species of 'iliau (*Wilkesia*), restricted to the island of Kaua'i, and 21 species in the genus *Dubautia*, found on all the major Hawaiian Islands. *Dubautia* plants are usually shrubs, but some species are small trees or vines. Some members of this genus are restricted to the wettest bog habitats, others are rain forest inhabitants, some specialize in colonizing new lava flows, and several live in dry subalpine environments.

Two species of *Dubautia* or na'ena'e are common in Hawaii Volcanoes National Park. *Dubautia ciliolata* (formerly known as *Railliardia ciliolata*; illustrated) is a small shrub, usually less than 3 ft tall, with stiffly erect, brittle branches. Lateral branches are generally covered with gray hairs and have conspicuous rings marking the points of attachment of fallen leaves. Leaves are narrow, thick, pointed, shiny or hairy, and are borne on branches in whorls of three. Often the tightly clustered leaves ascend branches in a neat linear formation. Inflorescences are found at branch tips and are composed of many small nodding heads of tiny yellow flowers. Flowers are most abundant in the summer and fall and develop into tiny seed-like dry fruits topped with tufts of white bristly hairs, an adaptation for wind dispersal. This na'ena'e is commonly found in rocky areas of the subalpine shrublands of Mauna Loa, but it also occurs in the dry open 'ōhi'a woodlands of Kīlauea Caldera and along Chain of Craters Road.

In Kīlauea Caldera, the range of *D. ciliolata* overlaps with that of *D. scabra* or kūpaoa, a common plant on recent lava flows and cinder fall areas and also a ground cover component of young rain forests and moist woodlands. *Dubautia scabra* is a creeping, vine-like shrub with linear, laxly spreading, alternate leaves with tiny marginal teeth. Its inflorescences are composed of upright heads of tiny white flowers. Where the two species grow together (*e.g.*, in the Pu'u Pua'i/Devastation Trail area), natural hybridization sometimes occurs. Hybrid plants have characteristics intermediate between the two species, with leaf arrangement varying between opposite and alternate and flowers a pale yellow.

Common Mullein (*Verbascum thapsus*)

Figwort family (Scrophulariaceae)

Alien; originally from Eurasia

Distribution in the Park: Mauna Loa Strip

290

The subalpine and alpine zones of the Park have been much more resistant to alien plant invasion and establishment than have zones of the lowlands and middle elevations. Above about 5,000 ft elevation, plant communities of the Park continue to be dominated by native plants, and above 6,000 ft only a handful of alien plants, mostly temperate grasses, have become well established. One of the successful invaders of the Park's subalpine zone is common mullein, a large, rosette-forming herbaceous plant in the figwort or snapdragon family.

When young, mullein plants consist of a ground-hugging rosette of thick, gray-green, woolly leaves. As the plant develops, the rosette grows spherically with the addition of new leaves and may occasionally reach a diameter greater than 3 ft. By its second year, mullein produces an upright leafy stalk, usually 3 to 6 ft tall, which eventually bears a dense spike of bright yellow, five-lobed flowers. Flowers develop into round capsules, which split when dry and release many tiny seeds. These seeds usually do not travel far from the parent plant but may be very long-lived in the soil. Elsewhere, mullein seeds have remained viable for up to 100 years. Because of this seed longevity, mullein may be extremely difficult to control in the Park.

While still relatively uncommon, mullein plants have been multiplying and expanding their distribution in the Park over the last 10 years. They are typically seen in rocky or cindery areas on the edges of old ‘a‘ā flows between 5,000 and 7,000 ft elevation but may also exploit the disturbed gravel verges of roadsides. Roads and trails appear to be corridors of invasion on Mauna Loa, perhaps implicating vehicles and hikers as agents of dispersal. Common mullein may have originally invaded the Park via a jeep road connecting Mauna Loa Strip Road with Saddle Road (between Mauna Loa and Mauna Kea). Mullein is much more abundant on the older cinder substrates of Mauna Kea.

It is not known when common mullein was introduced to Hawai‘i, but it was first collected by botanists on Hualālai Volcano about 60 years ago. Like so many other disruptive plants, mullein was probably brought to Hawai‘i as an ornamental plant. Mullein is native to Europe and Asia and has become naturalized in North America and other temperate regions of the world. In Europe and North America, mullein leaves and flowers are sometimes used medicinally in teas and tonics.

J. YOSHIOKA

Kūkaenēnē (*Coprosma ernodeoides*)

Coffee family (Rubiaceae)

Endemic to the islands of Maui and Hawai'i

Distribution in the Park: Mauna Loa Strip,
and open forests near Kīlauea Caldera

292

Although this shrub generally grows mixed with several other species (*e.g.*, pūkiawe, 'a'ali'i, and 'ōhelo) in the subalpine zone of Mauna Loa, it is distinctive because of its low, spreading, matted growth form. Long, sinuous, woody branches usually arch upward only 1 to 2 ft before descending to creep on the ground. The shiny, dark green leaves are less than 0.5 in. long, narrow, stiff, and crowded on lateral ascending branchlets. The inconspicuous flowers of kūkaenēnē are tiny, tubular, and unisexual. Male and female flowers are found on different plants; the male flowers bear four pollen-containing stamens, and female flowers have two long, velvety, white stigmatic surfaces. Female plants later develop shiny, black, rounded, berry-like fruits, which retain the female flower remnants as a crown of fine teeth. Although juicy and attractive, the fruits of kūkaenēnē are not palatable to humans but are readily eaten by birds. The plant's Hawaiian name, kūkaenēnē, literally means "goose droppings," and its fruits are eaten by the nēnē or Hawaiian goose.

Although very different in appearance and growth form, kūkaenēnē is related to the group of small coffee-family trees known as pilo, represented by a dozen species in Hawai'i. The Hawaiian members of this genus are thought to have developed from two or three colonizers, one giving rise to kūkaenēnē and the other(s) speciating into the dozen types of pilo occurring in the Islands today. The original immigrants to the Hawaiian Islands probably came from the South Pacific, as the genus is well represented in New Zealand, Australia, Indonesia, and islands southwest of the Hawaiian Archipelago.

Nohoanu, Hinahina, or Hawaiian Geranium
   (*Geranium cuneatum* subsp. *hypoleucum*)

Geranium family (Geraniaceae)

Endemic as species to Maui and Hawai'i islands

Distribution in the Park: Mauna Loa Strip above approximately 6,800 ft
   elevation

Elsewhere in the world, geraniums are usually small herbaceous plants, but in the Hawaiian Islands six endemic species have evolved that are woody shrubs. The native Hawaiian geraniums are all plants of higher elevations. Three species are restricted to bogs, one species each on Kaua'i, East Maui, and West Maui; the other three occur either in wet forest or subalpine shrublands. Maui Island has the greatest native geranium diversity; five of the species (or subspecies) are found there. Only one Hawaiian geranium occurs on more than one Island, and this single species (*Geranium cuneatum*) is divided into four subspecies based on leaf characteristics. One subspecies is found only on Maui, and three occur on Hawai'i Island.

The geranium of Hawaii Volcanoes National Park belongs to a subspecies found only on Mauna Loa. It has a limited distribution in the Park, where it appears to be restricted to elevations between 6,800 and 8,000 ft. Although it is uncommon and rarely grows taller than 3 ft, the native geranium is a conspicuous component of the subalpine shrubland because of its silvery leaves and showy white to pink flowers. The silvery color of leaves on Park geraniums (belonging to the subspecies *hypoleucum*) is due to soft white hairs densely covering the undersides of the narrow, wedge-shaped, inch-long leaves. The green upper leaf surfaces are prominently parallel veined, and leaf tips have about five sharp, triangular teeth. Leaves are usually clustered at the tips of many purplish branches, which bristle with pointed stipules where leaves were formerly attached. Flowers are borne on open inflorescences extending beyond the leaves. These are usually white but often have purplish pink veins streaking the petals. The fruits of the geranium are very narrow pods, held stiffly erect.

Hawaiian names for this native geranium are nohoanu, which means "cold dwelling," and hinahina, referring to the silvery or gray color of the leaves. Geraniums share the latter name with other plants bearing silvery foliage, such as the silverswords and beach heliotrope. In both high-elevation subalpine habitats and coastal environments, reflective silvery or white hairs serve to reduce water loss from leaves exposed to strong winds and harsh sunlight.

The best place to see the nohoanu in the Park is in the subalpine shrubland along Mauna Loa Trail. Here the geranium grows intermixed with pūkiawe, 'a'ali'i, the pilo *Coprosma montana*, and kūkaenēnē. Along with many other native plants, the geranium population was probably reduced by feral goat browsing in the past. Today, much of Mauna Loa Strip is fenced to exclude feral ungulates (hoofed mammals) and domestic cattle. Continued efforts to eradicate or reduce feral animals are also ongoing in the unenclosed upper reaches of the Strip. Elimination of browsing pressure should allow the native subalpine vegetation to regain its pre-disturbance species composition.

Domestic Goat (*Capra hircus*)

Hollow-horned Ruminant family (Bovidae)

Alien; first introduced to Hawai'i (Ni'ihau) in 1778 by
  Captain James Cook

Distribution in the Park: Formerly abundant in dry to moist areas,
  sea level to 9,000 ft; now limited to unfenced areas above 7,000 ft
  and to East Rift areas in very small numbers

Nobody really knows how many goats were once present in Hawaii Volcanoes National Park. The number most often mentioned is about 15,000 animals before 1970. Clouds of rising dust in the distance marked the locations of the largest herds; elimination of most vegetation and severe erosion even in semi-arid areas were the worst effects of this adaptable and widespread mammal. In some parts of the Park lowlands that should probably support dry forests, goat browsing has destroyed all trees except those out of reach on steep, rocky pali (cliff) faces. Goat removal efforts began in 1916 when Hawaii National Park was created. Hunting by the Territorial government from 1927 to 1931 destroyed over 17,000 animals. Control was interrupted by World War II and was generally ineffective in keeping up with goat reproduction. Feral goats are prolific animals, producing twins once or twice a year beginning at nine months of age. Populations can increase rapidly in Paradise, where the living is easy!

In the late 1960s, a critical decision was made: a series of small exclosures was constructed in the Park to determine what would happen without goat foraging pressure. Within a short time, all areas from which goats were excluded provided evidence that goats were damaging native Hawaiian plant communities. Within one lowland exclosure, at Kūkalau'ula, a viny jackbean, 'āwikiwiki, previously unknown to scientists, began to grow and dominate the landscape. Long-lived seeds and the absence of goats after about 120 years had produced a spectacular result! A multimillion-dollar, long-term goat control program became a classic conservation story, despite some political difficulties and opposition from local hunting interests.

Boundary-fence building became a top parkwide priority to reduce goat ingress from adjacent ranches, where goat hunting for sport continues even today. Barrier fences were constructed to concentrate animals driven by humans on horseback, on foot, or in helicopters. Hunters were deputized by the National Park Service to help with the control effort within the fences, and Park personnel were recruited to hunt, drive, and round up goats throughout the Park. Since the more-visible, light-colored animals are the first to be removed by hunting, the last animals were black or black and brown and difficult to find. They were adept at hiding in lava tubes and other places and learned to avoid humans and helicopters.

Because the last small groups of goats were difficult to remove, an innovative approach called the "Judas goat" technique was developed. Judas goats are wild or domestic animals that are fitted with radio collars and released to seek out others of their kind in the wild. Because feral goats are social creatures year round and are capable of moving long distances, radio-collared animals could be tracked to feral groups, locations radioed to hunters in helicopters, and the animals without collars dispatched through sudden air or ground attack. Today, a few Judas goats are released and monitored periodically to detect feral animals that occasionally breach Park boundary fences. Other feral goats have been almost eliminated. Using similar techniques goats have also been removed, or nearly so, from other important areas in the State, including Haleakalā National Park and the island of Kaho'olawe.

Where feral goats once roamed in large numbers in the Park, alien grasses often dominate now, but these coarse grasses were kept in check by goats only in the treeless western lowlands in the 1950s and 1960s. Increases in frequency, intensity, and size of fires in the Park in the 1970s can't really be attributed to goat removal, and goat reintroduction in the Park is not being considered. Management of alien grasslands by other means, such as fire prevention and firebreaks, biological control, and planting with native species after prescribed burning or herbicide use, is under study.

J. YOSHIOKA

Yellow-faced Bees (*Hylaeus* **spp.**)

Ant, Wasp, and Bee order (Hymenoptera),
  Yellow-faced Bee and Plasterer Bee family (Colletidae)

Endemic

Distribution in the Park: Sea level to alpine zone; dry to wet habitats

Over 60 species of yellow-faced bees occur in Hawai'i. These small (0.25-0.5 in.) fast-flying insects are unlike honey bees in many respects. Instead of the familiar black and yellow markings, yellow-faced or nesoprosopis (genus *Hylaeus*) bees are black, although limited white or yellow markings may be present. Yellow-faced bees have no external structures for carrying nectar and pollen on their hind legs. Instead, they carry a mixture of both in their stomachs and regurgitate to provision their nest cells. Also unlike their more conspicuous relatives, yellow-faced bees are solitary; they construct nests in burrows in the ground, in hollow twigs, or in holes bored in wood by other insects. Pollen and nectar deposited in such cavities serve as food for larvae that develop from eggs sealed in with a cellulose-like material.

Yellow-faced bees appear to have evolved from a single Asiatic colonizer. Some species have even become semi-parasitic, laying eggs in nests of related species. Different species of *Hylaeus* may be found in different biological communities, and many species use both native and alien flowering plants, especially in lower elevations. These mobile insects are able to fly to flowers blooming at different places, so they may appear very abundant or very scarce at different times. Unfortunately, many species are rare at all times; 22 species on Hawai'i Island are potential candidates for listing as Endangered Species. Look for yellow-faced bees around 'ōhi'a flowers (lehua), pūkiawe blossoms, or composites (sunflower family) in most areas of the Park, including the subalpine zone.

ALPINE AND AEOLIAN ZONES

ALPINE AND AEOLIAN ZONES

Alpine areas in Hawai'i (generally above 8,500 or 9,000 ft elevation) are found only on Mauna Kea and Mauna Loa on Hawai'i Island and on Haleakalā on Maui. The alpine zone extends upslope to include the vegetated portion of the high mountain slopes. The aeolian zone or alpine stone desert is that unvegetated area near the mountain summit, where living organisms depend on the wind to supply food and nutrients. Both these harsh zones are arid and windy, with extreme daily variation in temperature, usually greater than 50°F during the day but often dropping to below freezing at night. Volcanic features are prominent and are the most obvious attraction for the visitor. However, some life forms persist, including a few hardy plants such as the native grasses pili uka (*Trisetum glomeratum*) and *Deschampsia nubigena*, the alien Kentucky bluegrass (*Poa pratensis*), and the introduced sheep sorrel (*Rumex acetosella*). Small native shrubs that survive in the alpine zone include pūkiawe (*Styphelia tameiameiae*), 'ōhelo (*Vaccinium reticulatum*), and the tiny composite *Tetramolopium humile*. Shrubs in this harsh environment have compact, dense foliage and are either rounded or wind sculpted. They are low to the ground and are usually seen in cracks or depressions in the weathered lava surfaces. A few native lichens and mosses (*e.g.*, the white, leafy *Racomitrium lanuginosum*) may also be found. The paucity of vegetation is probably natural, although it may have been exacerbated by the presence of feral goats (*Capra hircus*) and sheep (*Ovis* spp.), notorious browsers of native vegetation at high elevations.

Animals found at high elevation in the Park include a number of invertebrates such as the endemic wēkiu bug (*Nysius wekiuicola*), several spiders, a centipede, the introduced western yellowjacket (*Vespula pensylvanica*), and a few alien and native flies. Many windblown invertebrates, collectively called "aeolian waifs," provide food for resident invertebrates. Dark-rumped petrels or 'ua'u (*Pterodroma phaeopygia sandwichensis*) and band-rumped (Harcourt's) storm petrels or 'akē'akē (*Oceanodroma castro*) may be heard over the high slopes during the breeding season, and a few breeding colonies of 'ua'u have been found in the alpine as well as the subalpine zones. Unfortunately, birds in burrows are easy prey for far-ranging feral house cats (*Felis catus*), which have destroyed most of the birds that have been found to date.

A large wolf spider (family Lycosidae) is fairly common in some alpine areas (*e.g.*, the trail between Pu'u 'Ula'ula [Red Hill] and Mauna Loa Cabin) and may be seen scurrying into cracks or under lava rocks during the day. These interesting animals catch prey on the ground rather than by weaving webs. Females care for their eggs and young, which may number in the hundreds. Lycosid spiderlings are among the best colonizers of new areas through a method comparable to hang-gliding. Gossamer lines spun from spiderling abdomens catch the wind to carry the tiny animals to new areas in the vast reaches of upper Mauna Loa and perhaps elsewhere.

The Park's alpine and aeolian zones are not accessible by road within the Park but may be reached by Mauna Loa Trail, which begins at the top of Mauna Loa Strip Road, near 6,700 ft elevation. Outside the Park, an alternate route begins at the Mauna Loa Observatory at 11,120 ft elevation, which can be reached from the Saddle Road. Using the latter approach, hiking distance to the summit and Mauna Loa Cabin is much shorter, but the trail is steeper. Regardless of the route chosen, backcountry use permits, obtainable at Park Headquarters, are required for all hikers planning overnight trips.

'Āhinahina or Silverswords (*Argyroxiphium sandwicense* and *A. kauense*)

Sunflower family (Asteraceae)

Endemic to the islands of Maui and Hawai'i; **Federally listed Endangered Species**

Distribution in the Park: Planted at the top of Mauna Loa Strip Road and along Mauna Loa Trail to Pu'u 'Ula'ula (Red Hill)

The Haleakalā 'āhinahina or silversword (*Argyroxiphium sandwicense* subsp. *macrocephalum*, underline) and two Hawai'i Island relatives have been planted in the alpine and subalpine zones of Mauna Loa and today grow at scattered localities not far from Mauna Loa Trail. Both the Haleakalā silversword and the Mauna Kea silversword (*A. sandwicense* subsp. *sandwicense*) were planted on Mauna Loa 20 to 40 years ago, before their taxonomic distinctness and potential for hybridization were recognized.

The Mauna Kea silversword is the rarer of the two subspecies and is listed by the Federal and State governments as Endangered. Naturally occurring plants of this species are today restricted to Waipāhoehoe Gulch above 9,000 ft elevation on the eastern slope of Mauna Kea. Approximately 50 naturally occurring individuals were counted at this site in 1993; these have now been supplemented by more than 200 Mauna Kea silverswords propagated and planted by the Hawaii State Division of Forestry and Wildlife, and the Mauna Kea site has been fenced to exclude feral ungulates (hoofed mammals).

Haleakalā 'āhinahina occur naturally only at Haleakalā National Park on Maui, where they today number approximately 50,000 plants, concentrated on cinder substrates within Haleakalā Crater. This subspecies has recently been listed by the U.S. Fish and Wildlife Service as Threatened. Seeds from Maui were brought to Hawaii Volcanoes as early as 1927, but most plantings on Mauna Loa probably date from the 1950s.

These two high-elevation 'āhinahina or silverswords are similar in appearance; both are giant rosette plants composed of a ball-shaped cluster of long, narrow, fleshy leaves covered with bright silvery hairs. Both are long-lived plants, which generally flower only once, producing a stout inflorescence containing many inch-wide, daisy-like heads of pink flowers. After flowering and producing seeds, single-rosette plants die, but those composed of several rosettes may live until each has flowered. Both Mauna Kea and Haleakalā silverswords may live more than 50 years before flowering.

A third type of 'āhinahina has been planted in Hawaii Volcanoes within the subalpine zone near the top of Mauna Loa Strip Road. This is the Ka'ū silversword (*A. kauense*), a species discovered early in the 19th century on Mauna Loa near 6,000 ft elevation and named as a distinct species only in the 1950s. A rosette-forming plant somewhat smaller than the Haleakalā and Mauna Kea silverswords, the Ka'ū silversword has narrower, more lax, and less silvery leaves than its relatives at higher elevations. Its flower heads are also smaller and bear fewer petal-like ray flowers. The Ka'ū silversword naturally occurs in wet subalpine forest and shrublands to the west of the Park and in one remote bog far to the northeast. Of all three silverswords planted in Hawaii Volcanoes, this one is most likely to have been distributed over the area of Mauna Loa now included in the Park, as populations have been discovered within a few miles of the Park's western boundary.

While there is no record of silverswords as original components of the natural vegetation of Hawaii Volcanoes, these rare taxa were planted within the Park because it was considered to be a safe and protected area for plants vulnerable to disturbance in their natural habitats. All silverswords (and related greenswords, *A. grayanum* on Maui) are susceptible to the depredations of feral pigs, goats, sheep, and mouflon. The browsing of feral ungulates, including wild cattle, is probably largely responsible for the decline of silverswords on Mauna Kea and Mauna Loa. Other factors have also contributed to the current rarity of these unusual endemic plants. Silverswords must be cross-pollinated with other individuals to set viable seeds, and when populations decline to low numbers, few plants flower at the same time, reducing the likelihood of successful outbreeding. Native insects (particularly bees) are the natural pollination agents for silverswords, and there is concern at Haleakalā that the populations of these native insects are being reduced by alien insect predators such as the western yellowjacket and the Argentine ant. House mice are known to eat silversword seeds, but few mice are present in alpine areas. In the past, there was great concern that seed-eating insects would decrease the number of potential propagules in each year's seed crop; today, these seed eaters are recognized as native species that rarely destroy all the seeds of flower heads and probably do not represent a serious threat to silversword survival.

Another source of mortality of the long-lived silverswords has been collection by people. In the past, many visitors to Haleakalā and Mauna Kea uprooted silversword plants, took them home, and dried them for display or as sourvenirs. Today, all silverswords or 'āhinahina are legally protected and may not be collected or harmed.

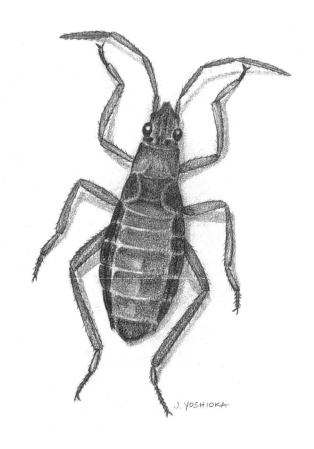

J. YOSHIOKA

Wēkiu Bug (*Nysius wekiuicola*)

True Bug order (Heteroptera), Seed Bug family (Lygaeidae)

Endemic

Distribution in the Park: Mauna Loa summit area (above 13,000 ft)

The wēkiu bug is one of the most remarkable examples of an "adaptive shift" among Hawai'i's invertebrates. Lifestyles of such species are radically different from those of close relatives. Although some 1,500 species of lygaeid bugs around the world have wings and can fly, the wēkiu bug is flightless. While other *Nysius* species are seed eaters, and some, outside Hawai'i, are important agricultural pests, the wēkiu bug survives by sucking the body fluids of dead and dying invertebrates blown to the tops of Mauna Loa and Mauna Kea. Included in this group of "aeolian waifs" (windblown invertebrates) are ladybird beetles, moths, spiders, flies, and even Kamehameha butterflies. The wēkiu bug has lost its wings in response to the fact that it takes a great deal of energy to fly in the cold, and because food, shelter, and mates can be found in its habitat by walking.

The black bodies of wēkiu bugs absorb the warmth of the sun; long black legs keep most of the body away from the cold ground. The blood of this animal contains glycerol, an antifreeze useful in the cold summit environment in which it lives. And wēkiu bugs are behaviorally as well as physically and chemically adapted to their harsh surroundings, seeking out warm spots and becoming most active in the summer when snows are melting. At this time they can be found at the edges of snow patches, where water and refrigerated invertebrates preserved from the winter months are available.

In addition to delicacies imported from lower elevations, wēkiu bugs on Mauna Kea and Mauna Loa sometimes dine on domestic fare. Some 18 resident species of invertebrates are known from Mauna Kea (which has a road to the top and has been better studied than Mauna Loa), including spiders, centipedes, and moths. Some of these invertebrates were probably originally brought to higher elevations by humans.

Did the wēkiu bug reach the tops of both Mauna Loa and Mauna Kea by way of human transport from one to another? Probably not. We know that bugs from the two mountains are nearly identical, so either separation occurred in recent times, or evolution has been conservative in the extreme conditions that prevail on peaks. During the last ice age (about 250,000 years ago), glaciers extended below 11,000 ft elevation in some places. Perhaps interchange of insects between the mountains was more common then because insects were more tolerant and climatic barriers were less prevalent. Now, the land between the peaks is unsuitable for wēkiu bug survival, and these unusual animals are found only on two cold and windy islands in the sky.

RARE AND MISSING PLANTS

The state of Hawai'i, despite its small size, has more endangered plant species than any state but California. As of October 1993, a total of 204 Hawaiian plants had been listed or formally proposed by the U.S. Fish and Wildlife Service as Federally Endangered or Threatened. More than 150 additional Hawaiian plant species are candidates under review for future Federal listing as Endangered. Factors contributing to the large number of Endangered plants in Hawai'i are the high degree of endemicity in the native flora, restriction of many taxa to limited habitats, loss of pollinators and dispersal agents, displacement by invasive alien plants, and disturbance by feral ungulates (hoofed mammals) and humans.

Although Hawaii Volcanoes National Park was not originally established with rare plants in mind, the protected habitats within its boundaries support at least ten plant species recently proposed for Endangered Species status and nearly 20 additional taxa that are candidates for Federal listing as Endangered. Apart from these plants, which are considered to be in danger of extinction throughout their ranges, at least 50 native species are unnaturally rare in the Park but may be more common elsewhere.

While the rain forests and upland forests of the Park have more intact vegetation and a greater diversity of native plant species, rare plants are found in every major Park zone. Several of the Park's proposed and candidate Endangered plant species are restricted to the coast or the adjacent lowlands. Two rare coastal species, a grass (*Ischaemum byrone*) and an 'ihi or purslane (*Portulaca villosa*), grew until recently at a site just west of Kamoamoa, but their habitat has been either destroyed or greatly altered by lava flows from the current eruption. While Kamoamoa was the only Park site known to support these two rare species, fortunately both occur outside the Park.

A third proposed Endangered plant species, the 'ōhai (*Sesbania tomentosa*, lower illustration) may still be seen at several coastal or lowland sites that are not currently threatened by lava flows. This low, spreading shrub is typically only 2 to 3 ft tall, but its trailing stems and grayish green foliage may cover many square yards of ground surface. Leaves of the 'ōhai are composed of 12 or more pairs of oblong leaflets with rounded tips. Stems and developing leaves at branch tips are often densely clothed in golden hairs, and leaves are usually covered with scattered hairs. Bright red curved flowers (1-2 in. long) are present throughout the year. Long, narrow seed pods are most abundant during the summer. Approximately 4 to 5 in. long, pods are less than 0.25 in. wide with shallow constrictions between seeds. Found in just a few sites on all the main Hawaiian Islands, 'ōhai occurs on Hawai'i Island only at South Point and within Hawaii Volcanoes. 'Ōhai is found in the Park at 'Āpua Point, Halapē, Ka'aha, near Kīpuka Nēnē, and at scattered sites in the remote western lowlands. Hikers and campers who use the Park's coastal trails and beaches should take care to avoid trampling or disturbing this beautiful rarity.

Rare plants of the mid-elevation zone include candidate and proposed Endangered Species such as 'ahakea (*Bobea timonioides*), a tree of dry and moist forests; hala pepe (*Pleomele hawaiiensis*), an unusual arborescent member of the agave family; Hawaiian catchfly (*Silene hawaiiensis*), a wiry shrub in the pink family; and 'ihi mākole or po'e (*Portulaca sclerocarpa*), a low-growing succulent herb. 'Ihi mākole (left illustration) occurs only on the island of Hawai'i (and one islet off Lāna'i) in dry habitats above 3,000 ft elevation. Hawaii Volcanoes National Park appears to have the largest population of 'ihi mākole known on the Island. Thirty years ago this rare plant was a frequent inhabitant in forests of the mid-elevation forests, but today it is restricted to only a few localities in the Park. The most important Park site, with approximately 1,000 individuals, is a geothermal area along the Chain of Craters. Only a few inches tall, 'ihi mākole has weak fleshy stems and narrow succulent leaves with tufts of hairs at leaf axils. Small open flowers are clustered at stem tips; these have five thin white petals and many golden-yellow stamens. The small fruits that develop from these flowers are round, dry capsules containing tiny dark seeds. The reasons for the rarity of this species are not known, but it is possible that feral goats (*Capra hircus*) and pigs (*Sus scrofa*) may have contributed to its decline, and alien grasses may have displaced it. An alien purple-flowered 'ihi (*Portulaca pilosa*) grows alongside 'ihi mākole at some sites; its impact on the endemic species is unknown.

Park rain forests are home to approximately 30 rare species of endemic plants, including two terrestrial orchids, four vines in the mint family, six lobelioids, several ferns, a palm, and more than a dozen types of trees and shrubs. Five of these rare endemics are proposed or candidates for Endangered Species status. They are a shrub in the African violet family (*Cyrtandra giffardii*); the lobelioids 'akū (*Cyanea tritomantha*) and koli'i (*Trematolobelia grandifolia*); ānini, a shrub in the tea family (*Eurya sandwicensis*); and two ferns (*Asplenium schizophyllum* and *Adenophorus periens*). These species are understory plants that require the cool, shady conditions of closed-canopy rain forests. *Adenophorus periens*, called *Oligadenus periens* by some (upper right illustration), a fern with no recorded Hawaiian name other than the nonspecific "kihi," is perhaps the rarest of the Park's rare rain forest plants. Formerly found in wet forests of six of the Hawaiian Islands, in the last 60 years this fern has been seen only on Kaua'i, Hawai'i, and Moloka'i. On the island of Hawai'i, *A. periens* seems to be restricted to closed-canopy 'ōhi'a (*Metrosideros polymorpha*) forests between Glenwood and Kīlauea's East Rift. This fern grows as an epiphyte on tree trunks, where it appears as clusters of pendulous fronds about 12 in. long. *Adenophorus periens* may be distinguished from more common relatives, such as *A. pinnatifidus* (*O. pinnatifidus* of some authors), by the greater length of its fronds, the perpendicular position of frond lobes, and the distinctive row of black hairs on the edge of each frond. The reduction in the historical range of *A. periens* indicates that it may not be able to tolerate disturbance to its rain forest habitat, but it is not understood why this fern is currently restricted to such a small geographical area.

Rare plants of the Park's upland forest and woodland zone are concentrated in the biologically diverse forests of Kīpuka Puaulu and Kīpuka Kī. More than a dozen rare woody species are found in these forests, including three that are proposed or candidates for Endangered Species status. The hau kuahiwi (*Hibiscadelphus giffardianus*) is essentially extinct in the wild but has been reintroduced in the upland woodlands in Kīpuka Puaulu. 'Aiea (*Nothocestrum breviflorum*), a tree of the nightshade family, is rarely seen in dry and moist forests of the kona (leeward) side of Hawai'i Island and may still occur in the Park's kīpuka forests. *Melicope zahlbruckneri*, an extremely rare tree of the rue or citrus family, has been collected from only two localities other than Kīpuka Puaulu, where approximately 30 individuals grow today. A fourth proposed Endangered Species, the Kīlauea hōlei (*Ochrosia kilaueaensis*), has not been seen in Kīpuka Puaulu in more than 60 years and apparently no longer grows in the Park.

The Park's subalpine zone is home to several rare plants found only at higher elevations, such as the silvery-leaved nohoanu (*Geranium cuneatum* subsp. *hypoleucum*) and the unusual, nearly leafless heau (*Exocarpos menziesii*), a shrub in the sandalwood family. In addition to these uncommon species, at least three proposed or candidate Endangered Species occur in the Park only in the subalpine zone. These include a tiny fern (*Asplenium fragile* var. *insulare* or *A. rhomboideum*), found only at the entrances of high-elevation lava tubes; an endemic raspberry or 'ākala (*Rubus macraei*); and laukāhi kuahiwi (*Plantago hawaiensis*), a perennial herb with narrow, strap-shaped leaves arising from a stout stem covered with reddish woolly hairs. Even the sparsely vegetated alpine zone of Mauna Loa probably supported rare plants in the past, but the only known rare species present there today are planted silverswords (*Argyroxiphium* spp.).

We will probably never know how many native plants became extinct before they could be collected and described by botanists. Lists of plants of the Park made earlier this century, however, indicate that several plant species have disappeared from Hawaii Volcanoes in the last 80 years. Kīpuka Puaulu, a forest well studied in the early 1900s, has lost at least seven species of native trees since 1913, when Joseph Rock documented the species composition of the Kīpuka. Among these disappearances is the exceedingly rare Kīlauea hōlei, known from only one locality other than Kīpuka Puaulu. Other apparent losses from the Park include *Neraudia ovata*, a small tree of the mid-elevation woodlands in the nettle family; pololei (*Ophioglossum concinnum*), a coastal fern; and *Spermolepis hawaiiensis*, an herb in the parsley family native to lowland forests. These missing species are now candidates for Endangered Species status, but they have not been seen in the Park since the 1940s. While future restoration of some of these species may be possible, the immediate goal of Park resource managers is to protect rare species habitat to prevent further losses of native plants.

Hau Kuahiwi (*Hibiscadelphus giffardianus*)

Mallow family (Malvaceae)

Endemic to Hawai'i Island.

Distribution in the Park: Planted in Kīpuka Puaulu

316

Some of the rarest trees in the Hawaiian Islands are the hau kuahiwi or upland hau, relatives of the better-known hibiscus. The entire genus *Hibiscadelphus*, which means "brother of hibiscus," is endemic or unique to the Hawaiian Islands, occurring on Kaua'i, Lāna'i, Maui, and Hawai'i. All six of the described species in this group are either extinct or exceedingly rare. All *Hibiscadelphus* species share the Hawaiian name hau kuahiwi.

The Park's hau kuahiwi, a candidate for Federal listing as an Endangered Species, was discovered in 1911 (five years before Hawaii National Park was designated) by the Austrian botanist Joseph Rock. Near Kīpuka Puaulu, which was then used for grazing cattle, he found only one tree growing. Seeds were collected from it, and one tree was established on private land in Volcano Village. Cuttings from this tree were propagated on Keauhou Ranch (adjacent to the Park) and in the Hilo nursery of the Territorial Division of Forestry. In the 1930s, the original wild tree died, but the plant still survived in cultivation and was replanted in Kīpuka Puaulu in the 1950s.

A small to medium-sized tree, often with multiple trunks, the hau kuahiwi resembles a large hibiscus. Its leaves are large, rough textured, and rounded, with an irregular margin and conspicuous palmate venation. Hau kuahiwi flowers are curved, 2 to 3 in. long, with a dark red corolla surrounding a prominent central column bearing the male and female floral parts. The exteriors of the flowers, both the corolla and the large calyx, are covered with soft, star-shaped, yellowish brown or greenish gray hairs. The flowers differ from those of a hibiscus in their curvature and the petals, which remain folded around the central part of the flower and never spread. The flowers develop into rough, woody, yellow-green capsules more than 1 in. long, containing seeds covered with light brown hairs.

Two other species of hau kuahiwi are known from Hawai'i Island. One (*H. bombycinus*) was collected near Kawaihae in the mid-19th century and is presumed extinct; the native forests of this region have been replaced by nonnative trees and grasses. The other hau kuahiwi (*H. hualalaiensis*) is native to the slopes of Hualālai Volcano, an area long used as a cattle ranch. In the 1950s, this Hualālai hau kuahiwi, reduced to only a few trees in its natural habitat, was planted in Kīpuka Puaulu, which was (and still is) one of the few examples of moist forest protected on the Island. By the early 1970s, researchers examining flowers for rat damage recognized variation in hau kuahiwi flower morphology that indicated hybridization between the species native to the Kīpuka and the Hualālai transplant. By this time more than 40 individual hau kuahiwi trees were growing in the Park, most of them first- and second-generation hybrids between the two species.

The Park was faced with a management dilemma. Should the vigorously growing hybrids be destroyed to protect the genetic integrity of the original Kīpuka Puaulu hau kuahiwi? What should be done with the planted Hualālai hau kuahiwi, also one of Hawai'i's rarest tree species? Although some people argued that the hybrids should be retained for possible use as rootstock for the two rare species, it would have been difficult to prevent the roots from forming shoots that would eventually flower and present opportunities for future hybridization. Park managers decided to kill the hybrid trees and dig up and relocate the Hualālai hau kuahiwi to arboreta and botanical gardens. The hybrids were relatively easy to identify when flowering because hybrid flowers were of an intermediate size and had a ring of narrow leaf-like structures or bracts that were intermediate in length between the two parent species. Today, remaining hau kuahiwi trees in Kīpuka Puaulu are those descended from the one individual discovered in the area 80 years ago.

Although hybridization is no longer a problem and plants are now protected from domestic cattle and feral ungulates, the Park's hau kuahiwi trees do not appear to be reproducing in Kīpuka Puaulu. The shape of the hau kuahiwi flower and its production of copious amounts of sweet nectar suggest adaptations for pollination by long-billed birds. Today few 'i'iwi occur in the Kīpuka, and native birds are probably not acting as pollinators of the plant. Pollination is taking place and seeds often develop, but most are taken by rats, animals introduced to Hawai'i. In one study, approximately 90 percent of hau kuahiwi seeds were eaten by rats, which also eat flower buds and pollen and chew into the base of flowers to get at the sweet nectar. Bark stripping and branch girdling by rats during dry periods has also been observed. Reduction in rat populations may be necessary to ensure the continued existence of hau kuahiwi in Kīpuka Puaulu.

J. Yoshioka ©
1988

Hawaiian Vetch or Hawaiian Broadbean (*Vicia menziesii*)

Pea family (Fabaceae)

Endemic to Hawai'i Island. **Federally listed Endangered Species**

Distribution in the Park: Not known to occur in
Hawaii Volcanoes National Park

The Hawaiian vetch was the first plant from Hawai'i to be listed as an
Endangered Species (in 1978). While not known from Hawaii Volcanoes, this

rare plant has been collected from sites both east and west of the Park's Mauna Loa Strip. A climbing vine in the pea family, the Hawaiian vetch is much larger and more woody than most temperate-zone vetches, which tend to be low, herbaceous vines. The Hawaiian vetch has angular stems and dark green, pinnately compound leaves tipped by curling tendrils, which allow the vine to attach itself to other plants and climb high into trees. Flowers, resembling those of a sweetpea, are borne in attractive, pendent clusters of 6 to 10, and usually appear in the summer. Flower petals are white when young and progressively darken to pink and dark rose. After fertilization by an unknown agent (possibly a species of Hawaiian honeycreeper), flowers develop into legumes, flattened pods that split when dry to reveal one to six round, dull black seeds.

The Hawaiian vetch was first discovered in 1794 by Archibald Menzies, a surgeon and naturalist on Captain George Vancouver's third voyage to the Hawaiian Islands. Menzies was the first European to climb Mauna Loa, and it was during this ascent that he collected the vetch, which was climbing on native shrubs at the upper edge of the forests of Kapāpala. Nineteenth century botanical explorers collected the Hawaiian vetch on windward Mauna Kea in the forests above Laupāhoehoe. In the early 1900s the vetch was found on Keauhou Ranch, to the east of the Park. For about 60 years, the Hawaiian vetch was not seen or collected, leading many botanists to assume that it had become extinct. Then in the early 1970s, the vetch was rediscovered on Keauhou Ranch and in Kīlauea Forest at about 5,000 ft elevation. These privately owned lands are almost the last refuge of this Endangered plant, which was also found on the slopes of Hualālai in the early 1980s and relocated in 1992. Unfortunately the vetch faces many threats to its continued existence at both sites. Much of its remaining natural habitat on Keauhou Ranch is used to graze cattle, which may browse or trample the vetch and open up the understory of forests used as pasture. Feral pigs are also a threat to seedlings and unprotected vines as they uproot and trample plants in their search for food. Beginning in the late 1970s, some of the disturbed forests containing Hawaiian vetch plants at Keauhou Ranch were bulldozed for a commercial silviculture project to grow koa, a commercially valuable native hardwood. Rats and insects have also been implicated as agents of damage to the vine.

Little is known about the natural pollinators or seed dispersal agents of the Hawaiian vetch, and its reproductive success has not been recently studied. The number of Hawaiian vetch plants surviving in their natural habitat is unknown, but the landowner of Kīlauea/Keauhou plans rare plant surveys in the near future.

The example of the Hawaiian vetch illustrates the difficulty of saving endangered species endemic to restricted localities, which may be under private ownership on lands where native plants and animals are not protected. Unless we are willing to settle for plantings in arboreta or maintenance of species as germ plasm in seed repositories, conservation of Endangered Species will require protection of their habitat as natural areas. An added benefit in habitat protection is the conservation of rare plant pollinators and other associated animal and plant species.

RARE AND MISSING BIRDS

J. YOSHIOKA

RARE AND MISSING BIRDS

Extinction is a natural phenomenon, but extinction rates of plants and animals in Hawai'i have increased considerably since the arrival of humans. Fossil finds of birds over the past 20 years or so demonstrate that most birds not known historically were extirpated from 1,900 to 900 years ago. Bird bones dating from pre-contact times (before Europeans) have often been found in "cultural contexts" (along with artifacts of Polynesian people) or with species, such as rats and snails, introduced by early Hawaiians; the reduction of bird bones over time at archaeological sites formerly used by Hawaiians suggests that these people could indeed reduce surrounding populations of some avian species. The effects of continental humans were even more severe and continue today.

Based on fossil records (actually subfossils, since they are not fully mineralized), we know that only 62 percent of Hawai'i's passerine (song-birds) and 12.5 percent of nonpasserine species survived until the late 1700s, when Europeans first arrived in Hawai'i. Clearing of lowland forests for agricultural purposes, together with predation by humans, dogs, pigs, and rats, probably accounted for most of the avian extinctions. Flightless nonpasserines such as geese (including a species weighing up to 50 lb -- five times the size of the nēnē or Hawaiian goose, *Branta sand-vicensis*), rails, and ibises would have been vulnerable to predation. Smaller birds, with typical island naivete, would have been easy prey for dogs and rats. Other native birds such as owls, a hawk, and an eagle probably vanished as prey disappeared. By the time Captain James Cook landed in 1778, extinct (or extremely rare) species included 10 or 11 geese and ducks, 8 flightless rails, 3 flightless ibises, 2 raven-sized crows, a honeyeater, a bird-eating hawk, an eagle, and 14 species of Hawaiian honeycreepers (subfamily Drepanidinae).

With the arrival of continental humans in Hawai'i, the avian extinction rate again became much more rapid than the prehistoric rate. Losses during the period 1890 to 1930 were especially great. An additional 11 species of unique Hawaiian honeycreepers have disappeared to date, and 13 of the 21 surviving species are Endangered Species; some of these are probably already extinct. A host of aggressive introduced animals, plants, and diseases plus further habitat destruction have resulted in severely restricted distributions in often marginal habitat for most remaining native birds. Hawai'i's avian species richness has now been reduced by some two-thirds through human-induced effects (Polynesian and continental peoples).

In Hawaii Volcanoes National Park, native species now constitute only 46 percent of the total bird species found in the Park. Although numerous alien species have been added, a number of natives once found in or near the Park have been lost. Those that are now extinct include the Hawai'i 'ō'ō (*Moho nobilis*), the kioea (*Chaetoptila angustipluma*), the Hawai'i 'akialoa (*Hemignathus obscurus obscurus*), the greater koa finch (*Psittirostra palmeri*), and the Hawai'i mamo (*Drepanis pacifica*).

The five species of birds described in this section are all Federally listed Endangered Species. The ʻalalā (*Corvus hawaiiensis*, illustrated on section title page) is arguably the most endangered bird in the world, and the Hawaiʻi ʻōʻū (*Psittirostra psittacea*) is possibly extinct. Small populations of the remaining three species (ʻakiapōlāʻau [*Hemignathus munroi*], Hawaiʻi ʻākepa [*Loxops coccineus coccineus*], and Hawaiʻi creeper [*Oreomystis mana*]) are still found on State or private lands near the Park; some of these birds may one day be used for repatriation to former habitat in Park forests.

Patterns of extinction for Hawaiʻi's birds are probably indicative of what happened to other animals that do not leave fossil "footprints." The loss of flightless insects, which evolved in Hawaiʻi in 10 of the 11 orders of flying insects, may have been as severe as that of flightless birds. Flightlessness (in animals) and loss of dispersal mechanisms (in plants) are common adaptations on islands. In the Park, two species of picture wing flies have apparently vanished from wet and moist forests since 1980. *Drosophila heteroneura* and *D. sylvestris* have suffered from reduction of *Clermontia* host plants by feral pigs, from predation by the western yellowjacket (*Vespula pensylvanica*), and possibly from collecting for scientific studies. As with the loss of Hawaiʻi's forest birds, it is difficult to say whether habitat loss and degradation, predation, or other limiting factors are primary causes.

Regardless of the reasons for losses, important components of Hawaiʻi's biota continue to disappear, resulting in biological communities that are impoverished in native species, altered and simplified in processes, less aesthetically diverse and valuable to humans in the long run, and more vulnerable to invasions by alien species. Changes in bird numbers, distributions, and species diversity provide a conspicuous index to less evident changes in structure and function of the entire biotic community. By this measure alone, Hawaiʻi's native communities are in drastic need of preservation and restoration. That much of the public is insensitive to the losses (a recent survey showed that most people in Hawaiʻi believe such problems are worse in other states) does not bode well for the future.

'Alalā or Hawaiian Crow (*Corvus hawaiiensis*)

Crow and Jay family (Corvidae)

Endemic to Hawai'i Island. **Federally listed Endangered Species**

Distribution in the Park: Missing

With perhaps a dozen birds left in the wild on the kona (leeward) side of the island of Hawai'i, controversy surrounds this species. Should 'alalā be removed from the private ranchlands that appear to be their last stronghold because the population may be too small to survive? Should wild birds be used to supplement gene pools of captive birds? Should 'alalā be studied to determine population health, despite the risk of disturbing the small population? Should supplemental feeding and predator control be conducted at public expense without evaluating responses of the 'alalā? Are we spending too much time and effort on a doomed species? Should we be focusing on ecosystems rather than "basket cases"? No completely satisfactory answers seem likely, but learning while managing the species seems a reasonable approach.

Many people predict that the 'alalā will be one of the next extinct species in Hawai'i. But steps are being taken to prevent this. The State operates a captive breeding facility on Maui with about 13 birds. Eggs and young have been produced by these captive birds in recent years. Another captive propagation facility is planned by the U.S. Fish and Wildlife Service for Hawai'i Island. In addition, a renewed emphasis on producing 'alalā from eggs taken from wild birds has begun and has supplemented production from captive crows. 'Alalā eggs are being incubated in an "egg house" in their breeding range on Hawai'i Island as well. Once young hatch they are raised in isolation from humans and returned to the wild.

'Alalā have declined drastically in distribution and numbers in the 20th century. The species once ranged from less than 1,000 to over 8,000 ft in elevation in dry to moist forests and parklands around the Island. 'Alalā were treated with respect by Hawaiians, although their black feathers were used in kāhili (long staffs topped with feathers, symbols of royalty). By the 1930s, crow numbers were greatly reduced, even though much of their geographical range was still occupied. By 1940, 'alalā were no longer found at lower elevations, and by the 1950s, they were present only in several remnants of their geographic range. In 1978, an estimated 76 birds remained in forest fragments between 3,000 and 6,200 ft elevation. The decline has continued, until today only one small group (at least 11 birds) remains, on McCandless Ranch in the central kona side of Hawai'i Island. What has happened to this social, seemingly "intelligent," but vulnerable black rascal of a bird should touch us all.

Although crows around the world tolerate humans to some degree and are able to adapt their diets to many different situations, destruction of 'alalā habitat for grazing and logging severely reduced favored native fruits from forest understories. On the kona coast, 'ōlapa and 'ōhā were common summer foods, and 'ie'ie and māmaki were common winter foods. Young birds were perhaps even more vulnerable to food shortages than adults. Because young crows leave the nest before they can fly (sometimes as long as two weeks before), introduced small Indian mongooses and feral house cats reduced reproductive success in many areas. Like other crows, 'alalā can fly strongly and for long distances, thus increasing the chances of contracting fatal diseases such as avian malaria and pox, especially at low to middle elevations where mosquito vectors thrive. And tragically, a shooting campaign by agriculturists in the early 20th century probably severely reduced numbers.

'Alalā were numerous in the Keauhou and Kapāpala areas near the Park around 1900. They once nested in koa forest 2 mi west of the Volcano House. Sporadic reports have occurred since then, especially in the Ka'ū area; the last reported sighting was in the winter of 1978 from Kalapana. Although the Park once provided habitat for only a few pairs, a high-elevation area along Mauna Loa Strip Road might someday serve as a secondary site for 'alalā reintroduction if enough 'alalā food plants can be encouraged there and if mongooses and feral house cats can be controlled. But holding crows in a presumably marginal area year round may not prove easy, and enhancing numbers on the kona side of the Island seems more feasible biologically. Considering social, political, and economic climates, in addition to the biological difficulties, 'alalā may not be heard in the Park again for years to come. How sad that such an interesting and conspicuous part of our unique avifauna is missing in so many places where it once was abundant. Let us hope it will not be lost forever from Hawai'i.

'Ō'ū (*Psittirostra psittacea*)

Finch family (Fringillidae),
  Hawaiian Honeycreeper and Finch subfamily (Drepanidinae)

Endemic to the Hawaiian Islands. **Federally listed Endangered Species**

Distribution in the Park: Probably missing. Formerly in wet 'ōhi'a forests primarily, but also dry 'ōhi'a woodland. Once found over a wider range of habitats, including koa forests and dry upland woodlands

The nest and eggs of this middle-sized (7 in.), olive-green honeycreeper with the bright yellow head (males) and pink legs have never been described. Although this is true of many of Hawaiʻi Island's extinct birds, the "Johnny, we hardly knew ye" poignancy of what may now be an extinct species has come to pass only within the past decade in the Park. In the 1890s, lower ʻŌlaʻa Forest was a stronghold for this once-abundant bird, and in the last 50 years most of the ʻōʻū observations have been made in upper ʻŌlaʻa. In the 1930s and 40s, the species was present in low numbers near Nāpau Crater, and five sightings were reported near Volcano House after 1960. ʻŌʻū were last seen in the Park (ʻŌlaʻa Forest) in 1985 to 1986.

What happened? Clearly, ʻōʻū are intolerant of forests opened up for agriculture and further degraded by feral cattle and pigs. The thick, pinkish, parrot-like bill of this species is adapted to feeding on the large female inflorescence of the ʻieʻie vine, although berries of the larger lobelioids were also eaten. These species of plants are also vulnerable to pigs and rats. Caterpillars favored by young ʻōʻū may have decreased with the introduction of parasitoids (parasites on insects) and habitat changes. Behavioral traits may also have worked against this mobile bird. Although large numbers of ʻōʻū once wandered upslope of wet forests to feed on concentrations of caterpillars, they also moved downslope from mid-elevation wet forests to exploit fruiting common guava, mountain apple, and other introduced fruits. In these journeys, they were vulnerable to malarial parasites and viral pox pathogens carried by introduced mosquitoes. ʻŌʻū were also at risk to introduced feral house cats in some areas of their range. Perhaps reduced numbers of birds were unable to effectively exploit decreasing food sources (were western yellow-jackets a factor late in the game?) or to breed successfully.

It is unlikely that ʻōʻū in the Park have been overlooked in the past several years. ʻŌʻū are hard to see in the forest as they sit sluggishly in the canopy, but their plaintive whistles (slurred up or down) and canary-like songs are loud and distinctive. And the species formerly took conspicuous flights in groups, often high in the air over open country, in contrast to many other more localized honeycreepers.

The palila, an Endangered honeycreeper closely related to the ʻōʻū, was once also much more widespread but not reliably recorded in the Park. Better adapted to drier habitats such as the māmane-naio forest on Mauna Kea than the ʻōʻū, palila populations seem to be rebuilding with drastic reduction of sheep and goats from the mountain. Observing the more sedentary palila can give us some idea of what their more mobile wet forest relatives must have been like, but each species is unique. When humans are responsible, the loss of any species truly diminishes life on earth.

J. YOSHIOKA

'Akiapōlā'au (*Hemignathus munroi*)

Finch family (Fringillidae),
 Hawaiian Honeycreeper and Finch subfamily (Drepanidinae)

Endemic to Hawai'i Island. **Federally listed Endangered Species**

Distribution in the Park: Missing

'Akiapōlā'au

Hawai'i's "woodpecker" (no true woodpeckers occur here) has perhaps the most bizarre bill of the extant honeycreepers. The lower mandible is stout and strong, but the upper is slender, curved, and somewhat flexible. Each is used independently, with the upper serving as a probe to pry burrowing insects from beneath bark, and the lower to hammer (with mouth agape) or chisel bark. Like woodpeckers, "aki's" -- as they are affectionately called locally in an effort to keep the name at least as short as the bird (4.5-5.5 in.) -- sometimes rear back and put their entire body into forceful blows. A considerable racket can be created, helping one to locate foraging birds.

Male aki's are olive-green above with yellow heads, short tails, and black lores (area between eye and bill). Females are smaller and duller, and bills and legs are black in both sexes. Aki's characteristically feed slowly along larger branches or trunks of koa and rarely are seen on 'ōhi'a, although they will use māmane and naio in proportion to availability. Family groups of two or three birds are often seen. Favorite foods are the larvae of wood-boring beetles (cerambycids) found in koa, māmane, and naio.

Aki's seem to have a prolonged breeding cycle, with young observed in all months and males singing year round. The song is a series of whistled notes described as "You-don't-see-me-but-I-SEE-you!" and males and young "chip" loudly. An upslurred note is also given, and call notes are louder than those of the common 'amakihi but similar.

'Akiapōlā'au are now found in four discrete and disjunct relict populations on the Island, from about 3,300 ft to 8,500 ft elevation (but mostly above 5,000 ft), with greater densities in koa/'ōhi'a forests than in māmane-naio forests. These small populations are at risk; allowing forest connections to regenerate between some of them would certainly help populations to increase. In the Park, aki's were once apparently common near Volcano House (1940s) and in Kīpuka Kulalio, off Mauna Loa Strip Road (until the 1950s). Much of the koa woodland habitat on the Strip is now recovering nicely since the removal of ungulates starting in the 1940s and concluding in the mid-1980s. However, the closest sizeable aki population to the Park is now about 6 mi away, on Kulani Correctional Facility lands, owned by the State. Aki populations are even closer together elsewhere on the Island, but the birds are not known to move far. If existing populations are large enough and recovering habitat in the Park is adequate to support 'akiapōlā'au, Hawai'i's version of the woodpecker may one day be reestablished in Park forests by humans, even if this intriguing species cannot return by itself.

331

Hawai'i 'Ākepa (*Loxops coccineus coccineus*)

Finch family (Fringillidae),
  Hawaiian Honeycreeper and Finch subfamily (Drepanidinae)

Endemic (subspecies) to Hawai'i Island. **Federally listed**
  Endangered Species

Distribution in the Park: Missing

'Ākepa are small (4.5 in.) warbler-like birds found on several of the main Hawaiian Islands. Among the most active of the honeycreepers ('ākepa means "sprightly" in Hawaiian), 'ākepa have short, conical bills that are slightly crossed at the tip, enabling them to pry open buds, bark, or plant material woven together by invertebrates. Although the crossed bill cannot usually be seen in the field, the long, notched tail and pale bill are good characteristics to aid in identification. The Hawai'i Island subspecies is noted for the beautiful reddish orange males; females and young males (one to two years old) are greenish above and yellow below (older immatures may have some orange). 'Ākepa forage in small groups for invertebrates high in 'ōhi'a trees. The reddish color of the males may have evolved because females prefer it (as a sign of successfully surviving males) rather than because it served as camouflage among 'ōhi'a lehua (blossoms) against now-extinct avian predators.

'Ākepa build cup nests of mosses and grasses inside tree cavities. Eggs are whitish, with fine dark speckles over the surface and blotches concentrated at the large end. The 'ākepa song is a listless, short, descending, variable trill that may be repeated for several minutes; calls include thin upslurred whistles and a "keewit."

Hawai'i 'ākepa are most common above 4,500 ft elevation in tall, moist to wet forests. They occur in widely separated habitats in low numbers on the Island. In the Park, they were abundant around Kīlauea Caldera in the 1890s in dry 'ōhi'a woodland at 3,600 ft elevation. 'Ākepa were found in the lower Chain of Craters area in the late 1930s and early 1940s. By the 1970s they were no longer present in the Park. Closest populations are now on Kamehameha Schools/Bishop Estate's Keauhou Ranch and Kūlani Correctional Facility State lands east of the Park. Perhaps someday 'ākepa can be returned to high-elevation Park forests recovering from damage caused by hoofed mammals, once enough cavities in old trees are available to support a nesting population. Tests are under way on Mauna Loa Strip to determine how frequently arboreal black rats use nest boxes; this would suggest how important rats might be as predators, should 'ākepa be restored to the Park. Artificial nesting cavities may eventually be needed to support breeding 'ākepa if not enough appropriate natural cavities are present in the regenerating forests.

Hawai'i Creeper (*Oreomystis mana*)

Finch family (Fringillidae),
  Hawaiian Honeycreeper and Finch subfamily (Drepanidinae)

Endemic to Hawai'i Island. **Federally listed Endangered Species**

Distribution in the Park: Missing

Four species of creepers are now recognized in the Hawaiian Islands, with a fifth, the Moloka'i creeper (*Paroreomyza flammea*), presumed extinct. The Hawai'i Island bird is olive green above and paler below, with a black face mask and a straight bill. Sexes look alike but immatures have white lores (area between eye and bill) and a stripe over the eye.

This species usually is seen working the interior portions of koa or 'ōhi'a on tops or bottoms of branches, or moving up and down trunks in search of invertebrates. Sometimes creepers also forage in foliage. Creepers prefer relatively undisturbed closed-canopy koa forests and are far less common in logged, grazed, and open areas. The ubiquitous introduced Japanese white-eye may compete with creepers for food or transmit avian diseases through use of similar foraging sites.

Like the 'akiapōlā'au, creepers are often found in family groups and sometimes join flocks of 'ākepa and 'akiapōlā'au. Hawai'i creepers are readily confused with common 'amakihi but are usually more deliberate in their movements and have slightly straighter, horn-colored bills, grayish throats and chins, and broader masks.

Creepers sing a rapidly descending trill that is softer and faster than that of the common 'amakihi. They utter a thin, quiet "sweet" call. Family groups give loud, wheezy chatter notes. Hawai'i creepers breed from February to June and build open, cup-like nests.

In the Park, creepers were common near Kīlauea Caldera in the late 1800s. They were present in 'Ōla'a Forest east of the Park (3,500 ft elevation) in lesser numbers in the late 1800s. The decline in Park populations probably began in the early 1900s, and creepers were seen only a few times near Nahuku (Thurston Lava Tube) and lower Chain of Craters in the late 1930s. Creepers were occasionally reported from Mauna Loa Strip in the early 1950s and from 'Ōla'a Forest until the early 1960s. This species is a possible candidate for restoration to Park forests someday, providing sufficient numbers remain elsewhere to allow birds to be taken for translocation.

SYSTEMATIC CLASSIFICATION OF
BIOTA DISCUSSED IN THIS BOOK*

KINGDOM MONERA (PROKARYOTES)
DIVISION OXYPHOTOBACTERIA
CLASS CYANOCHLORONTA (Blue-green Algae)

KINGDOM PROTISTA (PROTISTS)
DIVISION CHLOROPHYTA
(Green Algae)
Ulva spp. (Limu pālahalaha, Sea lettuce)

DIVISION RHODOPHYTA
(Red Algae)
Porolithon spp. (Coralline Algae)
Ahnfeltia concinna (Limu 'Aki'aki)

KINGDOM MYCETEAE (FUNGI)
DIVISION MYXOMYCOTA
(Slime Molds)

DIVISION LICHENES
(Lichens)
Cladoniaceae
    Cladonia sp.
    Stereocaulon sp.
Diploschistaceae
    Diploschistes
Usneaceae
    Usnea australis

KINGDOM PLANTAE (PLANTS)
DIVISION BRYOPHYTA
(Bryophytes -- Mosses and Liverworts)

CLASS MUSCI (Mosses)
    Dicranaceae
        Campylopus praemorsus
    Grimmiaceae
        Racomitrium lanuginosum

---

*   Not all taxa mentioned in the book are listed here; only those for which some information is presented in the text (beyond the scientific or common name) are included. The index provides scientific names for all species.

CLASS HEPATICAE (Liverworts)

DIVISION TRACHEOPHYTA
(Vascular Plants -- Ferns and Flowering Plants)

SUBDIVISION LYCOPODIOPHYTA (Fern Allies)[1]
    Lycopodiaceae (Club moss family)[2]
        Lycopodium cernuum [Palhinhaea cernua] (Wāwae'iole)
        Lycopodium phyllanthum [Phlegmariurus phyllanthus]
        Lycopodium polytrichoides [Phlegmariurus filiformis]
        Lycopodium serratum [Huperzia serrata]
        Lycopodium venustulum

SUBDIVISION PSILOTA (Whisk Ferns)
    Psilotaceae (Whisk Fern family)
        Psilotum complanatum (Moa, Pipi)

SUBDIVISION FILICOPHYTA = Pterophyta (Ferns)
    CLASS OPHIOGLOSSOPSIDA
        Ophioglossaceae (Adder's-tongue fern family)
            Ophioglossum concinnum (Pololei)

    CLASS FILICOPSIDA
      Order Filicales
        Aspleniaceae (Spleenwort family)
            Asplenium fragile [A. rhomboideum]
            Asplenium nidus (Bird's nest fern)
            Asplenium schizophyllum
        Athyriaceae[3]
            Athyrium microphyllum ('Ākōlea)
            Diplazium sandwichianum (Hō'i'o)
        Blechnaceae
            Sadleria cyatheoides ('Ama'u)
            Sadleria pallida ('Ama'u)
            Sadleria souleyetiana ('Ama'u)
        Cyatheaceae
        Dennstaedtiaceae
            Microlepia strigosa (Palapalai)

---

[1]   Classification of ferns and fern allies is according to Lamoureux (unpubl.). Scientific names in brackets are according to Wagner and Wagner (unpubl.).

[2]   Wagner and Wagner (unpubl.) subdivide Lycopodiaceae into subfamilies: Huperzioideae (*Phlegmariurus filiformis, P. phyllanthus, Huperzia serrata*), Lycopodioideae (*Lycopodium venustulum*), and Lycopodielloideae (*Palhinhaea cernua*).

[3]   According to Wagner and Wagner (unpubl.), both species here are in the family Dryopteridaceae, subfamily Athyrioideae; the scientific names are unchanged.

Dicksoniaceae (Tree fern family)[4]
  Cibotium glaucum (Hāpuʻu pulu)
  Cibotium chamissoi [C. menziesii] (Hāpuʻu ʻiʻi)
  Cibotium hawgiiense [C. chamissoi] (Meu)
Elaphoglossaceae[5]
  Elaphoglossum hirtum [E. paleaceum] (ēkaha)
Gleicheniaceae (Vine fern family)
  Dicranopteris emarginata (Uluhe, False staghorn fern)
  Dicranopteris linearis (Uluhe, False staghorn fern)
Grammitaceae (Grammitis fern family)[6]
  Adenophorus pinnatifidus [Oligadenus pinnatifidus]
  Adenophorus periens [Oligadenus periens]
  Adenophorus tamariscinus (Wahine noho mauna)
  Grammitis hookeri (Mākuʻe lau liʻi)
  Grammitis tenella (Kolokolo)
  Xiphopteris saffordii [Lellingeria saffordii] (Kihi)
Hymenophyllaceae (Filmy ferns family)
  Mecodium recurvum (ʻōhiʻa ku)
  Sphaerocionium lanceolatum (Palai hinahina)
Hypolepidaceae
  Pteridium aquilinum var. *decompositum* (Bracken)
    [Pteridium decompositum][7]
Nephrolepidaceae[8] (Swordfern family)
  Nephrolepis exaltata [N. exaltata var. *hawaiiensis]*
    (Swordfern, Kupukupu)
  Nephrolepis multiflora (Scaly swordfern)
Polypodiaceae
  Phymatosorus scolopendria (Lauaʻe)
Sinopteridaceae (Maidenhair fern family)
  Pellaea ternifolia (Kalamoho)[9]
Thelypteridaceae
  Pneumatopteris sandwicensis [Thelypteris sandwicensis]
    (Hōʻiʻo kula)

---

[4] Family Cyatheaceae, subfamily Dicksonioideae according to Wagner and Wagner (unpubl.).

[5] Family Dryopteridaceae, subfamily Lomariopsidoideae according to Wagner and Wagner (unpubl.).

[6] Wagner and Wagner (unpubl.) calls this family Grammitidaceae.

[7] Family Dennstaedtiaceae according to Wagner and Wagner (unpubl.).

[8] According to Wagner and Wagner (unpubl.), these species are in the family Dryopteridaceae, subfamily Nephrolepidoideae.

[9] Family Adiantaceae, subfamily Cheilanthoideae according to Wagner and Wagner (unpubl.).

SUBDIVISION ANGIOSPERMATOPHYTA (Flowering Plants)[10]
CLASS MAGNOLIOPSIDA (Dicotyledons)
  Subclass Magnoliidae
    Order Laurales
      Lauraceae (Laurel family)
        Cassytha filiformis (Kauna'oa pehu)
    Order Piperales
      Piperaceae (Pepper family)
        Peperomia spp. ('Ala'ala wai nui)
    Order Papaverales
      Papaveraceae (Poppy family)
        Argemone glauca (Pua kala or Hawaiian prickly poppy)
        Argemone mexicana (Mexican poppy)
        Eschscholzia californica (California poppy)
  Subclass Hamamelidae
    Order Urticales
      Moraceae (Mulberry family)
        Broussonetia papyrifera (Wauke, Paper mulberry)
      Urticaceae (Nettle family)
        Neraudia ovata
        Pipturus albidus (Māmaki)
        Touchardia latifolia (Olonā)
        Urera glabra (Ōpuhe)
    Order Myricales
      Myricaceae (Bayberry family)
        Myrica faya (Faya tree, Firetree)
  Subclass Caryophyllidae
    Order Caryophyllales
      Aizoaceae (Fig-marigold family)
        Sesuvium portulacastrum ('Akulikuli, Sea purslane)
      Caryophyllaceae (Pink family)
        Silene hawaiiensis (Hawaiian catchfly)
      Nyctaginaceae (Four-o-clock family)
        Pisonia brunoniana (Pāpala kēpau)
      Portulacaceae (Portulaca family)
        Portulaca pilosa ('Ihi)
        Portulaca sclerocarpa ('Ihi mākole or Po'e)
        Portulaca villosa ('Ihi or Purslane)
    Order Polygonales
      Polygonaceae
        Rumex acetosella (Sheep sorrel)
  Subclass Dilleniidae
    Order Theales
      Theaceae (Tea family)
        Eurya sandwicensis (Ānini)

---

[10] Taxonomic treatment of the flowering plants follows that of Wagner, Herbst, and Sohmer, 1990, pp. 128-130.

Order <u>Malvales</u>
   Malvaceae (Mallow family)
     Hibiscadelphus bombycinus
     Hibiscadelphus giffardianus (Hau kuahiwi)
     Hibiscadelphus hualalaiensis (Hualālai hau kuahiwi)
     Hibiscus tiliaceus (Hau)
     Thespesia populnea (Milo)
   Sterculiaceae
     Waltheria indica ('Uhaloa)
Order <u>Violales</u>
   Passifloraceae (Passion flower family)
     Passiflora edulis (Liliko'i)
     Passiflora ligularis (Sweet granadilla)
     Passiflora foetida (Love-in-a-mist or Foetid passion flower)
     Passiflora mollissima (Banana poka)
Order <u>Ericales</u>
   Epacridaceae (Epacris family)
     Styphelia tameiameiae (Pūkiawe)
   Ericaceae (Heath family)
     Vaccinium calycinum ('Ōhelo kau lā'au, Tree 'ōhelo)
     Vaccinium reticulatum ('Ōhelo)
Order <u>Ebenales</u>
   Ebenaceae (Ebony family)
     Diospyros sandwicensis (Lama)
Order <u>Primulales</u>
   Myrsinaceae (Myrsine family)
     Myrsine lanaiensis
     Myrsine lessertiana (Kōlea lau nui)
     Myrsine sandwicensis (Kōlea lau li'i)
Subclass Rosidae
Order <u>Rosales</u>
   Hydrangeaceae (Hydrangea family)
     Broussaisia arguta (Pū'aha nui)
   Rosaceae (Rose family)
     Acaena exigua
     Fragaria chiloensis subsp. *sandwicensis* (Strawberry)
     Osteomeles anthyllidifolia ('Ūlei)
     Rubus argutus (Blackberry)
     Rubus ellipticus (Yellow Himalayan raspberry)
     Rubus hawaiensis ('Ākala)
     Rubus macraei ('Ākala)
     Rubus rosifolius (Thimbleberry)
Order <u>Fabales</u>
   Fabaceae (Pea family)
     Acacia koa (Koa)
     Canavalia hawaiiensis ('Āwikiwiki, Viny jackbean)
     Erythrina sandwicensis (Wiliwili)
     Sesbania tomentosa ('Ōhai)
     Sophora chrysophylla (Māmane)
     Vicia menziesii (Hawaiian vetch, Hawaiian Broadbean)

Order Myrtales
    Melastomataceae (Melastoma family)
        Tibouchina herbacea (Cane tibouchina)
    Myrtaceae (Myrtle family)
        Metrosideros polymorpha ('Ōhi'a, 'Ōhi'a lehua)
        Psidium cattleianum (Strawberry guava, Waiawī)
        Psidium guajava (Common guava)
        Syzygium malaccense (Mountain apple)
    Thymelaeaceae ('Ākia family)
        Wikstroemia phillyreifolia ('Ākia)
        Wikstroemia sandwicensis ('Ākia)
Order Santalales
    Santalaceae (Sandalwood family)
        Exocarpos menziesii (Heau)
        Santalum ellipticum (Sandalwood)
        Santalum paniculatum var. *paniculatum* ('Iliahi, Sandalwood)
Order Celastrales
    Aquifoliaceae (Holly family)
        Ilex anomala (Kāwa'u or Hawaiian holly)
    Celastraceae (Bittersweet family)
        Perrottetia sandwicensis (Olomea)
Order Euphorbiales
    Euphorbiaceae (Spurge family)
        Aleurites moluccana (Kukui, Candlenut)
        Antidesma platyphyllum (Hame)
Order Sapindales
    Anacardiaceae (Mango family)
        Schinus terebinthifolius (Christmas berry)
    Rutaceae (Rue or Citrus family)
        Melicope clusiifolia (Alani)
        Melicope radiata (Alani)
        Melicope zahlbruckneri
    Sapindaceae (Soapberry family)
        Dodonaea viscosa ('A'ali'i)
        Sapindus saponaria (A'e, Mānele, Soapberry)
Order Geraniales
    Geraniaceae (Geranium family)
        Geranium cuneatum subsp. *hypoleucum* (Nohoanu, Hinahina, or Hawaiian geranium)
Order Apiales
    Apiaceae (Parsley family)
        Spermolepis hawaiiensis
    Araliaceae (Ginseng family)
        Cheirodendron trigynum ('Ōlapa)
Subclass Asteridae
Order Gentianales
    Apocynaceae (Dogbane family)
        Alyxia oliviformis (Maile)
        Ochrosia kilaueaensis (Kīlauea hōlei)
        Plumeria spp. (Plumeria)

Loganiaceae (Strychnine family)
  Labordia hedyosmifolia (Kāmakahala)
Order Solanales
  Convolvulaceae (Morning glory family)
    Ipomoea indica (Koali ʻawa)
    Ipomoea pes-caprae subsp. *brasiliensis* (Pōhuehue)
    Jacquemontia ovalifolia subsp. *sandwicensis* (Paʻū o Hiʻiaka)
  Cuscutaceae (Dodder family)
    Cuscuta sandwichiana (Kaunaʻoa kahakai)
  Solanaceae (Nightshade family)
    Nothocestrum breviflorum (ʻAiea)
    Physalis peruviana (Cape gooseberry, Pohā)
    Solanum pseudocapsicum (Jerusalem cherry)
Order Lamiales
  Lamiaceae (Mint family)
    Stenogyne calaminthoides (Hawaiian mint)
  Verbenaceae (Verbena family)
    Lantana camara (Lantana)
Order Plantaginales
  Plantaginaceae
    Plantago hawaiensis (Laukāhi kuahiwi)
Order Scrophulariales
  Gesneriaceae (African violet family)
    Cyrtandra giffardii
    Cyrtandra platyphylla (ʻIlihia)
  Myoporaceae (Myoporum family)
    Myoporum sandwicense (Naio)
  Scrophulariaceae (Figwort family)
    Verbascum thapsus (Common mullein)
Order Campanulales
  Campanulaceae (Bellflower family)
    Lobelioideae (Lobelia subfamily)
      Clermontia hawaiiensis (ʻŌhā kēpau)
      Clermontia parviflora (ʻŌhā)
      Cyanea pilosa subsp. *longipedunculata*
      Cyanea tritomantha (ʻAkū)
      Trematolobelia grandifolia (Koliʻi)
  Goodeniaceae (Goodenia family)
    Scaevola chamissoniana (Naupaka kuahiwi)
    Scaevola kilaueae (Kīlauea naupaka, Huahekili uka)
    Scaevola sericea (Naupaka kahakai)
Order Rubiales
  Rubiaceae (Coffee family)
    Bobea timonioides (ʻAhakea)
    Canthium odoratum (Alaheʻe)
    Coprosma ernodeoides (Kūkaenēnē)
    Coprosma menziesii
    Coprosma montana (Mountain pilo)
    Coprosma ochracea (Pilo)
    Coprosma rhynchocarpa (Pilo)

    Morinda citrifolia (Noni, Indian mulberry)
    Psychotria hawaiiensis (Kōpiko ʻula)
  Order <u>Asterales</u>
   Asteraceae (Sunflower family)
    Argyroxiphium grayanum (Greensword)
    Argyroxiphium kauense (Kaū silversword, ʻĀhinahina)
    Argyroxiphium sandwicense subsp. *macrocephalum*
     (Haleakalā silversword)
    Argyroxiphium sandwicense subsp. *sandwicense*
     (Mauna Kea silversword)
    Bidens hawaiensis (Koʻokoʻolau or Kōkoʻolau)
    Bidens pilosa (Spanish needle)
    Dubautia ciliolata (Naʻenaʻe)
    Dubautia scabra (Kūpaoa)
    Hypochoeris radicata (Gosmore)
    Pluchea symphytifolia (Sourbush)
    Tetramolopium humile

 CLASS LILIOPSIDA (Monocotyledons)
  Subclass Arecidae
  Order <u>Arecales</u>
   Arecaceae (Palm family)
    Cocos nucifera (Niu or Coconut palm)
    Pritchardia beccariana (Loulu)
  Order <u>Pandanales</u>
   Pandanaceae (Screwpine family)
    Freycinetia arborea (ʻIeʻie)
    Pandanus tectorius (Hala or Screwpine)
  Subclass Commelinidae
  Order <u>Juncales</u>
   Juncaceae (Rush family)
    Luzula hawaiiensis
  Order <u>Cyperales</u>
   Cyperaceae (Sedges)
    Carex wahuensis
    Fimbristylis hawaiiensis
    Gahnia gahniiformis
    Machaerina angustifolia (ʻUki)
   Poaceae (Grass family)
    Andropogon virginicus (Broomsedge)
    Anthoxanthum odoratum (Sweet vernalgrass)
    Deschampsia nubigena
    Ehrharta stipoides (Meadow ricegrass)
    Eragrostis variabilis (ʻEmoloa or Lovegrass)
    Heteropogon contortus (Pili)
    Holcus lanatus (Velvet grass)
    Hyparrhenia rufa (Thatching grass)
    Isachne distichophylla (ʻOhe)
    Ischaemum byrone
    Melinis minutiflora (Molasses grass)
    Panicum tenuifolium (Mountain pili)
    Paspalum conjugatum (Hilo grass)

            Paspalum dilatatum (Dallis grass)
            Paspalum urvillei (Vasey grass)
            Pennisetum clandestinum (Kikuyu grass)
            Pennisetum setaceum (Fountain grass)
            Poa pratensis (Kentucky bluegrass)
            Rhynchelytrum repens (Natal redtop)
            Schizachyrium condensatum (Bush beardgrass)
            Setaria palmifolia (Palm grass)
            Trisetum glomeratum (Pili uka)
Subclass Zingiberidae
  Order Zingiberales
      Zingiberaceae (Ginger family)
        Hedychium coronarium (White ginger)
        Hedychium flavescens (Yellow ginger)
        Hedychium gardnerianum (Kāhili ginger)
        Zingiber zerumbet (Shampoo ginger)
Subclass Liliales
  Order Liliales
      Agavaceae (Agave family)
        Pleomele hawaiiensis (Hala pepe)
      Liliaceae (Lily family)
        Astelia menziesiana (Paʻiniu)
      Smilacaceae
        Smilax melastomifolia (Hoi kuahiwi)
  Order Orchidales
      Orchidaceae (Orchid family)
        Anoectochilus sandvicensis
        Arundina graminifolia (Bamboo orchid)
        Liparis hawaiensis (ʻAwapuhi a Kanaloa)
        Phaius tankarvilleae (Chinese ground orchid)
        Spathoglottis plicata (Malaysian ground orchid)

KINGDOM ANIMALIA (ANIMALS)

PHYLUM MOLLUSCA
(Mollusks)

CLASS GASTROPODA (STOMACH-FOOTED MOLLUSKS)
  Order Prosobranchiata (Anterior-gilled Gastropods)
      Littorinidae (Periwinkle family)
        Littorina pintado (Pipipi kōlea)
      Neritidae (Nerite family)
        Nerita picea (Pipipi)
      Patellidae (Limpet family)
        Cellana sandwicensis (ʻOpihi)
        Cellana exarata (ʻOpihi)
  Order Pulmonata (Air-breathing Gastropods)
      Achatinellidae, subfamily Achatinellinae
        Achatinella
      Succineidae
        Succinea

Achatinidae
Achatina fulica (Giant African snail)
Family Spiraxidae
Euglandina rosea
Family Amastridae
Carelia
Family Limacidae
Limax maximus (Spotted garden slug)
Family Milacidae
Milax gagates
Family Veronicellidae
Veronicella

PHYLUM ANNELIDA
(Segmented Worms)

CLASS OLIGOCHAETA (Earthworms, Fresh or Brackish Worms, and Leeches)
Glossoscolecidae
Lumbricidae
Megascolecidae

PHYLUM ARTHROPODA
(Arthropods)

Subphylum Chelicerata
CLASS ARACHNIDA (SPIDERS, TICKS, MITES, PSEUDOSCORPIONS, AND SCORPIONS)
Order Pseudoscorpiones (False Scorpions)
Order Scorpiones (Scorpions)
Family Buthidae
Isometrus maculatus (Lesser brown scorpion)
Family Chthoniidae
Tyrannochthonius howarthi
Order Acari (Mites and Ticks)
Order Araneae (Spiders)
Araneidae (Orb-weaver family)
Gasteracantha crancriformis (Spinybacked spider)
Gasteracantha mammosa (Asian spinybacked spider)
Lycosidae (Wolf spiders)
Lycosa howarthi (Wolf spider)
Theridiidae (Comb-footed spiders)
Theridion grallator (Happyface spider)
Thomisidae (Spider crab family)

Subphylum Crustacea (Crustaceans)
CLASS MALACOSTRACA
Order Decapoda
Suborder Natantia
Atyidae
Halocaridina rubra ('Ōpae 'ula)

      Palaemonidae
        Macrobrachium lar (Tahitian prawn)
      Alpheidae
        Metabetaeus lohena
    Suborder Reptantia
      Paguridae (Hermit crabs)
      Grapsidae (Grapsid crabs)
        Grapsus tenuicrustatus ('A'ama, Rock crab)
      Ocypodidae (Ghost crab family)
        Ocypode ceratophthalmus (Ghost crab, 'Ōhiki)
        Ocypode laevis (Ghost crab, 'Ōhiki)

Subphylum Atelocerata
  CLASS MYRIAPODA (MYRIAPODS)
    Order <u>Diplopoda (Millipedes)</u>
        Trigoniulus lumbricinus
        Oxidus gracilis
    Order <u>Chilopoda (Centipedes)</u>
      Lithobiidae (Stone Centipede family)
        Lithobius
      Scolopendridae
        Scolopendra subspinipes

  CLASS INSECTA (INSECTS)
    Order <u>Collembola</u> (Springtails)
    Order <u>Odonata (Dragonflies</u> and <u>Damselflies)</u>
      Aeshidae (Darner family)
        Anax strenuus (Pinao)
      Coenagrionidae (Narrow-winged damselfly family)
        Megalagrion blackburni (Blackburn's damselfly)
        Megalagrion calliphya
        Megalagrion peles
      Libellulidae (Skimmer family)
    Order <u>Orthoptera (Crickets</u> and <u>Katydids)</u>
      Gryllidae (Cricket family)
        Caconemobius fori (Dark lava flow cricket)
        Caconemobius varius (Big Island cave cricket)
        Caconemobius sp. (Hawaiian splash zone cricket)
        Thaumatogryllus (Tree crickets)
    Order <u>Blattaria (Cockroaches)</u>
      Blattellidae
        Allacta similis
        Blattella germanica (German cockroach)
        Blattella lituricollis
      Blattidae
        Periplaneta americana (American cockroach)
        Neostylopyga rhombifolìa (Harlequin cockroach)
    Order <u>Dermaptera</u> (Earwigs)
      Carcinophoridae
        Anisolabis howarthi (Earwig)
    Order <u>Psocoptera (Psocids)</u>
      Psocidae (Book and Bark lice)

Order Heteroptera (True Bugs)
    Mesoveliidae (Water treaders)
      Cavaticovelia aaa
    Nabidae (Damsel bugs)
      Nabis tarai
    Reduviidae (Thread-legged bugs, Assassin bugs, Ambush bugs)
      Nesidiolestes ana (Thread-legged bug)
    Lygaeidae (Seed Bugs)
      Nysius wekiuicola (Wēkiu bug)
    Scutellaridae
      Coleotichus blackburniae (Koa bug)
Order Homoptera (Hoppers, Scale Insects, Etc.)
    Psyllidae (Jumping plant lice family)
      Trioza sp. ('Ōhi'a gall psyllid)
    Cicadellidae (Leaf hoppers)
      Pseudonirvana rufofasciata (two-spot leaf hopper)
    Cixiidae (Planthopper family)
      Oliarus polyphemus (Cave cixiid)
Order Neuroptera (Nerve-winged Insects)
    Chrysopidae (Green lacewing family)
      Anomalochrysa
    Hemerobiidae (Brown lacewing family)
    Myrmeleiontidae (Antlions)
      Eidoleon
Order Coleoptera (Beetles)
    Cerambycidae (Long-horned beetles)
      Megopis reflexa
      Parandra puncticeps
      Plagithmysus bilineatus ('Ōhi'a beetle)
      Plagithmysius varians (Koa beetle)
Order Lepidoptera (Butterflies and Moths)
    Carposinidae (Fruit moths)
      Carposina sp.
    Geometridae (Measuring Worm or Inchworm family)
      Eupithecia staurophragma (Brown grappler caterpillar)
      Eupithecia orichloris (Green grappler caterpillar)
      Eupithecia monticolens (Nectar-eating caterpillar)
    Nymphalidae (Brush-footed butterfly family)
      Vanessa tameamea (Kamehameha butterfly)
    Lycaenidae (Blue, copper, and hairstreak butterfly family)
      Udara blackburni (Blackburn butterfly)
    Notodontidae
      Cyanotricha necyria
    Pyralidae
      Pyrausta perelegans
Order Diptera (True Flies)
    Drosophilidae (Pomace fly family)
      Drosophila engyochracea
      Drosophila hawaiiensis
      Drosophila heteroneura
      Drosophila mimica
      Drosophila sylvestris

Tephritidae (True fruit fly family)
    Bactrocera cucurbitae (Melon fruit fly)
    Bactrocera dorsalis (Oriental fruit fly)
    Ceratitis capitata (Mediterranean fruit fly)
Culicidae (Mosquito family)
    Culex quinquefasciatus (Southern house mosquito)
Order <u>Hymenoptera</u> (Ants, Wasps, Bees)
Formicidae (Ant family)
    Anoplolepis longipes (Long-legged ant)
    Iridomyrmex humilis (Argentine ant)
    Pheidole megacephala (Big-headed ant)
Vespidae (Papernest wasp and yellowjacket family)
    Vespula pensylvanica (Western yellowjacket)
Colletidae (Yellow-faced bee and plasterer bee family)
    Hylaeus spp. (Yellow-faced bees)
Apidae (Carpenter bees, Bumble bees, Honey bees, and Others)
    Apis mellifera (Honeybee)

PHYLUM ECHINODERMATA
(Sea Urchins, Sea Cucumbers, Star Fish, Etc.)

CLASS ASTEROIDEA (STARFISH)
CLASS ECHINOIDEA (Sea Urchins)
Echinometridae
    Colobocentrotus atratus (Hā'uke'uke or Shingle urchin)
CLASS HOLOTHUROIDEA (SEA CUCUMBERS)

PHYLUM CHORDATA
(Chordates)
Subphylum Vertebrata (Vertebrates)
CLASS OSTEICHTHYES (BONY FISHES)
Order <u>Perciformes</u>
Kuhliidae (Flag-tail fishes)
    Kuhlia sandvicensis ('Āholehole)
Carangidae (Jack fish family)
    Caranx (Papio, Jack [crevalle], Ulua)
Pomacentridae (Damsel fish family)
    Abudefduf sordidus (Kūpīpī)
Bleniidae (Blennies)
Gobiidae (Gobies)

CLASS AMPHIBIA (AMPHIBIANS)
Order <u>Anura (Frogs and Toads)</u>
Dendrobatidae (Poison arrow frog family)
    Dendrobates auratus (Green & black poison arrow frog)
Ranidae (True frog family)
    Rana catesbeiana (Bullfrog)
Bufonidae (True toad family)
    Bufo marinus (Bufo, Marine toad)

CLASS REPTILIA (REPTILES)
  Order Chelonia (Turtles)
    Cheloniidae (Sea turtle family)
      Chelonia mydas (Green turtle)
      Eretmochelys imbricata (Hawksbill turtle)
    Dermochelidae (Leatherback sea turtles)
      Dermochelys coriacea (Leatherback sea turtle)
  Order Squamata
   Suborder Lacertilia
    Gekkonidae (Gecko family)
      Hemiphyllodactylus typus (Tree gecko)
      Hemidactylus frenatus (House gecko)
    Scincidae (Skink family)
      Cryptoblepharus boutoni (Snake-eyed skink)
      Emoia cyanura (Azure-tailed skink)
      Lampropholis delicata (Metallic or Rainbow skink)
      Lipinia noctua (Moth skink)
   Suborder Serpentes (Snakes)

CLASS AVES (BIRDS)
  Order Procellariiformes
    Family Procellariidae (Shearwaters and petrels)
      Puffinus pacificus (Wedge-tailed shearwater,
      'Ua'u kani)
      Puffinus newelli (Newell's shearwater, 'A'o)
      Pterodroma phaeopygia sandwichensis
      (Dark-rumped petrel, 'Ua'u)
    Family Hydrobatidae (Storm petrels)
      Oceanodroma castro ('Akē'akē, Band-rumped petrel)
  Order Pelecaniformes
    Phaethontidae (Tropicbird family)
      Phaethon lepturus (Koa'e kea, White-tailed tropicbird)
      Phaethon rubricauda (Koa'e kea,
      Red-tailed tropicbird)
    Sulidae (Boobies and Gannets)
  Order Anseriformes
    Anatidae (Waterfowl family)
      Branta sandvicensis (Nēnē or Hawaiian goose)
      Anas wyvilliana (Koloa maoli, Hawaiian duck)
  Order Falconiformes
    Accipitridae (Eagle and hawk family)
      Buteo solitarius ('Io or Hawaiian hawk)
  Order Galliformes
    Phasianidae (Gallinaceous bird family)
      Francolinus spp. (Francolins)
      Alectoris chukar (Chukar)
      Lophura leucomelana (Kalij pheasant)
      Phasianus colchicus (Common [Ring-necked] pheasant)
      Meleagris gallopavo (Wild turkey)
      Callipepla californica (California quail)
  Order Gruiformes
    Rallidae (Rails, moorhens, gallinules, and coots)

> > *Porzana palmeri* (Laysan rail)
> > *Gallinula chloropus sandvicensis* ('Alae 'ula)
> > *Fulica americana alai* ('Alae ke'oke'o, Hawaiian coot)
> Order Charadriiformes
> > Charadriidae (Plover and dotterel family)
> > > *Pluvialis dominica* (American golden plover)
> > > *Pluvialis fulva* (Pacific golden plover or Kōlea)
> > Recurvirostridae (Avocets and stilts)
> > > *Himantopus mexicanus knudseni* ('Ae'o,
> > > Hawaiian stilt, Black-necked stilt)
> > Scolopacidae (Sandpiper, phalarope, and relatives)
> > > *Heteroscelus incanus* ('Ūlili or Wandering tattler)
> > > *Numenius tahitiensis* (Bristle-thighed curlew or
> > > Kioea)
> > > *Arenaria interpres* ('Akekeke or Ruddy turnstone)
> > Laridae (Jaeger, gull, and tern family)
> > > Subfamily Sterninae (Tern subfamily)
> > > > *Anous stolidus pileatus* (Brown noddy, Noio kōhā)
> > > > *Anous minutus melanogenys* (Noio or Black noddy)
> Order Columbiformes
> > Columbidae (Pigeon and dove family)
> > > *Columba livia* (Domestic pigeon, Rock dove)
> > > *Streptopelia chinensis* (Spotted dove)
> > > *Geopelia striata* (Zebra dove)
> > > *Zenaida macroura* (Mourning dove)
> Order Strigiformes
> > Tytonidae (Barn owl family)
> > > *Tyto alba* (Common barn owl)
> > Strigidae (Typical owl family)
> > > *Asio flammeus sandwichensis* (Pueo or Hawaiian owl)
> Order Passeriformes
> > Corvidae (Crow and jay family)
> > > *Corvus hawaiiensis* ('Alalā or Hawaiian crow)
> > Pachycephalidae (Australo-Papua insect eater family)
> > > Subfamily Monarchinae (Monarch, Australian flycatcher,
> > > and fantail family)
> > > > *Chasiempis sandwichensis* ('Elepaio)
> > Muscicapidae (Old World insect eater family)
> > > Subfamily Turdinae (Thrushes)
> > > > *Myadestes obscurus* ('Ōma'o or Hawai'i thrush)
> > > Subfamily Timaliinae (Babblers)
> > > > *Garrulax canorus* (Hwamei or Melodious laughing
> > > > thrush)
> > > > *Leiothrix lutea* (Red-billed leiothrix or Japanese
> > > > hill robin)
> > Sturnidae (Starling and myna family)
> > > *Acridotheres tristis* (Common myna)
> > Meliphagidae (Honeyeaters)
> > > *Moho nobilis* (Hawai'i 'ō'ō)
> > > *Chaetoptila angustipluma* (Kioea)
> > Zosteropidae (White-eye family)
> > > *Zosterops japonicus* (Japanese white-eye or Mejiro)

Emberizidae (Cardinal and relatives family)
    Cardinalis cardinalis (Northern cardinal)
Fringillidae (Finch family)
  Subfamily Carduelinae (Cardueline finch subfamily)
    Carpodacus mexicanus (House finch)
  Subfamily Drepanidinae (Hawaiian honeycreepers)
    Telespyza cantans (Laysan finch)
    Psittirostra psittacea ('O'u)
    Loxioides bailleui (Palila)
    Rhodacanthis palmeri (Greater koa finch)
    Hemignathus virens (Common 'amakihi)
    Hemignathus obscurus obscurus (Hawai'i 'ākialoa)
    Hemignathus munroi ('Akiapola'au)
    Oreomystis mana (Hawai'i creeper)
    Loxops coccineus coccineus (Hawai'i 'ākepa)
    Ciridops anna ('Ula ai hāwane)
    Vestiaria coccinea ('I'iwi)
    Drepanis pacifica (Hawai'i mamo)
    Himatione sanguinea ('Apapane)
Passeridae (Old World sparrow family)
    Passer domesticus (House sparrow)
Estrildidae (Waxbills, mannikins, and parrotfinches)
    Lonchura punctulata (Nutmeg mannikin)

CLASS MAMMALIA (MAMMALS)
  Order Chiroptera (Bats)
    Vespertilionidae (Common bat family)
      Lasiurus cinereus semotus (Ōpe'ape'a or Hawaiian bat)
  Order Primates
    Hominidae (Human family)
      Homo sapiens (You and Me)
  Order Rodentia (Rodents, Gnawers)
    Muridae (Old World rat and mouse family)
      Rattus rattus (Black rat)
      Rattus exulans (Polynesian rat)
      Rattus norvegicus (Norway rat)
      Mus domesticus (House mouse)
  Order Mysticeti (Baleen Whales, Nontoothed Whales)
    Balaenopteridae (Fin-back whale family)
      Balaenoptera musculus (Blue whale)
      Megaptera novaeangliae (Humpback whale)
  Order Odontoceti (Toothed Whales and Dolphins)
    Delphinidae (Dolphins and allies)
      Tursiops truncatus (Bottlenose dolphin)
      Stenella longirostris (Spinner dolphin)
    Physeteridae (Sperm whale family)
      Physeter macrocephalus (Sperm whale)
  Order Carnivora (Flesh Eaters)
    Canidae (Wolf, jackal, and allies family)
      Canis familiaris (Dogs)

Viverridae (Civet and allies family)
    Herpestes auropunctatus (Small Indian mongoose)
Felidae (Cat family)
    Felis catus (House cat)
Order <u>Artiodactyla (Even-toed Ungulates)</u>
    Suidae (Old World swine family)
        Sus scrofa (Domestic pig)
    Bovidae (Hollow-horned ruminant family)
        Bos taurus (Domestic cattle)
        Capra hircus (Domestic goat)
        Ovis aries (Domestic sheep)
        Ovis musimon (Mouflon)

FURTHER READING AND REFERENCES

Armstrong, R.W., ed. 1983. *Atlas of Hawaii.* 2nd ed. Dept. Geography, Univ. Hawaii. Honolulu: Univ. Hawaii Press. 238 pp.

Balcomb, K.C., III. 1987. *The whales of Hawaii, including all species of marine mammals in Hawaiian and adjacent waters.* San Francisco: Marine Mammal Fund. 99 pp.

Berger, A.J. 1981. *Hawaiian birdlife.* 2nd ed. Honolulu: Univ. Hawaii Press. 260 pp.

[Bioscience] 1988. Hawaii's unique biology. *Bioscience* 38(4):220-304.

Carlquist, S. 1980. *Hawaii, a natural history. Geology, climate, native flora and fauna above the shoreline.* 2nd ed. Lawai, Kaua'i, Hawai'i: National Tropical Botanical Garden. 468 pp.

Cuddihy, L.W., and C.P. Stone. 1990 [reprinted 1991, 1993]. *Alteration of native Hawaiian vegetation: effects of humans, their activities and introductions.* Univ. Hawaii Coop. Natl. Park Resour. Stud. Unit. Honolulu: Univ. Hawaii Press. 138 pp.

Culliney, J.L. 1988. *Islands in a far sea. Nature and man in Hawaii.* San Francisco: Sierra Club Books. 410 pp.

Degener, O. 1973. *Plants of Hawaii National Park illustrative of plants and customs of the South Seas.* Ann Arbor, Michigan: Braun-Brumfield, Inc. 312 pp.

Fielding, A. 1979. *Hawaiian reefs and tidepools: a guide to Hawaii's shallow-water invertebrates.* Honolulu: The Oriental Press. 103 pp.

Harrison, C.S. 1990. *Seabirds of Hawaii: natural history and conservation.* Ithaca, New York: Comstock Publ. Assoc. (Cornell Univ. Press). 249 pp.

Haselwood, E.L., and G.G. Motter. 1983. *Handbook of Hawaiian weeds.* 2nd ed., revised and expanded by R.T. Hirano. Harold L. Lyon Arboretum. Honolulu: Univ. Hawaii Press.

Hawaii Audubon Society. 1993. *Hawaii's birds.* 4th ed. Honolulu: Hawaii Audubon Soc. 112 pp.

Higashino, P.K., L.W. Cuddihy, S.J. Anderson, and C.P. Stone. 1988. *Checklist of vascular plants of Hawaii Volcanoes National Park.* Tech. Rept. 64, Univ. Hawaii Coop. Natl. Park Resour. Stud. Unit. Honolulu. 82 pp.

Hoe, W.J. 1974. Annotated checklist of Hawaiian mosses. *Lyonia* - Occas. Papers Harold L. Lyon Arboretum. Honolulu: Lyon Arboretum. 45 pp.

Howarth, F.G., and W.P. Mull. 1992. *Hawaiian insects and their kin.* Honolulu: Univ. Hawaii Press. 160 pp.

Kay, E.A. 1979. *Hawaiian marine shells.* Reef and Shore Fauna of Hawaii Section 4: Mollusca. B.P. Bishop Mus. Spec. Pub. 64(4). Honolulu: Bishop Mus. Press. 653 pp.

Lamoureux, C.H. 1976. *Trailside plants of Hawaii's national parks.* Hawaii Natural History Assoc., Hawaii Volcanoes National Park. 80 pp.

Lamoureux, C.H. Unpub. Draft checklist of Hawaiian pteridophytes, March 1984. 10 pp. Typewritten.

Magnusson, A.H. 1956. A catalogue of the Hawaiian lichens. *Arkiv for Botan.* 3(10):223-405.

McKeown, S. 1978. *Hawaiian reptiles and amphibians.* Honolulu: The Oriental Publ. Co. 80 pp.

Morgan, J.R. 1983. *Hawaii: a geography.* Boulder, Colorado: Westview Press. 293 pp.

Nishida, G.M., G.A. Samuelson, J.S. Strazanac, and K.S. Kami, eds. 1992. *Hawaiian terrestrial arthropod checklist.* Bishop Mus. Tech. Rept. MS-092192. Honolulu: Bishop Mus. Press. 262 pp.

Porter, J.R. 1972. Hawaiian names for vascular plants. Hawaii Agric. Expt. Stn. Coll. Trop. Agric. Dept. Paper 1. Univ. Hawaii. 64 pp.

Pratt, H.D., P.L. Bruner, and D.G. Berrett. 1987. *A field guide to the birds of Hawaii and the tropical Pacific.* Princeton, New Jersey: Princeton Univ. Press. 409 pp. + 45 pl.

Pukui, M.K., and S.H. Elbert. 1981. *Hawaiian dictionary. Hawaiian-English, English-Hawaiian.* Honolulu: Univ. Press Hawaii. 402/188 pp.

Pukui, M.K., S.H. Elbert, and E.T. Mookini. 1974. *Place names of Hawaii.* 2nd ed., rev. and enlarged. Honolulu: Univ. Press Hawaii. 289 pp.

Sanderson, M., ed. 1993. *Prevailing trade winds. Weather and climate in Hawai'i.* Honolulu: Univ. Hawaii Press. 126 pp.

Scott, J.M., S. Mountainspring, F.L. Ramsey, and C.B. Kepler. 1986. *Forest bird communities of the Hawaiian Islands: their dynamics, ecology, and conservation.* Stud. Avian Biol. 9. Berkeley, Calif: Cooper Ornithol. Soc. 431 pp.

Sohmer, S.H., and R. Gustafson. 1987. *Plants and flowers of Hawaii.* Honolulu: Univ. Hawaii Press. 160 pp.

Stone, C.P., and J.M. Scott, eds. 1985. Hawai'i's terrestrial ecosystems: preservation and management. Univ. Hawaii Coop. Natl. Park Resour. Stud. Unit. Honolulu: Univ. Hawaii Press. 584 pp.

Stone, C.P., and D.B. Stone, ed. 1989 [reprinted 1992]. *Conservation biology in Hawaii.* Univ. Hawaii Coop. Natl. Park Resour. Stud. Unit. Honolulu: Univ. Hawaii Press. 252 pp.

Titcomb, M., with Collab. D.B. Fellows, M.K. Pukui, and D.M. Devaney. 1978. Native use of marine invertebrates in old Hawaii. *Pac. Sci.* 32(4):325-386.

Tomich, P.Q. 1986. *Mammals in Hawaii: a synopsis and notational bibliography.* 2nd ed. Bishop Museum Special Publ. 76. Honolulu: Bishop Mus. Press. 375 pp.

van Riper, S.G., and C. van Riper, III. 1982. *A field guide to the mammals in Hawaii.* Honolulu: The Oriental Publ. Co. 68 pp.

Wagner, W.H., Jr., and F.S. Wagner. Unpub. Revised checklist of Hawaiian pteridophytes as of July 1992. 8 pp. Typewritten.

Wagner, W.L., D.R. Herbst, and S.H. Sohmer. 1990. *Manual of the flowering plants of Hawai'i.* Bishop Museum Special Publ. 83. Honolulu: Univ. Hawaii and Bishop Mus. Presses. 1853 pp.

Zimmerman, E.C. 1948. *Insects of Hawaii.* Vol. 1. *Introduction.* Honolulu: Univ. Hawaii Press. 206 pp.

INDEX

Tree snails (*Achatinella*) 41, 220. See also *Succinea*
Trees 10-17, 58-63, 88-99, 129-133, 176-187, 191-193, 241-251, 316-318. See also Alien trees, Native trees, specific tree species
Trematolobelia 174, 193
Trematolobelia grandifolia (Koli'i) **191**, **193**, 314, 343
Trichinosis 218
Tricholaena rosea (Natal redtop). See Natal redtop
Trigoniulus lumbricinus (Millipede) 120, 347
Trioza ('Ōhi'a gall psyllid) 164, 348. See also Psyllids
Trisetum glomeratum (Pili uka) 286, 303, 345
Trophallaxis 44
Tropicbird family (Phaethontidae) 154, 350
True bugs (Heteroptera) 157, 308, 348
True flies (Diptera) 226, 348. See also Flies
True fruit flies (Tephritidae) 227, 349
Tuberculosis 218
Turdinae (Thrush subfamily) 211, 351
Turkey. See Wild turkey
Turtle. See Green turtle, Hawksbill turtle
Two-spot leaf hopper (*Pseudonirvana rufofasciata*) 133, 148, 348
Typhus 37
Typical owl family (Strigidae) 264, 351
Tyrannochthonius howarthi (Scorpion) 120, 346
Tyto alba (Common barn owl) **264-265**, 351. See also Common barn owl
Tytonidae (Barn owl family) 264, 351

'Ua'u, Dark-rumped petrel (*Pterodroma phaeopygia sandwichensis*) 30, 32, 303, 350. See also Dark-rumped petrel

'Ua'u kani, Wedge-tailed shearwater (*Puffinus pacificus*) 32, 350. See also Wedge-tailed shearwater
Udara blackburni (Blackburn butterfly) 239, **278-279**, 348. See also Blackburn butterfly
Udea (Moth) 127. See also Moths
'Uhaloa (*Waltheria indica*) 86, 107, 126, 169, 341
'Uki (*Machaerina angustifolia*) **202-203**, 344
'Ula 'ai hāwane (*Ciridops anna* [extinct honeycreeper]) 177, 352
'Ūlei (*Osteomeles anthyllidifolia*) 86, **100-101**, 135, 341
'Ūlili, Wandering tattler (*Heteroscelus incanus*) 56, 351
Ulua, [Jack] crevalle, Papio (*Caranx* sp.) 81, 349
Uluhe, False staghorn fern (*Dicranopteris linearis*) 127, **147-148**, 233, 257, 259, 269, 339
Ulva (Limu pālahalaha, Sea lettuce) 55, 337
Unauna, Hermit crab, Pāpa'i iwi pūpū (Paguridae) 75, 78. See also Hermit crab
Ungulates 2, 217, 247, 274, 275, 281, 331, 333, 353. See also Domestic cattle, Domestic goat, Domestic pig, Domestic sheep, Feral ungulates
Upland forest and woodland animals 238-240, 264-281, 328, 333
Upland forest and woodland plants 15, 67, 181, 192, 194, 202, 203, 204, 205, 237-238, 241-263, 285, 315
Upland forest and woodland species 24, 36, 67, 91, 101, 104, 237-240, 241-281
Upland forest and woodlands zone 5, 6, 11, 12, 14, 15, 17, 51, **235-281**, 286, 313, 327
Urera glabra (Ōpuhe) 173, 340. See also Ōpuhe

Waxbill, mannikin, and parrotfinch family (Estrildidae) 24, 352
Wedge-tailed shearwater, 'Ua'u kani (*Puffinus pacificus*) 32, 33, 350
Weeds. See Alien animals, Alien plants, Alien species, Invasive species, specific species
Wēkiu bug (*Nysius wekiuicola*) 47, **308-309**, 348
Western yellowjacket (*Vespula pensylvanica*) 2, 127, **156-158**, 227, 286, 307, 324, 329, 349
Wet forest. See Rain forest zone
Whales **70-71**, 352
Whisk fern family (Psilotaceae) 208, 338
White ginger (*Hedychium coronarium*) 197, 345
White-capped noddy. See Black noddy
White-eye family (Zosteropidae) 26, 351. See also *Zosterops japonicus*
Whitefly order (Homoptera). See Homoptera
White-tailed tropicbird, Koa'e kea (*Phaethon lepturus*) **154-155**, 350
Wikstroemia phillyreifolia ('Ākia) **134-135**, 342. See also 'Ākia
Wikstroemia sandwicensis ('Ākia) 86, **134-135**, 342. See also 'Ākia
Wildfires 126, 128. See also Fire, Management practices, problems
Wiliwili (*Erythrina sandwicensis*) **88-89**, 91, 341
Wild turkey (*Meleagris gallopavo*) 267, 350
Wilkesia ('Iliau) 289
Wind disturbance 3, 12, 199
Windborne Species. See Dispersal by wind
Wolf spiders (*Lycosa*) 47, 49, 87, 303, 346. See also *Lycosa*

Wood-boring beetles, Cerambycids 243, 331. See also Cerambycidae
Woodland habitat 27, 111, 211, 256, 261
World Heritage Site 5
Wright Road (Highway 148) 174, 177

Xiphopteris saffordii (Kihi) 207, 339

Yellow ginger (*Hedychium flavescens*) 197, 345
Yellow Himalayan raspberry (*Rubus ellipticus*) 175, 341
Yellow pear-shaped strawberry guava (*Psidium cattleianum* var. *littorale*) 187. See also Strawberry guava
Yellow-faced bee and plasterer bee family (Colletidae) 299, 349
Yellow-faced bees (*Hylaeus*) 127, 243, 286, **299-300**, 349. See also Bees
Yellow-foot limpet, 'Ālinalina (*Cellana sandwicensis*) **78**
Yellow-fruited strawberry guava (*Psidium cattleianum* var. *lucidum*) 187. See also Strawberry guava
Yellowjacket. See Western yellowjacket

Zebra dove (*Geopelia striata*) **115-116**, 351
Zingiber zerumbet (Shampoo ginger) 197, 345. See also Shampoo ginger
Zingiberaceae (Ginger family) 196, 345
Zosteropidae (White-eye family) 26, 351. See also Japanese white-eye
Zosterops japonicus (Japanese white-eye, Mejiro) **26-28**, 86, 127, 239, 286, 351. See also Japanese white-eye